995

High Times and Hard Times

Sketches and Tales by
GEORGE WASHINGTON HARRIS

Edited, with Introductory Essays, by
M. Thomas Inge

Drawings by Mary Alice Bahler

HIGH TIMES and

HARD TIMES

Vanderbilt ♒ *University Press:* 1967

Dedicated
with respect and admiration
to the memory of

RANDALL STEWART
July 25, 1896–June 17, 1964
Gentlemanly scholar, master teacher,
and genial friend.

" . . . *the kind of man who could love*
both Sut Lovingood and Henry James."

—Walter Blair.

ACKNOWLEDGMENTS

T HE completion of this edition has been made possible by a number of willing assistants. The one person responsible for first stimulating my interest in George Washington Harris and his inimitable Sut Lovingood was the late Randall Stewart, then Chairman of the Department of English, Vanderbilt University. Under his interested guidance, what began as a seminar paper soon grew into a master's thesis, then a doctoral dissertation, and has finally resulted in this edition. His quiet and steady confidence in me and in Harris largely accounts for whatever I have accomplished as an apprentice scholar.

When I informed author Donald Day of my interest in undertaking this project in 1960, he very generously turned over to me his entire collection of Harris material, including his personal copy of his doctoral dissertation. In accordance with his wishes, these materials have been deposited in the archives of the Joint University Libraries, Nashville, so that they will be available to future scholars. It should be noted that Day's findings had been based on the earlier research of Mr. Franklin J. Meine, retired editor of *The American People's Encyclopedia* and pioneer scholar of American literary humor, and through Day I have fallen heir to his scholarly generosity.

I am indebted to a number of people for various favors: Thomas Daniel Young, Associate Professor of English, Vanderbilt University, for his valuable criticism and comments on this edition as it progressed; Miss Clara Mae Brown, Head Reference Librarian, Joint University Libraries, for her persistent efforts in locating and ordering copies of Harris's most inaccessible pieces; Annabel S. Boyce and Ann W. Dorsey, Reference Librarians, Joint University Libraries, and Gertrude Parsley and Miss Kendall Cram of the Tennessee State Library and Archives, for their expert help in tracking down elusive information and various types of minutiae; Milton Rickels, Associate Professor of English, University of Southwestern Louisiana, for a stimulating exchange of ideas and correspondence, and for his intelligent criticism on Harris; Paul H. Bergeron, Assistant Professor of History, Vanderbilt, for his authoritative assistance in historical matters concerning Tennessee; Winston Smith, Assistant Professor of English, University of Alabama, for his shared enthusiasm over the humorists of the Old Southwest, and for locating an Alabama reprinting of a sketch by Harris; Norris W. Yates, Professor of English, Iowa State University, for answering a question about the *Spirit of the Times;* Ben Harris McClary, editor of *The Lovingood Papers,* who made this collection more nearly complete by his discovery of a lost story, "Sut Lovingood Escapes Assassination"; DeWitt Dykes, Instructor of American Thought and Language, Michigan State University, for performing some research in Knoxville; Robert P. Emmitt, Associate Editor, Vanderbilt University Press, who greatly improved the manuscript for this book in both content and quality; Theodore Johnson, Instructor of American Thought and Language, Michigan State University, for his expert assistance in identifying an elusive fragment of a song; and a host of librarians throughout the country who have kindly answered my queries about holdings.

For the one person who has shared this work and my life for the past eight years, my gratitude is inexpressible. She has devoted entirely too large a part of her time to any number of tedious tasks connected with my work on Harris, all performed while answering the demands of a family. For her endurance and unfailing encouragement, I am grateful.

M. Thomas Inge

Haslett, Michigan
March 1967

CONTENTS

High Times and Hard Times

INTRODUCTION

THE vigorous, masculine, and sometimes cruelly violent literature of the humorists of the Old Southwest has been important to subsequent American literature for several reasons.
Much of it contains the seeds and earliest examples of "realism"
in the accurate portrayal of regional characters and the preserva-
tion of folk speech often achieved by these writers. In the course
of provoking laughter, these writers created an impressive gal-
lery of memorable characters, such as Longstreet's Ransy Sniffle,
who anticipated Faulkner's Flem Snopes in both the appropriate
sound of his name and the malicious nature of his character;
Hooper's Simon Suggs, America's most notable contribution to
the literature of roguery; and Harris's Sut Lovingood, who stands
beside Shakespeare's Falstaff and Chaucer's Wife of Bath in his
spiritual freedom, his canny ability to see beneath appearances
to the heart of reality, and his unabashed reveling in things
sensual. The material also provided Mark Twain with some of
the basic themes and techniques for his major works, and its
influence continues to be felt in modern fiction through the work
of no less a writer than William Faulkner.

But Lovingood's creator, a Tennessean named George Washington Harris,[1] proved himself artistically superior to his contemporaries through highly effective characterization, a sharp eye

1. The first full-scale and authoritative biographical account of Harris
is Donald Day, "The Life of George Washington Harris," *Tennessee Historical Quarterly*, VI (March 1947), 3–38. Earlier and less dependable accounts include: J. Thompson Brown, Jr., *Library of Southern Literature*,
ed. E. A. Alderman and J. C. Harris, V, 2099–2102; George F. Mellen,
Knoxville *Sentinel*, XIII (February 13, 1909), 4; Franklin J. Meine, *Dictionary of American Biography*, VIII, 309–310; John J. Heflin, Jr., "George
Washington Harris, A Biographical and Critical Study" (unpublished Master's thesis, Vanderbilt University, 1934); Edd Winfield Parks, *Segments of
Southern Thought*, pp. 215–222. More recently, Donald Day prepared the
article on Harris for *Encyclopaedia Britannica*, XI, 217. The study *George
Washington Harris* by Milton Rickels in Twayne's United States Authors
Series is the definitive biographical and critical account.

for descriptive detail in action and surroundings, and a brilliantly complex command of the American vernacular and its potential for meaningful imagery. And he contributed to American literature one of its more controversial figures in Sut Lovingood, praised by William Faulkner for his unillusioned, unhypocritical view of himself and the world and condemned by Edmund Wilson as a "peasant squatting in his own filth."

Harris's critical reputation, which has increased considerably during the last three decades, has hitherto been based primarily on his one collected volume of stories, *Sut Lovingood, Yarns Spun by a "Nat'ral Born Durn'd Fool"* (1867). But his literary remains are considerably larger. During Harris's lifetime a body of his writings was published in newspapers and periodicals in New York, Nashville, Knoxville, Chattanooga, and elsewhere. Research has uncovered forty-nine separately published pieces by Harris: four sporting epistles, eight sketches and tales, four newspaper letters, fifteen stories about Sut Lovingood, seventeen satires (also using Sut Lovingood as a central figure), and one poem.

Harris had prepared a second collection of his stories for publication just before his death in 1869, but the manuscript was somehow lost. Much of the uncollected material was undoubtedly to be included in it. How much new material was prepared for the book is not known, but since two thirds of the twenty-four stories in the earlier book had not been published elsewhere, it seems likely that a good percentage of the new one was to be original. Years of persistent efforts on the part of several investigators to locate the unpublished manuscript have proved futile. I have thus presumed to adopt as a title for this collection the one Harris had intended to use, *High Times and Hard Times*. The title seems doubly significant, since the writings gathered here reflect the heights of Harris's artistic powers and the depths of his philosophical despair. They provide glimpses as well of the Southland during its most flourishing period before the Civil War and its bleakest days of the Reconstruction.

The purpose of this volume is to make available to both the scholar and the general reader, in an authoritative but readable text, Harris's uncollected writings, so that the development of his distinctive style may be traced and a fairer estimate may be made of his total achievement.

Any ultimate estimate of Harris's achievement must rest upon the complete canon of his writings. I have attempted to bring together in an annotated edition all of the known products of Harris's pen which were excluded from his one collection of *Sut Lovingood, Yarns*. A few of the uncollected sketches have been gathered in scattered places. Franklin J. Meine included two of them in *Tall Tales of the Southwest* (1930), "The Knob Dance —A Tennessee Frolic," and "A Snake-Bit Irishman," and Walter Blair included the first of these in *Native American Humor* (1937). The three Lincoln satires were collected and edited by Edd Winfield Parks in 1937 in a small volume published in Chicago, *Sut Lovingood Travels with Old Abe Lincoln*, but it was limited to 150 copies; Brom Weber also included them in his "translation" of *Sut Lovingood* (1954). Besides a healthy number of selections from the collected *Yarns*, the anthology *Humor of the Old Southwest*, edited by Hennig Cohen and William B. Dillingham for the Houghton Mifflin Riverside Editions in 1964, also reprinted "A Sleep-Walking Incident," although the editors failed to attribute it to Harris. It has been the purpose of *The Lovingood Papers* of the Sut Society to reprint only the uncollected stories about Sut, but they appear unedited, with all the typographical errors and inconsistencies of the original printings intact.[2] An authoritative text, edited to correct errors and facilitate readability, with obscure allusions and dialect words explained in annotations, is obviously needed. This edition is intended to fill that need.

The total collection is arranged chronologically in four divisions: Sporting Epistles; Sketches, Tales, and Letters; Sut Lovingood's Yarns; and Satires. The four sections represent the consecutive steps in the development of Harris's artistry. A few of the pieces have survived only in fragmentary form, and undoubtedly some stories are yet to be discovered. A good source could be a file of any nineteenth-century American journal or newspaper, since Harris was so widely reprinted.

Specific references exist to several stories still unearthed: paragraph one in the fourth installment of "Sut Lovingood's Love Feast Ove Varmints," and paragraph four of "Sut Lovingood at

2. Four issues of *The Lovingood Papers*, under the editorship of Ben Harris McClary, appeared for 1962, 1963, 1964, and 1965. The last three appear under the imprint of the University of Tennessee Press, Knoxville.

Bull's Gap" allude to a story in which Sut outruns old Burns's fox hounds; paragraph three of "Sut Lovingood, On the Puritan Yankee," along with references to two other events in *Sut Lovingood, Yarns,* mentions "sister Sall's onlawful baby"; Donald Day discovered allusions in the New York *Spirit of the Times* to a sketch William T. Porter thought "too highly seasoned to be published" and to a "Christmas Story" by Harris, both pre–Sut Lovingood pieces; [3] Henry Watterson quoted in an essay written in 1906 one paragraph from Parson Bullen's "funeral oration over the dead body of Sut Lovingood"; [4] Herman M. Doak once recalled reading a satiric sketch by Harris about Abraham Lincoln, "describing him, once at least, as climbing a tree in his shirttail . . . and telling how the old shellbark hickory tree grated, squealed, squeaked, and shrieked as 'the railsplitter' clomb aloft and came down." [5] None of these lost stories has come to light. But an exhaustive effort has been made to make this edition as nearly complete as possible, and perhaps little else of significance will be turned up in the future. Those stories which have been attributed to Harris on inconclusive evidence are not included. As an example of a poor attempt at imitating Harris, however, the decidedly spurious sketch, "Sut Lovingood at a Candy Pulling," is included in an appendix. Harris's poem, "The Coat of Faded Grey," which has little or no relation to the rest of his work, is of little value as poetry, and represents his one published effort in that line, is also placed in an appendix.

Not a single manuscript of Harris's stories has come to light. [6] Thus the copy text for each story is the earliest discovered printing. Only the first printing can have any independent value, since all successive reprintings only increase the possibility of

3. Donald Day, "The Life of George Washington Harris," *loc. cit.,* pp. 22–23.

4. Henry Watterson, *The Compromises of Life,* pp. 60–61. The full paragraph: "We air met, my brethering, to bury this ornery cuss. He had hosses, an' he run 'em; he had chickens, an' he fit 'em; he had kiards, an' he played 'em. Let us try an' ricollect his virtues—ef he had any—an' forgit his vices—ef we can. *For of sich air the kingdom of heaven!*"

5. See M. Thomas Inge, "A Personal Encounter with George W. Harris," in Ben Harris McClary, *The Lovingood Papers, 1963,* pp. 9–12.

6. The report of a Harris manuscript in the archives of the Historical and Philosophical Society of Ohio, as noted in *American Literary Manuscripts* (Austin, 1960) is erroneous, according to a letter to the writer from Ruth C. Brill, Curator of Manuscripts, dated June 5, 1962.

additional errors. Unless a derivative text offers evidence of revision by the author (and none of those discovered contains such evidence), it can be of little value in determining the definitive text, as Harris intended it. I have therefore not deemed collation of all printings necessary or useful. The text of the first printing has been reproduced with the following editorial changes: all obvious typographical errors have been corrected and textual alterations and additions made whenever it would improve the readability or comprehension of the text (usually in terms of punctuation). The punctuation has not been modernized, and nineteenth-century typography of the newspapers has been preserved (proper names, for example, were often printed entirely in capital letters). Since Harris regularly indulged in inconsistent dialect spellings and intentional misspellings, it has not seemed advisable to impose any consistency on them. The inconsistencies are preserved as found in the first printings, except when an obvious typographical error occurs or when they might impede comprehension. Readers interested in specific textual alterations are referred to my doctoral dissertation, "The Uncollected Writings of George Washington Harris: An Annotated Edition" (Vanderbilt University, 1964; published by University Microfilms, Inc., Ann Arbor, Michigan, in microfilm and xerox form), where all changes are noted. The establishment of a readable but authoritative text has been, in any case, the major aim.

All biographical, geographical, historical, and literary allusions are explained in annotations. Also, annotations are furnished for words which the modern reader might find obscure; the rule of thumb used to determine whether a word should be explained is the availability of a definition for it in an ordinary desk dictionary. Rather than develop a cumbersome system of references in the footnotes to the authorities used in establishing word definitions, none is cited, since all of the explanations are drawn from one or several of the following standard reference books: Lester V. Berrey and Melvin Vanden Bark, *The American Thesaurus of Slang,* Second Edition; William A. Craigie and James R. Hulbert, eds., *A Dictionary of American English,* 4 volumes; Mitford M. Mathews, *A Dictionary of Americanisms,* 2 volumes; Eric Partridge, *A Dictionary of Slang and Unconventional English,* Fifth Edition, Enlarged; Joseph Wright, *The English Dialect Dictionary,* 6 volumes; and *Webster's Third New*

International Dictionary. Wherever the editor has indulged in speculation about a word, the suggestion is always modified by the presence of an identifying "presumably" or "perhaps."

One other editorial practice should be noted. When Harris first created Sut, he spelled his surname "Lovengood," with an "e." But when the collected yarns appeared in 1867, the spelling was changed to "Lovingood." Accepting the latter as Harris's preferred spelling, the name is so spelled throughout this edition, regardless of the way it appears in the original texts.

M.T.I.

Sporting Epistles

How Harris came to learn the craft of writing, especially in view of his formal education of approximately eighteen months, we cannot tell. His innate talent was obviously nurtured by self-education. Perhaps he emulated and imitated classical and contemporary European authors in the beginning, although the certain influence of any one writer is not discernible in his ultimate and peculiarly unique prose style. He was known to be an omnivorous reader, and incidental comments and allusions in his writings indicate a familiarity with the Bible, Shakespeare, the classical epics, the fiction of Charles Dickens, the verse of Alexander Pope, the drama of William Congreve, and the romantic poetry of Byron, Burns, Elizabeth Barrett Browning, and Longfellow.[1] If he ever read them, and there is every likelihood that he did, Harris may have found literary and spiritual affinities with Cervantes, Rabelais, and Swift. The fact that Knoxville was becoming during the nineteenth century an educational and cultural center in Tennessee might also be of significance. Whatever first inspired him to write, enough of his early apprenticeship pieces remain to trace a definite line of development in the forging of his personal style.

The earliest products of his pen to reach print cannot be identified. These were a series of political sketches contributed around 1840, while Harris was farming, to the Knoxville *Argus*

1. Harris' general reaction to the false sentiment of romantic poetry is seen in his satirical attack on Longfellow's imitation ballad "Excelsior," in *Sut Lovingood, Yarns Spun by a "Nat'ral Born Durn'd Fool"*, pp. 123–124. Hereinafter referred to as *Sut Lovingood, Yarns*.

and Commercial Herald, an official organ of the Democratic party under the editorship of Elbridge G. Eastman.[2] Eastman, a native of New Hampshire, had been sent from Washington to Knoxville by James K. Polk to rally support in his bid for the governorship of Tennessee. Since the political polemics that appeared in the *Argus* were signed with such pseudonyms as Cato, Cicero, Franklin, or Hackberry, and none of the pieces contains stylistic elements identifiable with any certainty as Harris's, the locating of his contributions now appears impossible.[3]

Before Harris came upon the material and form of writing that distinguished him from the other yarn spinners of the Old Southwest, those early writings identifiable as his indicate that he experimented with a style unsuited to his temperament. Scholars have pointed out that from the beginning there have been two representative types of humor produced by American writers:

the one following closely English models, especially Addison, Steele, Defoe, and Goldsmith in the eighteenth century, and Lamb, Hood, Jerrold, and Dickens in the nineteenth century; the other springing from American soil and the new conditions of American life, and assuming a character as new to the world as the country that produced it.[4]

Although Harris may not have consciously imitated the genteel spirit and ornate rhetoric of the British epistle and sketch writers, much of his early writing was epistolary in form and rhetorically self-conscious (especially the sentimentally nostalgic sketch called "How to Marry"). But his material was always purely

2. In the "Dedication" to *Sut Lovingood, Yarns,* p. xiii, Harris wrote, "Dedicated to the memory of Elbridge Gerry Eastman, the able editor, and finished gentleman, the friend, whose kindly voice first inspired my timid pen with hope."

3. The following complete volumes of the Knoxville *Argus and Commercial Herald,* owned by the Tennessee Historical Society, are on deposit at the State Library and Archives: I (June 27, 1839–June 16, 1840), III (June 23, 1841–June 14, 1842), and IV (June 22, 1842–June 14, 1843). After a careful examination of these volumes, the present writer found only two letters signed by "A Farmer" (Harris was farming then) that Harris might have written (in the issues of July 30, 1839 and March 24, 1840). But this suggestion cannot be supported by internal or external evidence.

4. Will D. Howe, "Early Humorists" in *The Cambridge History of American Literature,* II, 148.

native American, and he soon discovered that the indigenous type of humor was his forte.

Besides Eastman's early patronage of Harris's literary efforts, the first man to provide him with an important audience for his talents was William T. Porter, influential editor of the weekly New York *Spirit of the Times*.[5] During 1843, Porter published four "Sporting Epistles" from Harris,[6] all of which were patterned after similar epistles from other parts of the country and were contributed under the pseudonym of "Mr. Free." [7] The first is dated January 23, 1843, from Knox County, East Tennessee. After listing the "cheaper sports" then occupying men in Knoxville due to "these times of scarcity and pressure," Harris concludes with a none too amusing and clumsily handled account of a coon hunt he went on with "the best rifle-shooter in all these parts." It is cluttered with frequent quotations from popular songs and verse, in conformity with the affected nineteenth-century epistolary style.

The second epistle, dated March 27, was brightened somewhat by an attention to regional atmosphere and characters, especially "some odd specimens of humanity . . . to be met with frequently in this mountain region." The scene is a quarter race held at the Stock Creek paths near Harris's farm. The first anecdote he relates is about a "right *verdant* Hoosier" who comes all the way to Knoxville to see the race only to miss it because of a visit to the local grog shop. In writing of this visitor, Harris attempts for the first time a bit of sectional dialect, none too

5. Porter's significance in the development of nineteenth-century American humor is ably explored in Norris W. Yates, *William T. Porter and the Spirit of the Times*.

6. Although the opening sentences of the first epistle indicate earlier correspondence with Porter ("How do you do sir! It has been so long since I have taken the Liberty of addressing an epistle to my dear 'Spirit,' that I think it right and proper we should exchange salutations before proceeding to business."), no earlier contributions by Harris were printed in the *Spirit of the Times*.

7. These sketches were first assigned to the pen of Harris by Franklin J. Meine, who based his argument on a statement in the obituary for Harris in the Knoxville *Press and Herald*, December 14, 1869. This and other supporting evidence has been summarized by Donald Day in "Appendix A" of "The Life and Works of George Washington Harris" (Doctoral dissertation, University of Chicago, 1942), pp. 102–103. The epistles also display a style, word choice, and phraseology too similar to that found in Harris's later work to be coincidental.

successfully. He goes on to describe the drinking and fighting following the race, but perhaps in only one scene do we get a slight glimpse of the mature Harris humor:

> I was gazing with admiration on such scenes as these when one much richer opened to my view. A flaxen haired youth, probably seventeen or eighteen years old, and about the height of a ten-year-old sapling, more or less, was running hither and thither through the crowd, with a six-by-ten ginger cake under his arm, off of which he was occasionally nibbling, the tears rolling down his cheeks, and enquiring—"Have you seen anything of Daddy!" And frequently he would break out with "*Dod rot* his skin, I told him he'd lose me!"

One might imagine that this was the young Sut Lovingood, before he substituted the whiskey jug for ginger cake. This letter closes with brief descriptions of the local political scene and deer hunting season.

A disconnected, rambling account of local sports and events composes the third epistle, dated June 6, 1843. "At the present time preaching thrives and matrimony is all the go," Harris notes and adds, "Such is always the case in times of pecuniary distress." After describing all the beauties and sporting opportunities in the area, Harris extends an invitation to Porter to

> venture out to these wild parts, . . . [as] here lies open a wide field, on which the lover of sports can roam at his pleasure and never tire; that is, if seeing an occasional race, hunting, fishing, contemplating the beauties of nature, and seeing humanity in all its varieties, possess for him any charms.

The remainder of the letter contains a few brief anecdotes.

The final epistle for the *Spirit of the Times* over the signature of "Mr. Free," dated August 15, 1843, reveals that Harris had been electioneering for some unrecorded political office. But an "honorable retreat," he notes, saved him "from an inglorious defeat," initiating a long series of abortive political endeavors. Harris goes on to record a lively account of a "logrolling" and a "quilting" in Tucaleeche Cove and a "corn shucking" in Morgan County, Tennessee, "places where things are done up brown!" His description here of a backwoods dance begins to show the lively action he was capable of imparting to the printed page:

> The music sounds high, and the wild woods ring; the feet of the company fly thick and fast; reels, cotillions, and waltzes, are all so mingled and blended together that it is a dance without a name. The mirth becomes uproarious, the men jump high, "cut the pigeon

wing," and crack their heels together; the women shed their brogans —here they come and there they go—and now in nature's slippers they feel more "at home," and "joy unconfined" continues as long as breath and toe-nails last.

Except for their biographical content and their reflections of the social side of Knoxville culture during this era, these four epistles have little value as literature. But the crude character portrayal and atmospheric details found in them demonstrate a keen eye for local color on the part of Harris. In his next pieces, he gave his undivided attention to local customs and characters.

SPORTING EPISTLE FROM EAST TENNESSEE

Knox County, East Tennessee, Jan. 23, 1843

*M*R. *Editor.*[1]—How do you do sir! It has been so long since I have taken the liberty of addressing an epistle to my dear "Spirit," that I think it right and proper we should exchange salutations before proceeding to business. Therefore, I beg leave to remark that I am in good health, or, in other words "in town with a shirt full of June apples." And—as is the custom of commencing communications in these parts—"hope these few lines will find you enjoying the same blessing."

In these times of scarcity and pressure,[2] the sporting men in this quarter have to amuse themselves with the cheaper sports: such as Quarter racing,[3] Cock-fighting, Deer-driving, Fox, Coon

This epistle appeared in *Spirit of the Times, A Chronicle of the Turf, Agriculture, Field Sports, Literature and the Stage*, XII (February 11, 1843), 596–597. Hereinafter referred to as *Spirit of the Times*.

1. William T. Porter. See Francis Brinley, *Life of William T. Porter*, for a contemporary biographical account. Porter's relations with Harris and other nineteenth-century humorists have been treated in full by Norris W. Yates in *William T. Porter and the Spirit of the Times*.

2. It has been reported that despite developments in transportation with the steamboat and railroad, an increase in land value, and prospering business houses, in Knox County between 1830 and 1860, "Recurring depressions caused people to seek new lands. Many Tennesseans moved on to Missouri, Illinois, and Iowa. An article appearing in the *Tennessee Farmer* in January, 1834, stated that many of the people, even the most industrious and frugal, were complaining of hard times, and of not being able to obtain reasonable rewards for their exertions. The writer attributes those conditions partly to migration of people from East Tennessee, who took with them their wealth and spending power. He also stated that back of this lay two more fundamental causes: first, the system of farming followed was soil-depleting, causing people to move rather than stay; and second, a lack of universal education." Mary U. Rothrock, ed., *The French Broad–Holston Country*, p. 76.

3. The racing of horses on a quarter-mile track. Racing flourished on a big scale in the agrarian South during the nineteenth century. As early as June 4, 1825, at Campbell's station, a community on the western edge of Knox County, fifteen miles from Knoxville, there was announced a one-

and 'Possum-hunting, Turkey-shooting, and Partridge-netting. By the way, Mr. Editor, if you have never experienced the pleasure of catching partridges as we catch them here, allow me to say, that there is one very pleasant sport you are unacquainted with. Some of our Bird hunters have caught, within a few weeks past, as many as three hundred partridges. I have known twenty-eight to be taken in one drive.

A COON HUNT IN HAUNTED HOLLOW

I must give you an account, Mr. Editor, of a Coon Hunt that Tom and myself took, not long ago. Not "Tom Owen the Bee hunter," [4] but Tom D., the best rifle-shooter in all these parts. He is known a hundred miles round, as the owner of "Old Turkey Reacher," the best rifle you ever heard tell of! A few minutes after the bright Orb of day had disappeared below the horizon, with our favorite coon dogs, Locksley and Thunderbolt—Tom and I set out with the intention of going over the Ridge into Raccoon Valley—and a beautiful valley it is for the *varmints*—but before we reached our place of destination, and while scrambling down the ridge, through brush, briars and brambles, Thunderbolt opened with a confident and delightful strain, and broke off at a rapid pace, with Locksley at his heels playing second fiddle. We followed as fast as the nature of the case would admit of,—our steps guided by the dogs, interesting music, until we reached "Haunted Hollow," a branch of the aforesaid valley, where we found our dogs snuffing about, barking, and occasionally looking up into a tall chestnut tree on which

> *"We soon saw by the light of the moon,*
> *Something that looked like an old raccoon."* [5]

almost at the top, laying very close to the body. And about ten feet below, we discovered another object—saw it move, and

---

mile dash for a purse of $200 at the local race course on August 2. Rothrock, pp. 329–331. Donald Day notes that "Harris's brother-in-law, Pryor Nance, owned the race track at Knoxville for years," in "The Life of George Washington Harris," *Tennessee Historical Quarterly*, VI (March, 1947), 13, note 45.

4. Thomas Bangs Thorpe's first published tale was about "Tom Owen, the Bee Hunter," in the *Spirit of the Times*, IX (July 27, 1839), 247. An excellent study of Thorpe's life and works is Milton Rickels, *Thomas Bangs Thorpe, Humorist of the Old Southwest*.

5. Harris sprinkled his early writings with brief quotations from currently popular songs and poems, many of them now unidentifiable.

then, Tom brought old Turkey reacher to bear,—fired—and brought lumbering down a fine, fat old *He*. Tom was now in his glory, for he had, for some time felt a particular spite at 'coons. He loaded again his favorite rifle, took aim, fired—but no 'coon! The object moved not. He fired again—and again, with no better success, until twelve good balls had whizzed in air, and there still sat, unmoved, "That same old 'coon."

Tom for the last ten years had never missed so many times. He began to suspect all was not right. The thousand reports of strange sights seen, and noises heard at the dead hour of night, in "Haunted hollow,"

> *"Where ghaists and oulets nightly cry,"* [6]

came rushing upon his mind with such rapidity as to induce him to believe the lead from his rifle was controlled by the "evil one." He said "Old Turkey-reacher is charmed, or else that is the 'same old 'coon' so celebrated in song." [7] This last thought gave him fresh courage, and soured all his malicious feelings towards the unfortunate coons. So he off with his coat and

> *"Climbed the tree*
> *This 'coon to see."*

He ascended within a few feet of the object. It moved not! He drew a pistol from his belt—discharged it with an aim that never fails! But what was his astonishment when he saw the object still immovable! He commenced backing out! His descent was in the same manner—as a matter of course—as a she Bear's—only more rapid—when urged downward by the wailings of her cubs. He reached the ground—seized "old Turkey-reacher," called Thunderbolt and Locksley—both having been squatting in anxious amazement for the last fifteen minutes—and took up the line of march, declaring he was agoing to leave that *Beat*,[8] never more to visit it after nightfall. I am not very superstitious; but on this occasion, I confess I was very willing to "follow in the footsteps of my illustrious predecessor!" Consequently, like a

6. This quotation is from the narrative poem "Tam O'Shanter: A Tale" by Robert Burns (1791), line 88.

7. Apparently a reference to the raccoon song quoted above.

8. A round or course habitually traversed by a particular animal and therefore frequented by hunters.

poor boy at a frolic, I had not one word to say, but shouldered the dead 'coon and "marched forward in order."

Tom on his homeward march said he believed he had encountered the "Prince of Darkness" in the shape of a 'coon, and that he had formed the resolution, never more to interrupt any of the 'coon family! We reached home about twelve o'clock, and spent the remainder of the night in troubled sleep. "When bright daylight came" Tom proposed to visit "Haunted Hollow" and see if any vestiges remained of the previous night's adventure. Accordingly, after breaking our fast with coffee, venison, and homony, we started. What was our astonishment when drawing nigh the tall chestnut we discovered the same appearance! But, when we drew *nearer,* and saw it was only a strange swelling on the body of the tree, and it scarrified with bullets, imagine our shame and mortification! We acknowledged ourselves out-'cooned, raised up "Turkey-reacher," each grasped it with the right hand, and made affirmation, never to mention it to any save the "Spirit."

We have lately had, in our vicinity, some Fox chases, Deer-drives, and Opossum hunts, equally as ludicrous as the 'coon hunt above related. But I will have to postpone an account of them to a more convenient season. In the meantime I beg leave to subscribe myself, at my residence on the sunny side of 'Possum Knob.[9]

Yours very respectfully,
MR. FREE.[10]

9. Harris left steamboating for farming in 1839 and settled on a tract of land in Blount County. "This land was on a branch of Nails Creek and the waters of Little River, close to 'Tuckalucky' (Tucaleeche) Cove, at the gateway to the Great Smoky Mountains." Day, p. 9.

10. The first of three pseudonyms employed by Harris during his writing career; the others: Sugartail (and the abbreviation thereof, "S———l") and Sut Lovingood.

QUARTER RACING IN TENNESSEE

'Possum Knob, East Tennessee, March 27, 1843

*M*R. *Editor:*—I believe the Long Islanders brag mightily on their Quarter Nags. To give you some idea of the fleetness of the Quarter Stock in this section, and to convince you and them that we have the only *real* Quarter nags in the Union, I think I need but relate an incident which occurred, at a race that came off not long ago at the Stock-Creek Paths,[1] in that rare place for sport south of the Holston River, known as "South America."

The day was fine, the Paths in good order, the horses in tip-top condition, and an immense crowd present to see the sport.

The nags were brought out—their trainers had been turning them, and making false starts, each trying to get the advantage of the other—you know a great deal depends on the start—for an half hour or such matter, when a right *verdant* Hoosier stepped up to me saying, "Stranger, won't they start afore long?" I told him I thought it highly probable they would. "Well," said he, "I wish they mort (might) for I come clean from Little Shinbone afoot, to see this ere race."

After a slight pause he continued, "Stranger, perhaps you'd drink something?" I declined the honor. "Maby you're temperance?" "Occasionally," I answered. On hearing this, he cast upon me such a look of contempt, as I am inadequate to describe, and thus remarked, "Well, I don't sign away *my* liberties no how you can fix it; I drinks whenever I likes, and I want a dram *now*, monstrous bad."

A few minutes after this conversation, I saw him wending his way to Old Keats' Jug-grocery, which is situated about a hundred

This epistle appeared in *Spirit of the Times*, XIII (April 15, 1843), 79.

1. Near where Harris had owned a farm. By February, 1843, he had lost or sold the farm and moved back to Knoxville. Donald Day, "The Life of George Washington Harris," *Tennessee Historical Quarterly*, VI (March, 1947), 11, 14.

yards from the Paths. Just as he entered the door the nags were turned loose. An instant more the shouts of the multitude told the race was run, and the loud buzzes of the friends of F. K.'s *Little Breeches*, showed that she was winner, and that the favorite before starting, W. R. B.'s *Brown Mary*, was beaten.

Directly, our Hoosier appeared again upon the ground, but with disappointment strongly depicted in his countenance. He had never seen a race in his life, though he had heard a heap talk of 'em—heard when this was to be—walked eleven miles, over knobs, that morning to see it, and after waiting an hour or so, had missed it! He waited a few minutes longer, then cut a stick and made a straight coat tail for Little Shinbone, musing, no doubt, as he went, upon the uncertainty of all human affairs, and thinking a race not exactly the thing it's cracked up to be.—I say, Mister, have you got any nags in 'York that can run a quarter before a man can drink a dram?

The sport seldom stops at the close of a race at the Stock Creek Paths: and on this occasion the choice "mountain dew" circulated as free as water:

"The mirth and fun grew fast and furious," [2]

and as I looked calmly on, I thought I never saw human beings more happy and so completely,

"O'er all the ills o' life victorious."

Here was a fight—the combatants gouging and biting each other—all for amusement of course—and then, the owner of a little sorrel pony on an elevation, calling out to the crowd!—"O, yes! O, yes! I've got the fastest horse in these United States, at any distance, and lots of castings [3] to back my judgment."

I was gazing with admiration on such scenes as these when one much richer opened to my view. A flaxen haired youth, probably seventeen or eighteen years old, and about the height of a ten-year-old sapling, more or less, was running hither and thither through the crowd, with a six-by-ten ginger cake under his arm, off of which he was occasionally nibbling, the tears rolling down his cheeks, and enquiring—"Have you seen any-

---

2. This and the following quotation is from "Tam O'Shanter: A Tale," lines 144 and 58.

3. Slang for coins or money.

thing of Daddy?" And frequently he would break out with *"Dod rot* his skin, I told him he'd lose me!"

He finally found the object of his search, who had just concluded a match on his mouse colored horse *Snapping Turtle,* against the aforesaid banterer's sorrel horse *Tarrapin,* for twenty-five bushels of corn,—to be run on the 4th of July next at the Tuckalucky Race Paths.[4]

It was now growing late, and having some distance to ride, I mounted my nag and started for the Knob, having seen some odd specimens of humanity, though such specimens are to be met with frequently in this mountain region. I might, did my paper afford room, give you some elegant extracts from eloquent harangues made by candidates for office before the *sovereigns* of this section of our country; but as you had a sample of stump oratory in the County of Knox, years ago, I do not deem it necessary.[5] I will barely remark, our public men are as eloquent and wise as they used to be. It is not a great while since one of our legislators located the Plymouth Rock in the Old Dominion, and another threw the tea overboard in the harbor of Baltimore!!

The frequent snows of late have made capital sport for our Deer hunters. The Deer in the county of Morgan have had great cause to exclaim,

"Now is the winter of our discontent." [6]

for no less than twenty-seven hundred have met death in that region in the last few months! The mountains in that and adjoining counties abound with Deer. You remember probably, the fine success some hunters from Knox had there last summer.—[Vide "Knoxville Post."] [7]

4. See note 9, first epistle.

5. In the autumn of 1838, Porter made an extensive tour of the South and West to meet his correspondents, develop new ones, and gather sporting information of interest to his readers. Norris W. Yates, *William T. Porter and the Spirit of the Times,* pp. 34–35.

6. William Shakespeare, *King Richard the Third,* Act I, Scene i.

7. Porter quoted the following description of the hunt from the Knoxville *Post* in *Spirit of the Times,* XII (November 26, 1842), 463: "The company consisted of four of our best marksmen . . . who together with some old hunters who were acquainted with every path in the mountains, were out four days, although they report the weather to have been unfavorable, they killed in all *twenty-two deer,* besides a quantity of smaller game, such as Pheasants, Turkeys, Wild Cats, &c. &c. In our next,

I must draw to a close. Before I do so, however, I will observe that it is the general impression hereabouts that your "Spirit" has played the *Dickens* with "Boz!" [8] The young man might have expected it.

Yours entirely.

Mr. Free.

---

if we have time and space, we will furnish the particulars in full, for the benefit of others who may hereafter engage in this delightful sport, in the interminable mountains of Morgan." Cf. introductory paragraph of Harris's tale "A Snake-Bit Irishman."

8. In February 1840, Porter, who gave more space in his journal than competitors to original material by native American authors, decided to perpetrate a hoax on those unscrupulous publishers who copied material by European authors from other American periodicals but claimed that it was obtained directly from Europe by contract. The trap took the form of a first installment of *Marmaduke Myddleton,* advertised as a new work by Charles Dickens. After the planned forgery was immediately reprinted by the gullible editors, Porter confessed to the hoax in the pages of the *Spirit* and thus caught the rival publishers red-handed. For a full account of the affair, see Lawrence H. Houtchens, "The Spirit of the Times and a 'New Work by Boz'," *PMLA*, LXVII (March 1952), 94–100.

SPORTING EPISTLE FROM EAST TENNESSEE

Possum Knob, East Tennessee, June 6, 1843

*D*EAR *Sir*—As regards the Spring Races over the Knoxville
Course, I send you bad tidings and little joy. The day set
apart for the races to commence—the 26th of April—came and
passed, Parson Miller to the contrary notwithstanding.—But to
those who expected to see the fleet courser, and hear his tramp
over the above mentioned course, it proved a perfect *April fool*.
The sun rose in the east, travelled his daily course, and set in the
west, as usual, the silence of the grave having reigned supreme
about our course, throughout the day. I witnessed not the "gathering of the clans," and heard not the joyful thanks of a multitude made glad by a glorious and exciting race. One reason there
was no running, there was not a purse offered. Had there been,
though it had been composed of coin of East Tennessee manufacture, we would not have wanted for nags to strive for the
prize. As we attribute almost every thing to the *hard times,* I
think we may safely lay the failure of our spring races to the
same account.[1] Why, my dear sir, the *needful* is so extremely
scarce hereabouts, that the issues from *Big Lands,* though not
particularly good (about one-eighth silver) are quite numerous
and pass very currently. You will see by the Knoxville papers that
the old advertisement is out, and that a new one is in for the Fall
Races. I trust and hope we may then—notwithstanding appearances are against us—be able to make, at least, a showing. At
the present time preaching thrives and matrimony is all the go.
Such is always the case in times of pecuniary distress.

I was highly interested in reading an account in the "Spirit,"
of pike and bass fishing in Illinois. That is pleasant sport no
doubt; in fact, it must be delightful to catch five and ten pound-
ers; but what say you when it comes to forty, fifty, sixty, and

This epistle appeared in *Spirit of the Times*, XIII (June 17, 1843),
187.

1. See note 2, first epistle.

23

even a hundred pounds each, and that with a hook and line? Would you not imagine that to be pleasure worth naming sport? Somehow it strikes me it would look so, even to a man pleasantly engaged hooking a trout every five minutes on Long Island. If the "Tall Son of York" [2] will venture out to these wild parts, I would be pleased to have the honor of conducting him to a place where, to me

> *"There is not in this wide world a valley so sweet*
> *As that vale in whose bosom the bright waters meet."* [3]

where the French Broad and Holston Rivers come together; the scenery is not to be surpassed, and from the very source of those waters to where the Tennessee empties into the Ohio, there is not better fishing ground. If you think I am telling you too strong a fish-story, just make it convenient to happen here some future Spring, and you shall be convinced of the truth of my assertions, by seeing and hooking catfish as tall as your own dear self, and perch, drum, red-horse, and various other kinds, of any size you fancy. What say you, stranger! can we ever have the pleasure and extreme felicity of shaking you by the hand and showing you all that is interesting in this Switzerland of America? May we ever hope to hunt, kill, and devour the bear and deer of our hills in your company? I am afraid not. You have so many stronger inducements to visit other parts, that I don't know as the few of "Ours" in this latitude can reasonably expect to see you here, though here lies open a wide field, on which the lover of sport can roam at his pleasure and never tire; that is, if seeing an occasional race, hunting, fishing, contemplating the beauties of nature, and seeing humanity in all its varieties, possess for him any charms.

I will relate to you what I witnessed once upon a time. I was at the county seat of —— county, some sixty or seventy miles from this. A menagerie of wild animals was being exhibited, Circuit Court was in session, and candidates for office were electioneering; so taken altogether, the little village of —— presented a more lively picture than it ever did before or probably

2. William T. Porter's younger sister, Sarah, gave him the nickname of "York's Tall Son" in 1837; see Francis Brinley, *Life of William T. Porter*, pp. 48–53.

3. Thomas Moore, "The Meeting of the Waters," in *Irish Melodies and Sacred Songs* (1834), lines one and two.

ever will again. Court adjourned at 12 o'clock M., on Tuesday, to give all a chance to hear the three rival candidates for the Legislature make an expose of their views. Each spoke on various measures of State and National policy from the Tipling act to the Bankrupt Law, declaring that *he* could do more for his constituents than either of his competitors, that *he* had the best rifle, the swiftest horse, &c., and finally, that *he* would treat to more good liquor than the next man. They all succeeded so admirably in sustaining this last pledge, that sometime before night, nine-tenths of their audience were calmly reclining on mother earth, dreaming, it is presumable, of everlasting happiness and ethereal bliss; and the other tenth very humanely busying themselves in hunting up their friends. When they discovered them, if their heads should be lying too low for comfort, they would gently raise, and quickly insinuate under them the softest limestone rock imaginable, ranging in size from an ordinary pillow to a Beegum [4] and then leave them to sleep the night away. O, I thought as I looked on this, that

> *"A fellow feeling makes us wond'rous kind."*

As day departed, and night crept on, I saw them lying there like an army encamped—and surely it was an army, commanded by "King Alcohol"—but when I rose in the morning, and issued forth, the camp was cleared. They must have

> *"Started up and away*
> *At the dawn of day."*

Wednesday passed off without anything extraordinary happening. Wednesday night a great many went to the show. Among the number was a grand juror, who gazed on the roaring lion with awe, saw the monkies stirred up with a long pole with delight, and to cap the climax of his wonder and astonishment, rode the elephant; after which he betook himself to his lodgings, thanking his stars that he had seen such an awful sublimity, and escaped unhurt. In the morning he rose early from his couch, and strolled forth to a place known as the "Old Fort," where, while musing on the rise, progress, and downfall of empires, he heard (to him) an unusual sound—he listened—it grew louder as it became longer, and more alarming as it was louder. In

4. A gum tree, hollowed by decay, in which bees construct a hive.

despite his fondness for the hallowed spot, and his desire to linger about it, his legs led him out at a race horse lick—his alarm and speed increased at every step, until in the very centre of the village, the former reached such a pitch that it caused him to send forth the startling cry, "the varmints are loose," which he kept on repeating until he sunk exhausted, and in horrid plight, at the door of the "Village Inn." By this time others had caught the alarm, and came forward to enquire the whereabouts of the "varmints." After proper restoratives had been administered, our juror was able to direct the curious to the "Fort," where they found safely ensconced behind a wall, not to be seen from the position occupied by our juror,—what would you imagine? Why, I'll tell you; a brute of that kind the Irishman shot as the father of all rabbits![5] One "of the long ear'd kind," which, as it proved, had been innocently singing his morning requiem, when the juror thought of the roaring lion he saw the night before, and was driven from his position as I have described. At the juror's request, the judge granted him an immediate discharge, and it is said he has never visited a village since.

Speaking of "the long-ear'd kind," reminds me of an anecdote I heard related of Col. S. He was riding a mule one day, and coming to where the road branched off in three or four directions, the mule refused to either advance or retreat, or to go to the right or the left. He was belaboring the animal pretty freely with hickory, and gracing him freely with oaths, when a preacher rode up, and reprimanded him for talking to one of God's creation in so unholy a manner. He replied,—"He is not of God's creation, Sir, but of man's invention."

W. R. B. and myself got up the other morning about 1 o'clock, and started with four couple of dogs for a fox-chase, but it was "great cry and little wool." We returned to breakfast without the fox.

I am told Col. Hampton's colts passed through Knoxville week before last, on their way to Nashville, to be trained for the Peyton Stake. Perhaps the editor of the "Spirit" will make his appearance at Nashville about the time that stake is run for? That race will be worth seeing.

5. Probably an allusion to another tall tale currently going the rounds. The animal referred to is a mule.

No more at present, but with a coat full of *Bar*-meat and cat-fish, and a pipe full of taloni [6] on fire, I am yours always,

MR. FREE.

6. This word, obviously having to do with smoking tobacco (perhaps a type or brand), cannot positively be identified.

SPORTING EPISTLE FROM EAST TENNESSEE

A Quarter Race—Corn Shucking—Quilting—Log Rolling

Possum Knob (East Tennessee), Aug. 15, 1843

*D*EAR *"Spirit,"*—Well, the canvass is over, and I am beaten, or I would have been, which is about the same thing, had I not believed "discretion the better part of valor," [1] and drawn back a few days before the election, and given the other candidates "a clear field and no favor." An honorable retreat saved *me* from an inglorious defeat. The others, more favored ones, fought the battle manfully, but were all conquered, save one! [2]

I have been so *monstrous* busy, riding about, making speeches, soliciting votes, cajoling the husbands, shaking hands with the wives, kissing the children, and giving them dimes and half dimes, treating temperance men to watermelons, and topers to *old Bald-face,* [3] that it was not possible for me to attend that Quarter Race on the 4th of July, in Tuck-a-lucky Cove, between those notorious crowders, *Tarrapin* and *Snapping Turtle.* But report says the match came off; that it was a fast thing, beyond all previous conception, and so extremely close, that the judges decided it a draw race, and that each party should keep his corn—as "crops is good, and no prospect of scarcity"—and treat: a quart of the *good,* just then being doubled by old Jo Cristy, to each of the judges, and a piggen [4] full to the crowd. This discussion was submitted to after a little fighting, biting, and gouging; and all ended in a perfectly *independent* row, and a jolly dance at night, to the music of a dulcimer, played by Sally Crisby, and a

This epistle appeared in *Spirit of the Times,* XIII (September 2, 1843), 313.

1. William Shakespeare, *The First Part of King Henry the Fourth,* Act V, Scene iv.

2. Always interested in politics, Harris apparently had been running for an unidentified office but withdrew before the voting began.

3. Whiskey fresh from the still without aging.

4. A small wooden pail or tub, usually spelled "piggin."

gourd fiddle, performed on by Jack Smackumsmooth, in true Paganini style.

I don't know of any more "matches to come," but I reckon we will have a little clattering [5] some of these days. There are two or three nags training at the Knoxville Course, and three or four stables expected to arrive from a distance. But it is all such "small fry," compared to the Nashville doings, that are to be, that "I beg you wouldn't mention it."

I imagine there would be some novelty even to you, Mr. Editor, in a "logrolling" and "quilting" in Tuck-a-lucky, or a "corn shucking" in Morgan; for those are places where things are done up brown! So here goes for a faint outline.

The news goes forth that on such a day there will be a "log-rolling" and "quilting" at Capt. Dillon's. The sun has scarcely risen on that day, when every strong yeoman and buxom lass in the neighborhood are up and stirring, preparing for the "merry meeting." Hugh Dillon is started with the well-worn keg for first proof "mountain dew;" his sisters are preparing a sumptuous breakfast; corn-meal, eggs, and a large brown ham, are called into requisition, all of which are fast assuming "other shapes"; the fire's crackling, the fat (or sop, as it is better known by that name in the Coves) is hissing, ham frying, hoe-cake baking, and everything in a complete bustle, when the neighbors begin to arrive. The men are dressed out in strong linsey-woolsey, the women in neat checked or striped dresses, made of a similar material, with bonnets large, flaring, and over-commodious, trimmed with broad striped and spangled ribbons; in short—

> "Their dress, taken altogether, we may safely say
> The same was in vogue in their grandmother's day."

The guests have assembled. Hugh has returned; all partake of the "sparkling bowl"—though it don't sparkle much—but it makes the eyes of those fair maids that participate sparkle; that is, if you would call eyes which twinkle like diamonds, and rival the beams of the "god of day," sparkling—why, then, they sparkle *some!* as Dan Looney would say. The hospitable board is spread, all gather round in joy and gaiety, and administer to appetites such as are ever strangers to your city belles and beaux. Their fast being broken, the sexes separate, the males to the

5. Noisy and idle talk, gossip.

clearing, there to display as extraordinary feats of strength with the handspike, to win partners for the dance, as did ever knight-errant perform with his implements of warfare to gain the favor of some "ladye love;" the females to the quilting frame, where they ply the needle, pass their harmless jests, and "carol lays of love." The day passes—the shades of evening approach—the quilting is finished—the room is cleared—the puncheon floor is neatly swept. In another cabin the Miss Dillons have the evening meal prepared, when the woodmen return. All partake of food, and some of drink; mirth is beaming in every eye; the music's enchanting strains burst upon the ear, and all repair to the quilting-room, to engage in a furious dance. And if you have never seen a backwoods' dance, your imagination must help to complete the picture.

The music sounds high, and the wild woods ring; the feet of the company fly thick and fast; reels, cotillions, and waltzes, are all so mingled and blended together that it is a dance without a name. The mirth becomes uproarious, the men jump high, "cut the pigeon wing," and crack their heels together; the women shed their brogans—here they fly and there they go—and now in nature's slippers they feel more "at home," and "joy unconfined" continues as long as breath and toe-nails last. Occasionally some fair one can be seen resting on the knees of her partner, who, for the want of a chair, is "half sitting, half reclining," with feet firmly fixed, and his back braced against the wall, his arm around her—taper waist, I was about to say, but pardon me; you must bear in mind that "stays" or "bustles" never found their way into Tuck-a-lucky Cove. The Cove girls believe in the stay of a healthy spine, an ample waist, and Nature's, their only bustle. The panting and hard breathing over, their lips meet with a mighty rush, give a hearty smack, and up they jump for another whirl in the "mazy dance." "Thus on and on, till the night is gone"—and the whiskey, too, the dulcimer stops, and the gourd fiddle gives out, the hour for parting is come, when they bid the Dillons farewell, and set out for their several homes, not know-ing when they will meet again.

But the way they do things in Morgan pleases me, especially deer hunting and corn-shucking, and corn-shucking in particu-lar. All the corn on the farm is gathered and heaped at the crib, and then gather the maids and men. They are divided into com-panies, and the corn into as many heaps. At it they go—hurrah,

men, women, boys, and girls, for a race! Singing, talking, bet-
ting, drinking, shucking, or husking, as you call it; and last,
though not least, kissing who, when, and where they please, and
as often as they wish for the red ears; though the excitement of
the race is such that they generally prefer keeping count—and
I'll warrant you they count fast enough—and take the kissing
out at a more leisure moment, which is usually at night, while
resting from the fatigues of the dance—for every day's shucking
is wound up with a dance at night. Their music and dancing are
about the same as in the Cove I have described.

> "Now waving grain, wide o'er the plain,
> Delights the weary farmer."

In a few weeks the "tillers of the soil" will be "gathering it
into their garners." And any gentleman wishing for "variety,"
which, you know, is the "spice of life," can have the pleasure of
being shucked into one end of Morgan County, and danced out at
the other, by applying to

Your humble-cum-tumble,[6]

MR. FREE.

6. An admirer, or more frequently a beau, usually spelled "humble-
come-tumble."

Sketches, Tales, and Letters

Following his fourth sporting epistle, Harris ceased to contribute to the *Spirit of the Times* until he was provoked by
another correspondent into composing his first full-length story.
The correspondent was a native of Vicksburg, Mississippi, who
signed his letters with the pseudonym of "The Man in the
Swamp." He wrote to question Porter's use of a particular phrase
which could have been heard nowhere "but in East Tennessee"
and went on to describe the virtues and vices of the area with
apparent authority but erroneous geographical information. His
errors seem not to have provoked Harris as much as one statement in particular: that East Tennesseans "have no amusements
save politics and religion, and in these they fairly run the thing
into the ground!" [1]

"The Knob Dance—A Tennessee Frolic," written in reply to
this charge, is examplary of the transition Harris was making
from the epistolary to the fictional form of composition. The
piece is still structured as a letter addressed to editor Porter,
dated from Knoxville, July 16, 1845, and in the first paragraph
"The Man in the Swamp" is set straight on his geographical
errors. And then in answer to his statement that religion and
politics had replaced the old-fashioned frolics and entertain-
ments, Harris introduces a fictional raconteur named Dick Harlan ("Hear him bust!" exclaims Harris), who describes a frolic
recently held in the neighborhood. Dick Harlan's narration is
important for several reasons. This is the first time Harris used
the device of permitting a fictional character to tell a story entirely from his point of view and in his own native vernacular, a

1. *Spirit of the Times,* XV (June 21, 1845), 194.

crucial device in the later development of Sut Lovingood—a device the value of which Mark Twain would recognize more than thirty years later when he began to create the adventures of Huckleberry Finn.

The discovery of this device also permitted Harris for the first time to translate effectively the sights and events of his regional experience into the vividly active and colorfully metaphorical language which later flowed so easily from his pen. Seldom has the rich texture of folk speech been so imaginatively handled in the accurate delineation of backwoods America in the pursuit of food, dancing, fun, women, and fighting for the sheer hell of it. At a time that most American fiction was either overly sentimental, enigmatically symbolic, or morbidly gothic, Harris's mythical-realistic portrayal of Jo Spraggins is refreshingly human.

He's a squire, a school comishner, . . . a fiddler, a judge of a hoss, and a hoss himself! He can belt six shillins worth of corn-juice at still-house rates and travel—can out shute and out lie any feller from the Smoky Mounting to Noxville, and, if they'll bar one feller in Nox, I'll say to the old Kaintuck Line! (I'm sorter feared of him for they say that he lied a jassack to death in two hours!)—can make more spinnin-wheels, kiss more spinners, thrash more wheat an more men than any one-eyed man I know on. He hates a circuit rider, a nigger, and a shot gun—loves a woman, old sledge, and sin in eny shape. He lives in a log hous about ten yards squar . . . has all out ove doors fur a yard, and all the South fur its ocupants at times. He gives a frolick onst in three weeks in plowing time and one every Saturday-nite the ballance of the year, and only axes a "fip" for a reel, and two "bits" fur what corn-juice you suck; he throws the galls in, and a bed too in the hay, if you git too hot to locomote.

Here stands the epitome of nineteenth-century Southern manhood, to be matched in congeniality and hospitality perhaps only by Chaucer's archetypal hosts, Harry Bailey and the Franklin.

The lively exchange between Harris and "The Man in the Swamp" apparently led the two to further correspondence and a recognition of kindred spirits. Whether they ever got together personally is not known, but they did make plans somehow for a collaboration on a book which was never completed. This we learn from a letter written for Porter's paper by a mutual friend of theirs who used the pseudonym of "Roderick"; the epistle is entitled "Sayings and Doings in East Tennessee" and one paragraph states:

Have you heard anything of the "Smokey Mountain Panther?" a book to be published by "Sugartail" [Harris] and "The Man in the Swamp?" It is now in the womb of the future, but I trust they will bring it forth 'ere long. It is to be illustrative of the manners and customs of East Tennessee—containing an account of Bear and Panther fights, quarter racing, card playing, anecdotes of the Rev. Anley, etc., etc., with illustrations.[2]

This may be an indication that Harris up to this time had written and published a good many more than the five pieces now extant.[3]

For "The Knob Dance," Harris adopted a new pseudonym which he was to retain for the next ten years: Sugartail, and the abbreviation thereof, S_____l, a regional name for a donkey because of the resemblance of its tail to a stalk of sugar cane. The following year, 1846, Harris wrote two more sketches for the *Spirit of the Times* over this signature: "A Snake-Bit Irishman" and "A Sleep-Walking Incident." Both were ostensibly based on personal experiences and related, therefore, in the first person. The first describes an occurrence Harris says he observed on a hunting party in the mountains of Morgan County, Tennessee. An unwelcome Irishman with an inordinate fear of snakes is chased out of the camp, and the country, by a crude practical joke which takes advantage of his fear. Some of the descriptive action is vivid and extravagant, but much of the humor relies too heavily upon conventional Irish racial satire. Although the handling of the Irish dialect is inept, and in general the piece is poorly written, it brought Harris a sudden popularity when it was widely reprinted in other periodicals. For some time afterwards, Harris was known as "the author of the 'Snakebit Irishman.' "[4]

2. *Spirit of the Times,* XV (November 15, 1845), 441.

3. Another indication of this probability is a statement made two years later by the editor of the Knoxville *Standard* in the issue of October 10, 1847, upon reprinting "There's Danger in Old Chairs," Harris's fourth extant full-length story: "By the by, Captain, wouldn't it be a good idea to call your children home, and only let them out in a manner by which they will furnish you some recompense for all the trouble you have had with them? There are enough travelling through the country to make a neat little family, if collected." It would presumably take more than four stories to compose a collection.

4. When Harris lost the original draft of "A Snake-Bit Irishman," he rewrote it from memory recast in the form of a Sut yarn and included it in *Sut Lovingood, Yarns,* pp. 108–113. The second version was a great improvement over the first.

"A Sleep-Walking Incident" purports to relate a personal incident which harks back to Harris's apprenticeship as a metal worker, when, he says, "I was sent into the upper counties of this State, on a trip of business, and which I contrived to make a trip of pleasure, save the 'scrape' about to be narrated." But the tale is actually an American variation on the age-old European *fabliau* theme of the traveling stranger who stays overnight in the one-room house with a farmer and his family, which includes several young daughters of marriagable age. Such a theme is found in the work of Chaucer and Boccaccio, and it may well be one of the germs of modern traveling-salesmen jokes. Harris appears to have resisted the subtle possibilities for ribadlry in the situation, or he wasn't yet skilled enough to take advantage of them, as the story is only mildly amusing, although one editor thought well enough of it to include it in an early collection of American humor.[5]

After a year's silence, Harris's next story was written at the request of Elbridge G. Eastman, his old friend who had just returned from Washington to edit a Democratic paper in Nashville. The tale, "There's Danger in Old Chairs," appeared in the October 6, 1847, issue of the *Weekly Nashville Union* and was based on an incident said to have occurred "at one of the first class hotels, in a western city." Although the straight narrative prose is smoother and more Addisonian than anything Harris had done to date, the sketch is again no more than an undistinguished variation on an old theme—that of the uneducated country bumpkins who come to town and encounter difficulties among more sophisticated citizens. Harris gave Eastman a promise of future stories,[6] but he failed to fulfill it, and it was not until

5. T. A. Burke, ed., *Polly Peablossom's Wedding and Other Tales,* pp. 166–175. Harris's first full-length sketch, "The Knob Dance," was also reprinted in two contemporary anthologies: William T. Porter, ed., *A Quarter Race in Kentucky, and Other Sketches,* pp. 82–90; [Thomas C. Haliburton], ed., *The Americans at Home; or, Byeways, Backwoods, and Prairies,* vol. II, pp. 99–110.

6. Eastman noted in the editorial column: "We presume most of our readers have seen the story of 'the Snakebit Irishman,' which originally published in the Spirit of the Times, went the rounds of all the papers some two years ago, and was universally pronounced the best story of its kind.—We introduced the writer of that story to the public several years since, in the Knoxville Argus; and he continued, until we left Knoxville, occasionally to set our readers in a roar. He performs the same kind office for the readers of the Union to-day; and we have much pleasure in

nine years later that he began to write for Eastman regularly. In fact, seven years lapsed before he published anything again,[7] perhaps because of time-consuming business and political concerns.

Harris did, however, write a piece for the *Spirit of the Times* during 1848 which was apparently never printed. Harris's good friend and Porter's Knoxville correspondent, who signed his epistles simply as "Charlie," made a trip to New York in October of 1848, and delivered into Porter's hand personally a story from Harris. When Porter failed to publish it, "Charlie" wrote him:

> Know that you have offended me, in that you have neither published nor made any mention of the paper by 'S—l,' which I left with you sometime last month. . . . my character is in danger with that story's author, and sundry other good fellows, who were cognizant of the fact that the document was given to my charge. . . . They began to 'have their suspicions' that I made way with the story in some way or other—perhaps sold it for a price to an English magazine. . . . I leave this whole business to be settled with your conscience; but should the world never see that story, written, as it is, in George's best vein, I say it, and will stand to it, though all the critics in the world dispute the position, the world will have lost an uncommon amount of good fun.

In a note appended to "Charlie's" inquiry, Porter noted, "The communication of 'S____l' has been long under consideration. It is too highly seasoned to be published as it is, but we will try to

---

recording a promise of him to make our paper a medium through which many of his future sketches will appear."

7. In Appendix B, "The Life and Works of George Washington Harris" (unpublished Ph. D. dissertation, University of Chicago, 1942), p. 104, Donald Day assigns a story to Harris called "Old Man Nincum's Horse," which appeared in the *Spirit of the Times* on July 29, 1848, over the pseudonym of "Zip." He admits that his evidence is "not conclusive" and indeed it is unconvincing. Both the affected language (especially the use of such learned words as "diminutive," "supposition," "risibilities," "patronymic," "sobriquet," "cognomen," "denizen," etc.) and the clumsy narrative quality indicate an author other than Harris. In fact, Harris appears in the story along with several other of Porter's correspondents from Knoxville, and "Zip" notes that he hopes his attempt at narration, "although unused to such a task," will induce them to share with "the laughter-loving public" a great many more of their "thousand and one ludicrous adventures." There would be little logic in Harris's adopting a new pseudonym and writing of himself in an attempt to inspire himself to write again.

'fix it.' " [8] This is the only evidence we have of the suppression of a story by Harris on account of its ribaldry, a vein of writing he would later utilize with a frankness shocking in view of nineteenth-century Victorian literary standards.

Perhaps Porter's treatment of his "highly seasoned" sketch piqued Harris, because it wasn't until 1854 that he made another contribution to the *Spirit,* and the piece was so innocent and free of scurrility that the most orthodox Victorian prude would have heartily approved of it. "How to Marry" describes a romantically idyllic episode which took place while Harris was purportedly "one of the seventy-nine passengers on board the fast steamer 'Emily Barton', bound up the Tennessee." A wedding occurs during the trip between a man and woman so handsome and attractive that a tall, masculine Tennessean steps forth from the witnesses and is inspired to declare, "Now I will marry on *this spot* any lady in the crowd who has the nerve to face such music; look at me, and if you can love me as *she* loves (pointing full at the bride) I'll promise to be a husband to you, such a husband as *she* deserves. . . . Who'll take me?" A "Fawn-like, blue-eyed girl, from the flowery banks of the Alabama," steps forth to accept his proposition, and a double ceremony ensues. Harris's use of the steamboat locale and descriptions of natural scenery (somewhat conventional in imagery) were probably a result of impressions gained during his brief return to steamboating as captain of the steamer "Alida" in February of 1854. The entire sketch is most uncharacteristic of Harris, and it has been suggested that it is comparable to the work of N. P. Willis,[9] the American journalist and poet who wrote sentimental and didactic sketches at the same time Harris wrote. It does provide, however, a very brief glimpse into Harris's religious philosophy by the phraseology of one particular sentence which takes a swipe at New England transcendentalism (Emerson was in his prime and Thoreau had just published *Walden*): "we instinctively made way to let them pass to the altar, and where *that* was we had about as clear an idea as a transcendentalist generally has of what he's talking about."

Harris's next and last contribution to the *Spirit of the Times,*

8. "Letter From a Tennessee Joker," *Spirit of the Times,* XVIII (December 23, 1848), 517.

9. Donald Day, "The Humorous Works of George W. Harris," *American Literature,* XIV (January, 1943), 394.

published on November 4, 1854, only six days after "How to Marry," offers quite a contrast to it in style, tone, and artistry. This was "Sut Lovingood's Daddy, Acting Horse," marking both the discovery of the vein of writing which would best tap the imaginative talents of Harris and the birth of one of American literature's most lively comic personalities. Harris seemed to realize that Sut offered the best vehicle for having a say on the world at large in at least one manner when so many attempts in other directions, especially business and politics, had proved unsuccessful. Except for a few instances, all of his subsequent writings involved Sut, either as further chapters and escapades in the life of his creation, or as political polemics in which Sut served as a mouthpiece for Harris, sometimes ironically and sometimes literally.

The post-1854, non–Sut Lovingood material which has survived consists of what appears to be an excerpt from a longer sketch, four letters on miscellaneous subjects addressed to the Nashville *Union and American* and its editor, Elbridge G. Eastman, and two humorous stories about friends of Harris's who also happen to have been eminent Tennesseans.[10]

The first of these, a brief anecdote published under the title of "The Cockney's Baggage," concerns the encounter of a Tennessean and a "fullblooded Cockney . . . taking notes on the United States." The former plays a little trick to counter the Briton's nosiness and overinquisitiveness, and the result is not especially amusing. But it was written at a time when more and more visitors, especially Europeans, were traveling through the South and returning home to write rather biased and prejudiced

10. Excluded from discussion and from the present collection is the anecdotal epistle called "The Speaking at Fayetteville," published over the name of "John T. Swawb" in the Nashville *Union and American* of July 17, 1861, and tentatively attributed to Harris by Donald Day, "The Life of George Washington Harris," *Tennessee Historical Quarterly*, VI (March, 1947), 31, note 138. Day offers no evidence for his assumption, and there is neither internal nor external evidence to support it. Except for a similarity in subject matter and point of view, the style and language are unlike Harris's (aside from a liberal use of such curse words as "damned" and "H-ll," and a reference on the part of the writer to himself as a "d—d fool"). Possibly the author was consciously or unconsciously imitating Harris. E. G. Eastman once refused to publish a contribution to his paper simply "because it treats of characters which are the peculiar property" of Harris (see the July 28, 1858 issue of the Nashville *Union and American*).

accounts of what they saw there. The anecdote is very likely but a small portion of a larger piece now lost, perhaps a full-scale satire on the subject, because such activities would easily have raised the ire of an ardent Southern patriot of the calibre of Harris.

Resorting once more to the epistolary form for the relation of disconnected anecdotes and comments, the form he had first used to participate in the spirited interchange of stories among the correspondents of the *Spirit of the Times,* Harris contributed a series of "Letters from Sut Lovingood of Tennessee" in the summer of 1858 to the Nashville *Union and American.* They were not written in the person or language of the fictional Sut. But Harris had by now become identified with him to such an extent that he used the name as a pen name and was called "Sut" by his friends.[11]

Eastman had instigated the series by printing a brief report on a hyperbolic "fish story" related to him personally by George Harris, a story which, he said, "we don't believe." Not one to let the opportunity of adding to the proportions of a tall tale slip by, Harris responded with additional details, noting facetiously, "The *Union* last received makes me irate, exceedingly. . . . A veritable historical fact is tinged with a light shade of improbability, by his [Eastman's] willful omission of a point stamping the whole as an indisputable truth." While he was at it, Harris also threw in an anecdote about a misunderstanding that developed between the Postmaster of Knoxville and two of the city's fresh German immigrants because of a language difficulty. Harris's attempt at a reproduction of their speech is very clumsy and in the main constitutes senseless double talk.

A week later, Harris composed another letter primarily political in content and directed against some of the activities in Washington and at home in Knoxville. Unless one is thoroughly familiar with the persons and events to which Harris vaguely alludes, the letter is all but meaningless. Harris's fish yarn meanwhile had prompted a correspondent from Georgia to write for further information in the case. The writer purported to be one

11. Unlike Johnson Jones Hooper, who rankled when he was addressed by the name of his humorous creation "Simon Suggs," Harris never objected to being known as "Sut Lovingood." The story of Hooper's reaction is recounted in W. Stanley Hoole, *Alias Simon Suggs, The Life and Times of Johnson Jones Hooper,* pp. 102–103.

"Fredreica Muller," a "scientific lady" whose "passion" is natural history. Conceivably Eastman was himself responsible for the letter since this ruse could have prompted more writing from Harris and kept his readers interested. For some reason, however, Harris was unable to rise to the occasion and swallow Eastman's bait. He replied with a one-paragraph note expressing his "sorrow that he is unable to throw more light on the 'fish business'. . . ."

Harris did contribute one more letter to the series, anecdotal like the others, consisting of two brief stories about the adventures of an unscrupulous "shell bark lawyer" and one account of a "scrimmage" between a railroad conductor and a lady passenger. Except for the brief insights these letters provide into Harris's interests and activities at this time, and the fact that they probably reveal Harris at his worst as a literary comedian, none of them is noteworthy.

Another non-Sut story, "The Doctor's Bill," published in the *Union and American* three days after his final letter, is Harris's version of a story told about himself by Dr. J. G. M. Ramsey, one of Knoxville's most distinguished citizens and the author of one of the earliest histories of the state of Tennessee. The crux of humor in the story is a medical bill submitted by the doctor to the local court to receive payment from welfare funds for his treatment of a pauper. But the young physician makes the mistake of submitting it in Latin, as any good doctor of the time would, and the ill-educated country squires who must approve it become suspicious of the doctor's erudition, a reflection of the suspicion in which the nineteenth-century American grass-roots citizenry held education. One exclaims, "That ar dockymint aint 'cordin to law; hit's writ in Cherakee in part, and the balance in nigger, to mistify *this court*." Some of the misunderstandings that develop, especially those with a touch of ribaldry, still retain their comic appeal, and the general narrative quality is skillful. We already see in Harris's comments an element of conservative nostalgia for the rapidly receding past and a sense of dissatisfaction with the modern and progressive young professional men. Of the medical profession in particular, he notes, "I must say that in those good old days [1828] the title of M.D. meant something more than an assumption of the affix with a corresponding prefix as a balance-weight, composed too often of impudence and empiricism."

Although Harris's final sketch appeared under the title of "Sut Lovingood's Hark from the Tombs Story," it does not involve the fictional Sut. The piece is simply the retelling of a tale about an event in the life of Major Campbell Wallace, a noted Southern railroad superintendent and commissioner. Its interest remains primarily historical.

If Harris's reputation had to rest upon all the writing he did aside from his yarns about Sut Lovingood, he would be remembered as no more than a second-rate local wit and would hardly merit the attention of posterity. It is odd that few of the non-Sut tales contain even a suspicion of the richly complex command of imagery and language later so characteristic of the best Sut stories. It was fortunate for Harris, and fortunate for American literature, that he stumbled across Sut, who seemed to uncork the stopper of his imagination in a way that nothing else in his creative life had.

THE KNOB DANCE—A TENNESSEE FROLIC

Dick Harlan's Story

Knoxville, July 16th, 1845

*M*R. *Editor.*—Your Mississippi friend "In the Swamp," in spite of his pathetic appeal not to "crowd the mourners," seems very much inclined to do that same to a considerable extent.[1] He crowds "Old Knox" jist a leetle closer to Louisville,

This story appeared in *Spirit of the Times,* XV (August 2, 1845), 267.

A Quarter Race in Kentucky, and Other Sketches, ed. William T. Porter, pp. 82–90. Reprinted under the title "Dick Harlan's Tennessee Frolic" without editorial revision, except for the omission of the first and last two paragraphs. Porter wrote as a headnote to the sketch, "We wish we were at liberty to disclose the name and habitation of the writer of the incident annexed, for then we are assured his friends would insist upon his becoming a more regular correspondent of the 'Spirit of the Times,' in the columns of which he made his *debut.*"

The Americans at Home; or, Byeways, Backwoods, and Prairies, ed. Author of "Sam Slick" [Thomas Chandler Haliburton], II, 99–110. Reprinted under the title "Dick Harlan's Tennessee Frolic, or a Nob Dance," with extensive editorial revision, mostly concerned with Harris's erratic spelling and punctuation (especially the use of the comma and apostrophe in dialect contractions) for the benefit of British readers. Sentences containing references to tumbling on the bed and the use of bedsheets for table cloths were prudishly omitted, as were such indelicate phrases as "pot-gut" and "rot-gut." Dick Harlan's description of his girl friend's legs, "they make a man swaller tobacker jist to look at 'em," was changed to the less vivid but more decorous "they make a man wink jist to look at 'em." The first and the last two paragraphs of the original were omitted. Haliburton added this note at the beginning: "This sketch will doubtless appear exaggerated and over-drawn; it is, however, true to nature, and there are some places in the British provinces where similar scenes are still enacted, although old settlements before Tennessee was colonized at all."

1. The identity of Porter's Mississippi correspondent, "The Man in the Swamp," has never been determined; see Norris W. Yates, *William T. Porter and the Spirit of the Times,* p. 78. Harris's comments here were occasioned by a letter from the Mississippian, published in the *Spirit of the Times,* XV (June 21, 1845), 194, commenting upon Porter's use of the phrase "Don't crowd the mourners"; it opened: "*Mr. Editor.*—Now 'where in the name of all the gods at once,' did you get that; I have travelled from Maine to Mexico, via. the Smoky Mountains—looked good through the

44

Charleston, and Winchester, than ever I expected to see it.² It
makes the old town quite restive, it does. He says Knoxville is
200 miles from each of the places above named. Now *that's hot!*
Geographys wouldn't sell in that "swamp" if they happened to
insinuate that the man thar, was wrong, perhaps, a few hundred
miles. I think if he was to *occur* in this rootin, somebody would
see *one* dead man *twice* if they never saw two dead at one time,³
and *he* would *"See the Elephant,"* ⁴ sure! His sketch is good and
true, though, all save placing us so *near* where somebody lives.
Wonder if he was at "ar-a-frolick" while he was in East Tennessee? ⁵ I reckon not or you would have *hearn* of it before now in
the "Spirit of the Times." My friend DICK HARLAN tells of one
that took place somewhere in the neighborhood of Stock Creek ⁶
that "crowds the mourners." Hear him bust!

　　You may talk of your bar hunts, Mister Porter, and your deer

---

West India Islands, and Texas, and overlanded the Mississippi and its
tributaries from one end to the other, and never heard that 'Don't Crowd
the Mourners' anywhere but in East Tennessee, until I found you making
use of it: d—d if you was ever in East Tennessee." The phrase is explained
towards the end of the letter, where "The Man in the Swamp" describes a
visit to an East Tennessee religious camp meeting: "They were yelling and
shouting, the preacher kicking and banging the pulpit, with several exhort-
ers striding through the crowd gesticulating like maniacs and all preaching as loud as they could bawl. In an open space were the 'mourners'; the
females appeared to be in hysterics, and the bucks were boo-hooing at a
great rate; some of the old brethren were down with the 'mourners'
praying at the top of their voices. . . . Others of the old brethren were
engaged clearing the ring, begging the people *not to 'crowd the mourners'*—occasionally patting a mourner on the back and telling him to
'agonize!' (don't know what it meant). Never was there such a pandemo-
nium."

　2. "The Man in the Swamp" had noted, "Knoxville being near the
centre of East Tennessee is distant from Nashville about two hundred
miles, about the same distance from Louisville, Charleston, S. C., and
Winchester, Va." *Ibid.*

　3. "They [East Tennesseans] live to an extreme old age, and few of
them ever leave the valley; when one gets out and returns he gives
news,—an old preacher in East Tennessee said to his congregation 'My
friends—here is a man amongst you who has just returned from New
Orleans, where he saw *two dead men at once!*'" *Ibid.*

　4. See the world; gain worldly experience.

　5. The "Man in the Swamp" had charged that the East Tennesseans
"have no amusements save politics and religion, and in these they fairly
run the thing into the ground!" *Loc. cit.*

　6. Stock Creek is a tributary of Little River in the southern part of
Knox County, Tennessee.

hunts, and knottin tigers' tails thru the bung-holes of barrels, an cock fitin, and all that but if a regular bilt frolick in the Nobs of "Old Knox," don't beat 'em all blind for fun, then I'm no judge of fun, that's all! I said *fun*, and I say it agin, from a *kiss* that cracks like a wagin-whip up to a *fite* that rouses up all outdoors—and as to laffin, why they *invented* laffin, and the *last* laff will be hearn at a Nob dance about three in the morning! I'm jest getting so I can ride arter the motions I made at one at Jo Spraggins's a few days ago.

I'll *try* and tell you who Jo Spraggins is. He's a squire, a school comishner, overlooker of a mile of Nob road *that leads towards Roody's still-house*—a fiddler, a judge of a hoss, and a hoss himself! He can belt six shillins worth of corn-juice at still-house rates and travel—can out shute and out lie any feller from the Smoky Mounting to Noxville, and, if they'll bar one feller in Nox, I'll say to the old Kaintuck Line! (I'm sorter feared of him for they say that he lied a jassack to death in two hours!)—can make more spinnin-wheels, kiss more spinners, thrash more wheat an more men than any one-eyed man I know on. He hates a circuit rider, a nigger, and a shot gun—loves a woman, old sledge,[7] and sin in eny shape. He lives in a log hous about ten yards squar; it has two rooms one at the bottom an one at the top of the ladder—has all out ove doors fur a yard, and all the South fur its ocupants at times. He gives a frolick onst in three weeks in plowin time and one every Saturday-nite the ballance of the year, and only axes a "fip"[8] for a reel, and two "bits"[9] fur what corn-juice you suck; he throws the galls in, and a bed too in the hay, if you git too hot to locomote. The supper is made up by the fellers; every one fetches sumthin; sum a lick of meal, sum a middlin[10] of bacon, sum a hen, sum a possum, sum a punkin, sum a grab of taters, or a pocket full of peas, or dried apples, an sum only fetches a good appetite and a skin chock full of perticular deviltry, and if thars been a shutin match for beef the day before, why a *leg* finds its way to Jo's sure, without eny help from the ballance of the critter. He gives Jim Smith, (the

7. A popular nineteenth-century American card game.

8. Abbreviation for fippenny bit (the half *real*, a Spanish silver coin), formerly passing current in the U.S. with a value of about six cents.

9. Originally two pieces of money each valued at a bit (the Spanish silver *real*, valued at about twelve and one-half cents); later, a quarter of a dollar.

10. A portion of meat comprising the middle side of a hog between the ham and the shoulder.

store-keeper over Bay's Mounting,[11]) *warnin* to fetch a skane [12] of silk fur fiddle-strings, and sum "Orleans" [13] for sweetnin, or not to fetch himself; the silk and sugar has never failed to be thar yet. Jo then mounts Punkinslinger bar backed, about three hours afore sun down and gives all the galls *item*.[14] He does this a leetle of the slickest—just rides past in a peart rack,[15] singin,

> *"Oh, I met a frog, with a fiddle on his back,*
> *A axin his way to the fro-l-i-c-k!*
> *Wha-a he! wha he! wha he! wha ke! he-ke-he!"*

That's enuf! The galls nows *that* aint a jackass, so by sundown they come pourin out of the woods like pissants [16] out of an old log when tother end's afire, jest "as fine as silk" and full of fun, fixed out in all sorts of fancy doins, from the broad-striped homespun to the sunflower callico, with the thunder-and-lightnin ground. As for silk, if one had a silk gown she'd be too smart to wear it to Jo Spraggins's, fur if she did she'd go home in hir petticote-tale *sartin*, for the homespun wud tare it off of hir quicker nor winkin, and if the sunflowers dident help the homespuns, they wouldn't do the silk eny good, so you see that silk is never ratlin about your ears at a Nob dance.

The sun had about sot afore I got the things fed an had Barkmill saddled, (you'll larn directly why I call my poney Barkmill,) but an owl couldent have cotch a rat afore I was in site of Jo's with my gall, JULE SAWYERS, up behind me. She hugged me mity tite she was *"so feerd of fallin off that drated poney."* She said she didn't mind a fall but it mought break hir leg an then good bye frolicks—she'd be fit fur nuthin but to nuss brats ollers arterwards. I now hearn the fiddle ting-tong-ding-domb. The yard was full of fellers and two tall fine lookin galls was standin in the door, face to face holdin up the door posts with their backs, laffin, an castin sly looks into the house, an now an then kickin each other with their knees, an then the one kicked wud bow so perlite, and quick at that, and then they'd laff agin an turn red. Jo was a standin in the hous helpin the galls to hold the facins up, an when they'd kick each other he'd wink at the

11. A prominent ridge located in the extreme southeastern part of Knox County.
12. Skein.
13. New Orleans sugar.
14. A hint or a warning.
15. A pert gait.
16. Colloquial name for the ordinary ant.

fellers in the yard an grin. Jule, she bounced off just like a bag of wool-rolls,[17] and I hitched my bark-machine up to a saplin that warnt skinned, so he'd git a craw-full of good fresh bark afore mornin. I giv Jule a kiss to sorter molify my natur an put hir in heart like, and in we walked. "Hey! hurray!" said the boys, "my gracious!" said the galls, "if here aint Dick an Jule!" jist like we hadent been *rite thar* only last Saturday nite. "Well, I know we'll have a reel now!" "Hurraw!—Go it while you're young!" "Hurraw for the brimstone kiln [18]—every man praise his country!" "Clar the ring!" "*Misses* Spraggins drive out these dratted tow-headed brats of your'n—give room!" "Who-oo-whoop! whar's that crock of baldface, and that gourd of honey? Jim Smith, hand over that spoon, an quit a lickin it like "sank [19] in a bean-pot." "You, Jake Snyder, don't holler so!" says the old oman—"why you are worse nor a painter." "Holler! why I was jist *whispering* to that gall on the bed—*who-a-whoopee!* now I'm beginning to *holler!* Did you hear *that,* Misses Spraggins, and be darned to your bar legs? You'd make a nice hemp-brake,[20] you would." "Come here, Suse Thompson, and let me pin your dress behind? Your back looks adzactly like a blaze on a white oak!" "My *back* aint nuffin to you, Mister Smarty!" "Bill Jones, quit a smashin that ar cat's tail!" "Well, let hir keep hir tail clar of my ant killers!" "Het Goins, stop tumblin that bed an tie your *sock!*" "Thankee marm, its a longer stockin than you've got—*look at it!*" "Jim Clark has gone to the woods for fat pine, and Peggy Willet is along to take a lite for him—they've been gone a coon's age. Oh, here comes the lost 'babes in the wood,' an *no lite!*" "Whar's that lite! whar's that torch! I say, Peggy, whar *is* that bundle of lite wood?" "Why, I fell over a log an lost it, and we hunted clar to the foot of the holler for it, and never found it. It's no account, no how —nuthin but a little pine—who cares?" "Hello, thar, gin us 'Forked Deer,' [21] old fiddle-teazer, or I'll give you forked litnin! *Ar* you a goin to tum-tum all nite on that pot-gutted old pine box of a fiddle, say?" "Give him a soak at the crock and a lick at the

17. Quantities of wool rolled or twisted into cylindrical shapes.

18. Hell.

19. A sank was a tailor employed by a clothier to make uniforms for soldiers. The meaning here is not clear.

20. A machine in which dried kempstalks are beaten to remove the bark and cellular pith from the fiber.

21. "Forked Deer," a popular fiddle tune. The music and a discussion of its origin appears in Ira W. Ford, *Traditional Music of America,* pp. 45, 184–85.

patent bee-hive [22]—it'll *ile* his elbows." "Misses Spraggins you're a hoss! cook on, don't mind me—I dident aim to slap *you*; it was Suze Winters I *wanted* to hit; but you stooped so fair—" "Yes, and it's well for your good looks that you didn't hit to hurt me, old feller!" "Turn over them rashers [23] of bacon, they're a burnin!" "Mind your own business, Bob Proffit, I've cooked for frolicks afore you shed your petticotes—so jist hush an talk to Marth Giffin! See! she is beckonin to you!" "That's a lie, marm! If he comes a near me I'll unjint his dratted neck! No sech fool that when a gall puts hir arm round his neck will break and run, shall look at *me*, that's flat! Go an try Bet Holden!" "Thankee, marm, I don't take your leavins," says Bet, hir face lookin like a full cross between a gridiron and a steel-trap.

Whoop! hurraw! Gether your galls for a break down! Give us "Forked Deer!" "No, give us 'Natchez-under-the-hill!' " [24] "Oh, Shucks! give us 'Rocky Mounting,' or 'Misses McCloud!' " " 'Misses McCloud' be darned, and 'Rocky Mounting' too! jist give us

> *"She woudent, and she coudent,*
> *and she dident come at all!"*

"Thar! that's it! Now make a brake! [25] *Tang!* Thar is a brake—a string's gone!" "Thar'll be a head broke afore long!" "Giv him goss [26]—no giv him a horn [27] and every time he stops repeat the dose, and nar another string'll brake tonite. Tink-tong! Ting-tong! all rite! Now go it!" and if I know what *goin it* is, we *did* go it.

About midnite, Misses Spraggins sung out "stop that ar dancin and come and get your supper!" It was sot in the yard on a table made of forks stuck in the ground and plank of the stable loft, with sheets for table cloths. We had danced, kissed and drank ourselves into a perfect thrashin-machine apetite, and the vittals *hid* themselves in a way quite alarmin to tavern-keepers.

22. The honey is being used as a chaser to follow the whisky.
23. Thin slices cut for broiling or frying.
24. "Natchez Under the Hill," a popular fiddle tune. The music appears in Ira W. Ford, p. 56. The other two titles mentioned here were undoubtedly traditional tunes of the day also.
25. Presumably a step in the breakdown, a noisy, lively dance performed in a stamping manner.
26. A severe scolding or harsh treatment.
27. A drink of whisky.

Jo sung out "nives is scase, so give what thar is to the galls an let the ballance use thar paws—they was invented afore nives, eneyhow. Now, Gents, jist walk into the fat of this land. I'm sorter feerd the honey wont last till day break, but the liquor will, *I think,* so you men when you drink your'n, run an kiss the galls fur sweetnin—let them have the honey—it belongs to them, naturaly!"—"Hurraw, my Jo! You know how to do things rite." "Well, I rayther think I do; I never was rong but onst in my life and then I mistook a camp meetin for a political speechifyin, so I rid up an axed the speaker 'how much Tarrif there was on rot-gut?' [28] and he said 'about here there *appeared* to be none!' That rayther sot me, as I was right smartly smoked,[29] myself, jist at that time. I had enough liquor plumb in me to swim a skunk, so I come agin at him. I axed him 'who was the bigest fool the Bible told of?' and he said 'Noah for he'd get *tite!*' I *thought,* mind, I only thought he might be a pokin his dead cat at some-body what lives in this holler; I felt my bristles a raisin my jacket-back up like a tent cloth, so I axed him if he'd '*ever seen the Elephant?*' He said no, but he had seed *a grocery* [30] *walk,* and he expected to see one *rot down* from its *totterin* looks, purty soon!' Thinks I, Jo you're beat at your own game; I sorter felt mean, so I spurr'd and sot old Punkinslinger to cavortin like he was skeered, and I wheeled and twisted out of *that* crowd, and when I *did* git out of site the way I *did* sail was a caution to turkles and all the other slow varmints."

Well, we danced, and hurrawed without eny thing of *very* particular interest to happen, till about three o'clock, when the darndest muss was kicked up you ever did see. Jim Smith sot down on the bed alongside of Bet Holden (the steeltrap gall,) and jist fell to huggin of her bar fashion. She tuck it very kind till she seed Sam Henry a lookin on from behind about a dozen galls, *then* she fell to kickin *an* a hollerin, *an* a screechin like all rath. Sam he come up an told Jim to let Bet go! Jim told him to go to a far off countrie whar they give away brimstone and throw in the fire to burn it. Sam hit him strate atween the eyes an after a few licks the fitin *started.* Oh hush! It makes my mouth water now to think what a beautiful row we had. One feller from Cady's

28. Whisky of a cheap, inferior quality.
29. Excited.
30. Early grocery stores sold whisky.

Cove,[31] nocked a hole in the bottom of a fryin pan over Dan Turner's head, and left it a hangin round his neck, the handle flyin about like a long que,[32] and thar it hung till Jabe Thurman cut it off with a cold chissel next day! That was *his share*, fur that nite, sure. Another feller got nocked into a meal-barrel; he was as mealy as an Irish tater, and as *hot* as hoss-radish; when he bursted the hoops and cum out he rared a few. Two fellers fit out of the door, down the hill, and into the creek, and thar ended it, in a quiet way, all alone. A perfect mule from Stock Creek hit *me* a wipe with a pair of windin blades;[33] he made kindlin-wood of them, an I lit on him. We had it head-and-tails fur a very long time, all over the house, but the truth must come and shame my kin, he warped me *nice*, so, jist to save his time *I hollered!* The licken he gave me made me sorter oneasey and hostile like; it wakened my wolf[34] wide awake, so I begin to look about for a man I *could* lick and *no mistake!* The little fiddler cum a scrougin[35] past, holdin his fiddle up over his head to keep it *in tune*, for the fitin was gettin tolerable brisk. You're the one, thinks I, and jist I grabbed the dough-tray[36] and split it plumb open over his head! *He* rotted down, right thar, and I paddled his 'tother end with one of the pieces!—while I was a molifyin my feelins in that way his gall slip'd up behind me and fecht'd me a rake with the pot-hooks.[37] Jule Sawyer was *thar*, and jist *anexed to her* rite off, and a mity nice fite it was. Jule carried enuf har from hir hed to make a sifter,[38] and striped and checked her face nice, like a partridge-net hung on a white fence. She hollered fur hir fiddler, but oh, shaw! he coudent do hir a bit of good; he was too buisy a rubbin first his broken head and then his blistered extremities, so when I thought Jule had given her a plenty I pulled hir off and put hir in a good humor by given hir about as many kisses as would cover a barn door.

Well, I thought at last, if I had a drink I'd be *about done*, so I

31. Cades Cove, a small settlement in southeastern Blount County, Tennessee.
32. Queue: a braid of hair on the back of the head; a pigtail.
33. Spindles upon which yarn is wound.
34. Wrath, desire to fight.
35. Crowding.
36. A wooden tray in which bread dough is kneaded, used here to designate the fiddle.
37. Hooks for suspending a pot over a fire.
38. A sieve for separating the coarse from the fine particles in flour.

started for the creek; *and* the first thing I saw was more stars with my eyes shut than I ever did with them open. I looked round, and it was the little fiddler's *big brother! I know'd what it meant*, so we locked horns without a word, thar all alone, and I do think we fit an hour. At last some fellers hearn the jolts at the house, and they cum and *dug us out*, for we had fit into a hole whar a big pine stump had burnt out, and thar we was, up to our girths a peggin away, face to face, and *no dodgin!*

Well, it is now sixteen days since that fite, and last nite Jule picked gravels out of my knees as big as squirell shot. Luck rayther run agin me that nite, fur I dident lick eny body but the fiddler, and had three fites—but Jule licked her gall, that's some comfort, and I suppose a feller cant *always* win! Arter my fite in the ground we made friends all round (except the fiddler—he's hot yet,) and danced and liquored at the tail of every Reel till sun up, when them that was sober enuff went home, and them that was *wounded* staid whar they fell. *I* was in the list of wounded, but could have got away if my bark-mill [39] hadn't *ground* off the saplin and gone home without a parting word; so Dick and Jule had to ride "Shanks' mar," [40] and a rite peart *four-leged* nag she is. She was *weak* in *two* of hir legs, but 'tother two—oh, my stars and possum dogs! they make a man swaller tobacker jist to look at 'em, and feel sorter like a June bug was crawlin up his trowses and the waistband too tite for it to git out. I'm agoin to marry Jule, I swar I am, and *sich* a cross! [41] Think of a locomotive and a cotton gin! Who! whoopee!

That's Dick Harlan's story, Mr. Editor, and if the man "In the Swamp" could see Dick at a *Knob Dance* he would think that something besides politicks and religion occupied the mind of *some* of the inhabitants of the "peaceful valley."

Is Mr. Free [42] dead? I have a yarn to spin on him, also, one about "Sleep Walking," [43] and I will do it some day if I can over come my laziness. You see I am a *hot* hand at the *location* of capital letters and punctuation, (the spelling is Dick's.) If you

---

39. A mill for grinding bark, used here to designate the horse.
40. To go on foot.
41. A mixture of breeds.
42. A facetious reference to Harris's abandoned pseudonym.
43. See "A Sleep Walking Incident."

think I have made *one* "capital" letter I shall be agreeably disappointed.

Your Friend,
SUGARTAIL.[44]

Tom Warner says he saw the man "In the Swamp" at the Warm Springs, and he knows him by his style, and thereupon tells a very good yarn on him. Shall I tell you privately? say? [Yes "hoss."] [45]

44. Harris's second pseudonym, adopted from the "designation given in the mountainous regions to a donkey because of the resemblance of its tail to a stalk of sugar cane." Donald Day, "The Life of George Washington Harris," *Tennessee Historical Quarterly*, VI (March, 1947), 16.

45. Porter's reply in brackets.

A SNAKE-BIT IRISHMAN

An Original Tennessee Hunting Incident

AS a "Mounseer" [1] would say, "one gran, magnifique, pretty good" Deer Hunt came off a few weeks since in the mountains of Morgan county, Tennessee. [2] The party—made up of the best materiel—consisted of Judge A——, J. M. W—, J. A.—, and some two or three veteran hunters, rife for sport and full of fun. As my object is not to give a detailed account of the hunt, but only one of its incidents, I shall content myself with merely saying, that after a four days' hunt the three gentlemen named returned with twenty pair of hams and divers specimens of smaller fry. J. A. killed a fine buck at 160 yards off hand, shooting at the head and hitting it. Judge A—— (an ardent sportsman and splendid rifle shot) also killed at "long taw." [3] But a truce to this, and now for the incident.

As every day hath its night and every rose its thorn, so this mirthful party had its "pest," in the shape of a huge raw-boned loquacious Irishman, who, uninvited, had quartered himself in the camp, boarding and lodging at the expense of the crowd and contriving in countless ways to render himself a nuisance when awake, and when asleep accomplishing the same praise-worthy

This story appeared in *Spirit of the Times*, XV (January 17, 1846), 549–550.

Yankee Notions, I (May, 1852), 150–152. Reprinted under the title "The Snake-Bit Irishman, A Tennessee Hunting Incident," with extensive editorial revision and condensation by a hand other than Harris's.

This story was rewritten from memory as a Sut yarn for Harris's collection *Sut Lovingood, Yarns Spun by a "Nat'ral Born Durn'd Fool"* (New York, 1867), pp. 108–113. Harris added the following footnote: "This story was originally prepared for, and published in the *New York Spirit of the Times*, when that splendid paper was under the control of the lamented William T. Porter [he died in 1858]. Having lost the original draft, it has been re-written from memory and adapted to the genius of 'Sut'." Understandably, there is little similarity between the two versions.

1. Slang for Frenchman.
2. See footnote seven, "Quarter Racing in East Tennessee."
3. At a distance.

end without any contrivance at all—it being a natural gift, and used by the possessor with most tormenting effect. *The man snored,*—and how he snored, will presently appear; suffice to say, a more unmitigated nuisance was never abated in a more summary manner.

They soon learned by his conversation and behaviour that he was afraid of snakes [4] generally, and "ould *snakes*" in particular; indeed, I think that the sequel warrants the bold assertion that he would have given long odds in favor of a Stock Creek gouging, rather than face an 18 inch moccasin with "bells on his tail," as he termed rattles.[5] The man *had* heard some awful snake yarns or *tales* since his "laving the sod;" this was evident from the morbid dread, yes, horror, he felt of the crawling tribe. Well, with the Queen of Sheba he might truly say that "the half had not been told him," [6] after a night's experience at a hunters' camp in Tennessee.

On the second night of his intrusion he made himself more than usually welcome, by "getting, sir, somewhat, sir, shot!" as Tom Murry said when an ounce of lead took up its lodgings in the "fork" of his breeches, thinking (if lead can) no doubt, that it had more *room* there than in the powder bed of an old brass boring iron. He told long dry yarns, all having a more or less remote bearing on his own prowess or skill, and more than once insinuated a desire to make a demonstration, by having the use of the skull of "ony jintlemin present, and a two fut thorn,[7] fur jist a minit!" Well, all this was very pleasant, and I have no doubt perfectly satisfactory, so far as he individually was concerned, but with his hearers it was quite a different thing; yet still they endured it; but the cup of patience was nearly full, and that night it overflowed, bearing off on its boiling current, the "cause" of the "rise," to regions far away and unknown. After he had wearied

---

4. Snake yarns such as this one form one of the most popular and numerous groups of tales found in Porter's *Spirit of the Times;* for a discussion of these, see Norris W. Yates, *William T. Porter and the Spirit of the Times*, pp. 177–178. An interesting analogue to Harris's story is recounted in John Hallum, *The Diary of an Old Lawyer*, pp. 438–441, about a victim's wild race with a rattlesnake hanging by the fangs to his shirt tail.

5. A surprising error, for Harris: moccasins, of course, have no rattles.

6. I Kings 10:7.

7. A walking cane made from a thorn plant.

him with his "blather," [8] and showed symptoms of turning in, Jim A — — told *him* a *few* yarns bearing on the much dreaded snake subject, and particularly on their size, variety, and amiable temper in those parts, dwelling at length upon their *apparent* social disposition, assumed only with fell intent to those whose *nearer* acquaintance they sought. This evidently did not sit well on the excited stomach of this pugnacious sprig-of-shillalah, as was manifested by the furtive and uneasy glances he ever and anon cast at his blanket and "location." But bed time came, and after reconnoitering his sleeping ground he proceeded to count his beads and the chances of being "snake-bit" before day, then "tucking in" his blanket and wishing "the sowls ov all snakes in these perts in purthiculer," in a country where, to say the very least, they would have but a slim chance for indulging in their natural torpidity, he fell asleep.

And now the storm began. His snoring grew fast and furious, loud and long; occasionally a sort of half snort, half grunt, terminated with "snakes, by jabers,[9] blast their sowls!" "Ugh! ugh!" when there came the variation or chorus in the shape of a grind of his teeth that threatened to drive them through his jaw or crush them to powder; by way of variety he would hold his breath a few seconds and then snore again, and such snoring! my stars, that I could spell it! It was a sort of cross between the breathing of an asthmatic elephant and the braying of a superannuated donkey, whose will lasted longer than his wind. Well, it thus continued with the regularity of the whip-poor-will's cry until, say half an hour before daybreak, when J. M. W. (Jim W. we'll say) whose stock of patience had long ago evaporated, unrolled himself from his blanket, saying in his usual quiet way, "Humph! I'll *stop* that infernal concert or *start* the maker of it, see if I don't! Umph!" He then awoke Jim A. and the Judge, when a plot was laid and thus carried into execution.

W. got his hunting-knife and going to where the offal of a large deer had been thrown he cut off about seven feet of *gut,* and securing the ends with twine to retain the contents, he tied one end of it fast and tight to a corner of Paddy's shirt-tail that had wandered through a "rint" [10] in the seat of his breeches,

8. Vapid or noisy talk.

9. An oath, presumably a corruption of *Jesus* by way of the Anglo-Irish *Jasus.*

10. Rent.

coiling it all up smooth by his side, snake-like and true. All things thus arranged, the conspirators laid down again, and at the conclusion of one of the stage-horn[11] snores with the "snakes sowls" variation, Jim A. roared out at the top of his voice, "HU WEE! HUW WEE! *A big copperheaded black rattle-snake, eleven feet long, has crawled up my breeches and is tying himself into a double-bow-knot round my body!*" giving the Irishman, with every word, a furious dig in the side with his elbow, with a running accompaniment on his shins with his heels! Of course, all this noise and hurting awoke him quick and wide; in his first movement he laid his hand on the nice cold coil of gut at his side. Hissing out a "Jayzus" from between his clenched teeth, he made a bound that carried him some ten feet clear of the camp, and with a force that straightened out the coil and made the snake's tail crack like a cart whip! Casting one wild blazing look behind he tore off with the rapidity of lightning around the camp in a circle of some forty feet across, and at every bound shouting, or rather yelling, "Saze 'im! saze 'im by the tale! Oh, howly Vargin, stop 'im! Och, Saint Pathrick! tare 'im in till jabletts![12] A wha! A wha! Bate 'im to smittereens wid a gun, can't yees! He's got me fast howld by me—! och he has, by Jabers! *an he's a mendin his hoult,* a wha! Howly Father, he's got a shark hook on 'is tale! Och, murther, he's forty fut long! !" On making this last circuit he ran through a part of the smouldering campfire, and the twine at the aft end of the gut caught fire; this brought a new terror, and added a strong inducement for him to put on more steam and increase his rate; round and round he went! "He's a fiery sarpint. Och, murther! Howly Vargin, he carries a lite to see how to bite by! Och, help! I'm swallowed (jumping a log) intirely all but me hed! He's saxty fate long, if he's a fut! Thread on his bloody, fiery tale, will yees? Thry to save me!" then, as if inspired with new life and hope, he roared out, "Shoot 'im! shoot 'im! *but don't aim at 'is hed!* Shoot! shoot!"

Now here was a picture! There stood the Judge hugging a sapling with both arms and one leg, his head thrown back emitting scream after scream; here lay Jim W. on his back, with his feet against a tree, his arms elevated like a child's when he wants you to help him up, and it was scream for scream with the Judge. All sounds, at all like ordinary laughter, had ceased, and the

11. Horn used to announce the arrival of a stagecoach.
12. Giblets.

present notes would have rendered immortal the vocal fame of a dozen panthers, accompanied in their concert by the fog whistle of a steam boat. Yonder stands Jim A.—"fat Jim"—with his legs about a yard apart, his hands on his hips, shouting at regular intervals of about five seconds, "*Snake!—Snake! !—*SNAKE! ! !" at the same intonation, but so loud that the echoes mocked each other from fifty crags, and "Snake! Snake!" reverberated loud and long among those mountain slopes, while his eyes carefully and closely followed the course of poor Paddy round the camp. After running round it about thirty times, the persecuted one flew off in a tangent into the dark woods, and the medley sounds of "snake! murdther! help! fire! saxty fut! Howly Vargin!" &c. gradually died away in the distance, and the hunters were alone.

"Umph," said Jim W. (after stopping his laughing hiccough,) "umph, I thought *that gut* would stop snoring at *this* camp at least! Umph." The next evening the Patlander [13] was seen traveling at a mighty rate through Knoxville, with a small bundle under one arm and a huge shillalah in the other hand, poked out ahead of him in a half defensive, half exploring attitude, when he was hailed by Archy Mc— with, "Which way, Paddy?" Casting round at the speaker a sort of a hang-dog, sulky glance, he growled forth, a word at a step, "Strate to Ireland, by Jayzus, where there's no snakes!"

You cannot say "snake" to either member of the party yet, without its costing a set of vest buttons or producing a "stitch in the side."

SUGARTAIL.

KNOXVILLE, TENN., Dec. 25th, 1845.

13. Slang for Irishman.

A SLEEP-WALKING INCIDENT

*D*EAR P.[1]—Many, very many years have taken their turn in making me older, if not more wise, since the sunny days of youth, when there was not a sallow leaf on life's tree—when all was light and glow, and I felt but the present, the past unheeded, and the future unknown. Oh, joyous fifteen, that green isle now dimly seen over life's waste of waters, how we look and long to tread thy shores again! But our bark of life is speeding away. Small—smaller still. The dim eye of age can see thee no more—*thou* art "the past."

Soon after this hour in life's morning, I was sent into the upper counties of this State, on a trip of business, and which I contrived to make a trip of pleasure, save the "scrape" about to be narrated.[2]

Night had overtaken me some miles short of my intended stopping-place, so I hailed the first house that I came to—a large square cabin sort of a house, with but one apartment, which served as "parlour, hall, kitchen and all,"—to know if I could obtain shelter for myself and horse? A stout, iron-looking little old man answered the summons, and after resting his arms and chin on the gate for some seconds, he said, rather deliberately, that he "didn't adzactly know, seeing as how his house was small, and he had company; but seeing as how I was a benighted [3] boy,

This story appeared in *Spirit of the Times*, XVI (September 12, 1846), 343.

Polly Peablossom's Wedding and Other Tales, ed. T. A. Burke, pp. 166–175. Reprinted under the same title with minor editorial revision in terms of punctuation and spelling, and attributed to "An Old Tennessee Correspondent."

1. William T. Porter.

2. Although Harris ostensibly recounts this story as an actual experience, it is clearly related to a number of European *fabliaux* with similar plots, two notable examples being the sixth story of the ninth day in Boccaccio's *Decameron* and the Reeve's tale in Chaucer's *Canterbury Tales*.

3. Overtaken by night or darkness, with perhaps a subtle hint of the secondary meaning, morally and intellectually ignorant.

he reckoned I mought jist lite." I did so, and found the house "full of gals." First, there was the "old oman," of course, all tidiness and check apron—then three blooming daughters, all shyness and blushing—a married daughter and her yearling child (these were the "company" alluded to), and *then* there was that everlasting, long-legged, ubiquitous, eighteen-year-old boy, who is to be seen at all houses in the country with that everlasting tight roundabout,[4] strained across his shoulder blade, which seems to belong inherently to all chaps of his class, and he patronized mixed socks and low-quartered shoes. That specimen of the class "green boy" deserves more than a passing notice at my hands, if I had the talent and room, but I must content myself by merely saying that his name was TEWALT, and that I will never forget him, or the service he rendered me in my "hour of great peril," although for a time he annoyed me not a few; and I may hazard the assertion, that if he remembers all that was gleaned from me that night, and all that occurred next morning, he is a perfect locomotive encyclopaedia of useful knowledge.

Supper passed off, during which, and the interval preceding bedtime, I was subjected to a categorical examination on matters in general, and my business in particular, the old lady acting as principal inquisitor, prompted in whispers by the girls. They listened and giggled, the married daughter nursed and tried to look matronly, the dog lay at the corner of the hearth, and dreamed perhaps of his last rabbit chase; the cat washed her face, as all well-ordered cats will do, after a hearty saucer of milk, and I, poor I, wished it well over. I counted the minutes as indicated by a twenty-four-hour Yankee clock, which, nailed against the log wall, ticked off the time most methodically; and surveyed the prospect for bed *room*, with deep interest. I counted the beds (three, all in a row, across the back of the house,) over and again; then I counted noses, and found an awful disproportion between them and the beds. I resolved divers arithmetical problems of position in my mind, to ascertain if possible how to class said noses, so as to violate no known and acknowledged law of usage and propriety, in sleeping matters, made and provided. But all in vain. I was beginning to entertain serious thoughts in relation to the stable-loft, when the old lady opened the first act by peremptorily ordering TEWALT off to one bed, then with the

4. A short, close-fitting jacket.

help of the girls she metamorphosed another into a gigantic "shake-down" [5] before the fire; she managed to increase its dimensions prodigiously, until it attained at least the size of an ordinary onion-bed. This encampment, as I said, was spread before the fire, and was for the benefit of the girls, married and single, rank and file. Now my mind was at rest; they (the girls), baby and all, were safely disposed of, and the horrid suspicion had passed away that I might have to sleep "spoon fashion" [6] with perhaps three, and that fat baby at the foot. I now saw as clearly through the old lady's sagacious arrangements as if they had been the result of the aforesaid abortive mathematical calculations. *Tewalt* and myself were to have one bed, and the old folks the other; to my unsophisticated boyhood, this arrangement was the best that possibly could be made under the circumstances. The old lady, considerate old soul, hung a quilt over two chairs, as a kind of flattery for me to undress behind, and cautioning the girls in an undertone not to *look*, she told me I might go to bed as soon as I liked. I, nothing loth, obeyed the intimation, and in spite of the stray eye-shots fired at me from the region of the fire-place, got safely to bed, and was soon in the land of dreams.

The first thing I remember, I felt some one inflicting furious digs in my side; it struck my dreaming imagination that it was the aforesaid Tewalt, who wanted some incomprehensible point in the evening's conversation elucidated, so I moved not. Soon I saw him standing over me, his legs at least sixty feet long, and kicking me in the ribs at a smashing rate, with a foot about the size of a steamboat's yawl. Then he changed and had on petticoats of the proportions of a circus tent, with a huge big-top on for a night-cap, and nursing the Yankee clock for a baby, and every blow it struck resembled a blast from a pair of infantile lungs highly inflated! Anon, he became a gigantic pair of fire-tongs, with red-hot feet, and he pinched me on the arm until it *scizzed* again! This awoke me, sure enough, and I found the pinching still going on at about the rate of 120 to the minute.

"Hello, old fellow!" says I, "that'll do. What in the name of the Lunatic Asylum *do* you want?"

5. An improvised bed usually made on the floor by spreading bed-clothes over straw; sometimes called a pallet.
6. To sleep on one's side, facing the back of another in the same position.

"It aint no *old* feller, an' you may thank gracious goodness that it aint, but you jist git rite up an' mosey, afore I calls the old feller!"

This was spoken close to one ear in a good round whisper, while a suppressed sort of giggling appeared to originate about a foot from the other. I lay perfectly still, and tried to arouse my faculties as to the cause of all this rumpus. I then ventured to raise my head a fraction and saw that the fire was not in the same place that it occupied when I went to bed. Had Tewalt turned my bed round by the furious kicks above named? No, that must have been a dream, and I was awake *now*—as wide as ever you saw a cat, with all the dogs in the neighborhood at the foot of the apple-tree, and she on the first limb. I listened, and the blessed old clock had moved towards another point of the compass, and was boxing away as if nothing had occurred to disturb its equanimity; the old man's snoring, too, had partaken of this general first-day-of-May excitement, and, like the clock and the fire, had changed its quarters. Strange, that, but may be I had only heard the echo on the wall. But the old man being sedate, it was not presumable that he would patronize other than a becoming and sedate snore, and would tolerate no other, however sonorous, nor be guilty of playing such fantastic tricks before—a stranger! And the heavy breathing of Tewalt, too, had retired to a respectful distance in the rear, but it *was* his breathing, and no mistake; I was familiar with the sound. Well, what was the matter? Was I tight? No, I had drank nothing. Was I crazy? No, for I was fully aware of everything, save that my ideas of relative position had become confoundedly mystified.

"I say, cuss your sassey little picter, are you gwine to leave afore I calls dad, for he'll jist give you goss in a minit, little hoss, and we gals couldn't save your cussed ternal scalp if we wanted tu! Say, ar ye gwine, *durn* yer imperdence?"

Oh, my stars! the awful truth flashed on my mind in an instant. I had got in bed with the girls, and would soon be a lost boy, barrin' better luck than John Tyler [7] ever had. But my pres-

7. Presumably a reference to the tenth President of the United States, John Tyler (1790–1862), long considered by many the poorest to serve in the office. His sorry reputation is based in part upon his strict adherence to political beliefs which led him to forsake both the Democrat and Whig parties. His name became so notorious that it gave birth to a verb, "Tylerize," which meant to forsake the party or side to which one owes

ence of mind came to my aid, so I replied to this whispered tirade by giving a heavy groaning sort of snore, and turning over from my tormentor, I reconnoitred my location by throwing out first an arm and then a leg. The arm lit across the heaving warm breast of *somebody* with considerable muscular energy, for quick as light it was seized, and no rocket ever flew with more of a "vim," than it did from its soft resting place, and lit smack across the face of my pinching friend, the married daughter, who was unmasked by this move of her sister, for in its descent it chanced also to hit the "yearling" a wipe in the neighborhood of the nose, and such a yell as followed, or rather such a series of yells, I never before heard. My leg, I suppose, had lit upon forbidden ground also, for it followed the arm with no bad consequences, only a wicked sort of a dig in my side, which I thought might be inflicted with the naked elbow; this was intended as a kind of interest on the operation, given in "have-the-last-lick" spirit of mind.

Well, after calculating the probable location of my own bed, I made one bound, which cleared me of the enemy's camp, and I lit alongside of Tewalt.

"Well, durn your carcass," says he, "you wanted to sleep *warm*, did you, so you jist goes atween the gals! They warmed ye, didn't they? drat your picter! Ha! ha! ha! Well, now, if that aint hot, I'm d-a-r-n-e-d!"

A running-fire of conversation was kept up between the shake-down and the old folks' bed for some time, but as it was not of a *very* complimentary nature, so far as I was concerned, I will not inflict on the reader what both pained and scared me. After rolling about for some time in a rather perturbed state of mind, I fell asleep, and was awoke by the old lady to come to breakfast. Tewalt was gone, I knew not where, the shake-down had vanished, and things looked tidy and clean.

When we set up to breakfast I felt like a criminal, and I know that I looked like one; the girls blushed, the married one was serious, the old lady seemed pious, and the old man looked devilish; so you may guess how I relished my breakfast. Not a word did I say that I could help, and the old lady's disposition of

office or allegiance. See Hugh Russell Fraser, *Democracy in the Making;* Oliver Perry Chitwood, *John Tyler, Champion of the Old South;* Robert J. Morgan, *A Whig Embattled, The Presidency Under John Tyler.*

the previous evening to ask questions seemed to have vanished, so I was not interrupted in my taciturnity.

The meal over, I asked the old man the amount of my bill. "I don't charge ye a cent." This was said in a tone and manner that I neither liked nor understood; so, as my horse was at the gate, with Tewalt holding the bridle, I turned around to bid the girls "good morning," and there they were, holding up the log that served for a mantle-board with their foreheads, and seemed to be in tears. This mystified me more than ever; the old man had taken down an old black snakish looking rifle, and was changing the priming. I enquired if he was agoing to hunt? "Y-a-s," he drawled out—"I'm agwine to kill a mink what's been among my pullets!" Well, I didn't like *that,* either; so, without more ceremony, I started to the horse, and as I left the door, I heard one of the girls (a sweet, blue-eyed damsel she was, too), and the one who had converted my arm into a projectile with such dire effect the night before, say—"Oh, daddy, now don't; we all know he *was* asleep, poor little fellow! Don't, daddy, don't!"

The old scoundrel growled a reply which I did not hear, and followed me.

When I reached my horse, I mounted, and Tewalt, who stood beyond the horse, drew from the leg of his breeches, a long, keen hickory, and stealthily gave it to me, saying:

"Don't hold it so, dad'll see it, and when ye *get the word,* jist gin that hoss of yourn hot darnation about his tail, or maybe ye won't ride long if ye don't!"

He was cut short in his charitable speech by the approach of the old *he* shark, *gun* in hand.

"Now, sir," says he, "ye come here benighted, didn't ye?"

"Yes, sir," said I, submissively.

"I took ye in like a gentle*man,* didn't I?"

"Yes, sir, you did, and I am"—

"Stop! that ain't the pint. I fed you an your hoss on the best I had didn't I?"

"Yes, sir," replied I, "and I am willing"—

"Stop! *that* ain't the pint. I give you a *good* bed to sleep on, didn't I?"

"Yes, sir," said I, "you did all"—

"Stop! *that ain't the pint.* Ye got your breakfast, didn't ye?"

I nodded assent.

"My boy and gals treated you like a gentle*man,* didn't they?"

I nodded again.

"Well, I've refused yer money, hain't I?"

"Yes, sir, and I wish you would"—

"Stop! that ain't the pint; *but this is the pint!*" and the fire simmered in his eyes like molten iron in glass globes; all his forced calmness had left him, and he was an old Tiger *all over.* "You've eat my bread—yer hoss eat my corn—ye smoked my pipe—ye had my bed, an all fur nuthin—an then ye wanted to circumvent, not one, but all my gals, married and single, at one bite, darn yer little snakish gizzard; an now we'll settle, *or I can't draw a bead!* I never vierlates the law of horspitality at this house, nur on my grit [8]—so ye see that cross-fence, down *thar?*" (it was about 150 yards off.)

I barely nodded my head, and in looking, my eye caught the form of Tewalt and the girl with the blue eyes, behind the stable, busily enacting a piece of pantomime, evidently for my benefit. Tewalt gave an imaginary horse an awful imaginary thrashing, leaning forward, and occasionally stealing a look over his shoulder, as if he expected to see the devil. She took very deliberate aim at him with a corn stalk, and then poked him between the shoulder-blades with it, in no very slight manner.

"Well," continued the *old he,* "when I give you the word, you may start, and if ye start too soon I spile yer hide on my own grit, an I don't want to do *that.* I say, when I give the word ye may go, an perhaps you'd use them long boot heels of yourn *some,* fur when you start *so do I,* an when I gets to that fence—mind, it's *my line,* then we are off my grit—*I'm jist agwine to shute you, jist like a cussed mink* fur getting among my hens! I'll only spile ye with two holes, one behind, an t'other before, jist sixty-three to the pound,[9] adzactly, and yer kin can't say I hurt ye on my land!"

He began to hitch up his breeches with the disengaged hand, and laid off his hat, so I ventured to ask—more dead than alive—what the "word" would be?

"It'll be 'the old quarter tackey [10] word.' I'll ax ye if yer ready, an when ye ar, jist say 'go!' If ye ain't, say 'no,' but mind yer dont

8. Soil.

9. This obscure phrase perhaps refers to the size of the rifle ball and therefore the size hole it would make. The size of rifle and pistol balls was expressed in the number that could be made from a pound of lead.

10. A small, unkempt or ill-conditioned horse.

balk often, or I mite git to ravin an fittin, an go off afore you want me to, an then ye'll be *dead* beat sartin!"

During this preliminary direction I was gently playing my horse on the off side with my heel and hickory, to stir him up a little. I had ridden a few quarter races in my time, and was pretty well up to the dodge.[11] The old villain asked, between his set teeth, "ar ye ready?" I shouted "go!" and away we went. My hickory now fell ten times faster on the real horse than Tewalt's did on the imaginary one, and as soon as the old cuss heard it he bawled out to his boy, "Oh, dat rat yer heart, I say; I'll bore a hole in *you,* when I get to ye."

I ventured to turn my head and take a look at him; he had foamed at the mouth until it adorned each corner like a pair of whiskers, made of whipped eggs, and he was running *some,* I tell *you!* My horse, perfectly astounded at such unusual treatment, fairly flew; the panels of fence looked like a continuous stripe alongside the road, and the wind whistled a merry jig in my listening ears. *Spang!* whiz—phit! the ball had sped, and it had *missed!* I saw it tear the bark from a hickory, a few yards ahead. Oh, how fresh and warm the blood rushed back around my heart. I felt safe, mischievous, and glad, and began to rein up my horse. When I succeeded in doing so, I wheeled him in the road to reconnoitre. There stood the old Tiger, leaning on the muzzle of his gun, as if in a brown study; so I resolved to give him a parting "blizzard." I shouted, "hello, old cock; you have good victuals and a fine family, your gals in particular; but I would not give a button for your gun or your temper! You can't shoot for sour owl bait! Tell the girls 'good bye,' and the same to you, you old scatter gun!"

He began to re-load furiously, so I whistled to my horse, and left those parts—for ever, I hope. I have often wondered since, what he *did* do to poor Tewalt, for smuggling me the hickory which enabled me to tell this story.

SUGARTAIL.

KNOXVILLE, TENN., August 21st, 1846.

11. An act of evasion by some cunning trick.

THERE'S DANGER IN OLD CHAIRS!

A MOST amusing incident took place not long since at one of the first class hotels, in a western city, which, if it reads only half as well as it appeared, will most certainly raise the price of buttons, and depress "doctors' truck" in a proportionate ratio. The chairs in the dining room were of the best quality, and most fashionable style; but there being an overflow of guests at the time, a draw was made upon some depot of odds and ends, and among others two old chairs were hustled up, that had seen their best days on board the now defunct steamboats Bolivar and Plough Boy,[1] and given a place near the foot of the table, among their more pretending and gold-clad compeers—grim, gaunt, consumptive-looking old fellows they were, too, and reminded one strongly of a charity hospital or a sheriff's sale. Well, there they stood, with the names of the respective boats to which, in better days, they had belonged, traced in large bronze letters across the back rail, patiently awaiting some hungry guest to oppress them once more in their last and worst days.—Well, it chanced that two customers arrived in the city: the one the pilot of an ox-wagon, and the other its engineer; that is, he locked the wheels, "scotched"[2] them, and occasionally fired up on the oxen with a snake pole, when a hard hill had to be stemmed. They were as nice a pair of spectacles—no *specimens*—of the genus Hoozier,[3] as you could wish to look at. The driver rejoiced in the

This story appeared in *Weekly Nashville Union*, XIII (October 6, 1847), 3.

Knoxville *Standard*, III (October 19, 1847), 1. Reprinted without editorial revision.

Spirit of the Times, XVII (December 4, 1847), 480. Reprinted without editorial revision.

1. The "Bolivar" was a regular Cumberland River packet during the period 1830–1840 and later. Byrd Douglas, *Steamboatin' on the Cumberland*, p. 327. The Kentucky steamboat "Plow Boy" plied the Tennessee River between 1824 and 1832. Bert Neville, *Directory of Tennessee River Steamboats*, p. 22.

2. To block a wheel by placing a wedge under it.

3. Hoosier, an inhabitant of Indiana.

name of Bolivar, but was called in his neighborhood Bottletail, for short. He was "one of 'em," as sure as you live. He was as long as a covenanter's sermon, and about as fat as a "stall-fed sitting pole;" [4] his head was about the size and shape of a cocoa nut water-dipper, and his nose as sharp and thin as the gnomon of a sundial. His eyes were small and twinkling, his under lip gave back from the upper, and his chin receded from that again; his hair was thin, straight, and a flax color, and no two of a length; his feet were encased in number twelve brogan boots, and he made a track about the size and shape of the half head of a flour barrel. He wore tight red jeans, "oh no we never mention 'ems," [5] and a flax colored coat with ham cracker tails,[6] that came to a point about a foot from his heels.—His legs were remarkably small, but what they wanted in diameter they made up in length.—The fact is, he was split up to his shoulders—he was. He chewed tobacco, sung Barbara Allen nasally, and went about four feet at a stride, and slow at that. His mate was a fat, a *very* fat, overgrown green boy, about 18 years old, and the most remarkable feature about him for a fat one was *his* nose; it was an outrageous nose, and made after the pattern of a goose-wing broad axe.[7] It was said of him by the facetious J——— ——— that he got into a fight once, during which a man hit him on his nose with a handspike, when thirty-eight bats and a kingfisher blew out of it; but be that as it may, it was, as I said before, a most outrageous nose.

Well, they concluded, in solemn council, after they had fed their oxen, to take supper and breakfast at the hotel, or "grub at the tavrin," as they called it. When the bell rang, the driver took the lead for the supper room, with the fat one holding on to one of his coat tails. Slowly and warily, thus they marched along the table in quest of a seat, when at length the driver's eye fell on the Bolivar's chair on the opposite side, and next on the Plough Boy's.—Turning with a slow and labored wink on his companion, "Legs" said, "I *be* durn'd if these fellers don't adzactly know

---

4. Stall-feed means to keep and fatten an animal in a stall, usually for killing; a setting pole is a pole used to propel a boat. The combination implies a pampered but skinny man.

5. Trousers, in the nineteenth century, were generally known as "unmentionables."

6. Swallow-tails, as on a full dress coat.

7. An ax with a broad cutting edge for hewing timber.

how tu du it about plumb. See thar!" pointing to the vacant chairs, "du you know what them ar letters spells and what they're for?" The fat one gave a long, fixed, bewildered sort of stare, whistled, and shook his head. "Ah! son, you is green, I sees, yet; you knows nothing about a city;" and planting one of the brogan boots well forward, drawled out, "that ar cheer thar has on it B-o-l, Bol-i, Boli-v-a-r, var—Bolivar! thats *my* name, and that cheer's for *me*. The tother one is yourn, becase it has on it P-l-o-u-g-h, Plough—B-o-y, Boy—Plough Boy; and you *is* one, you know, and I *be* durn'd if them chaps ain't smart some—found out my name without axin, and your trade by your looks! Well, I *will be* durn'd!" The fat one was in the most profound amazement at the novelty of the thing, and people's smartness generally, and Legs' in particular; and during the time occupied in reaching the vacant seats had his oleaginous mind in a beautiful state of mystification in regard to the whole proceeding. When he sat down he shook his head mechanically, and turning in his seat, spelled out the words, tracing the letters with his finger. This appeared to satisfy him, and he "set to" on his supper in good earnest.

After stowing away as much provision as they well could, they disappeared until breakfast, when the grand finale of the thing came off.

They marched in to breakfast with much more confidence and deliberation than they had exhibited on the preceding evening, and found the table nearly full. After diligently searching among the vacant seats for their "cheers," and not finding them, they determined to examine those occupied, and at length found the Bolivar's chair supporting an effeminate, dandified person, with a thin mustache, very white hands, and long-toed boots. The Plough Boy's held a meek, pale-looking, sleek-headed man, with a white cravat, and who ate fried chicken and hot biscuit. Our hero peeped first on one side and then on the other, until he became satisfied of the identity of his "cheer." So he craned his neck over the dandy's shoulder and accosted him with, "See a-here! I *be* durn'd, mister, if I don't hate to stop a feller when he is a boltin his grub, 'specially when it seems to do him so much good as that ar flitter cake [8] is a doing you; but I be durn'd if you ain't made a small mistake, owin to the fog this mornin—you've

8. Fritters or flapjacks.

got my cheer!" "Oh—ah! *your* chair fell*ow!* who—how come you to own this chair?" He looked up at Legs, who stood leaning over him as solemn as a clock, and the mustache slightly curled. "Go away, fell*ow,* or-a-I shall call the landlord." "Now, see ahere, mister! that ar cheer is mine. I *be* durn'd if it ain't. It's got my name, my *cristen* name, on this here board; and if you don't vacate quick I'll mix with you so durn'd intimately that these fellers can't sort us without a sifter. We'll be like two pints of red eye in one jug! I *be* durn'd if we don't! *I* ain't feard of any thing that wears har this side Tar river,[9] so that you neednt set thar on my *pre*-mises, and turn up that hary lip at me! I cum from the forks of Beaver-dam,[10] I *be* durn'd if I didn't; and I'll grub right *thar,* or die on this dung-hill; I *be* durn'd if I don't! Ar ye gwine to *vac*ate?"

The dandy affected to pay no attention to this belligerent talk, but sipped away at his coffee, when quick as lightning our hero swung his huge fist around in a circle and brought it down on the poor effeminate's head, with a force that nearly drove him through the chair, and sent his coffee cup bounding across the table, whilst its contents flew in spray in all directions. The next instant he gave the chair a jerk that dislodged his victim, and he fell stunned on the floor.

A long, pendulum-like swing of one of the brogan boots shot him under the table, where he staid until the fray ended. A negro servant seeing the dandy disappear so mysteriously, sung out, "De great golly! if he haint druv 'im frew de floor!—run Pete, down in de cellar, an bring him up, while I gits de curiner."

During this time, the fat one had been singing a kind of second to the conversation of his patron in the ear of the sleek-headed man, who ate on without paying the slightest attention; but when he heard the crash, and, looking, saw that the dandy was invisible, he concluded that it was a perfect grease spot affair; so up he bounced, and retreating to a side table, locked his hands before him, and stood silently and meekly awaiting the end.

No sooner did he leave his seat than the fat one took possession, and fell to work on his predecessor's biscuit, coffee, and

9. The Tar River, located in Beaufort county, North Carolina, rises into the wide estuary known as Pamlico River.

10. Beaverdam is a small town in Kosciusko county in the northern central part of Indiana.

chicken, at a most frightful rate, without once raising his head. By the time our hero was fairly seated in his Bolivar chair, the landlord came, backed by a whole squadron of sleek negroes, and two or three bar-keepers, and without a word hustled him off towards a side door, with a negro hanging to each arm, his long legs making fearful gyrations and sad havoc among the negroes' shins the while; then, aiming one tremendous and well directed kick at his rear, sent him flying like a pair of scissors across the street. When they turned to wreak vengeance on the fat one, he was not there; he had made good his escape, and carried with him every particle of the meek man's "chicken fixens."

When the two friends met at the wagon, our hero asked the fat one, in a very dejected tone of voice, "I say, did that feller get a swing at *your* rear?" "No, by gravy! he didn't that; I seed his foot go plumb out of sight in the fork of your coat tail, and you rise from that yearth like shootin; so I moseyed quick the other way, but (slapping his hand on his stomach) I saved that feller's biscuit and chicken, and what little coffee he had on hand, afore times got too hot. I've got it right *here*." "Well, I *be* durn'd if it aint good luck for you, my son—*if* he had a planted that boot of his'n in your rear, he'd a busted grease enuff out at the top of your head to have greased a cotton factory. When he *raised* me I thought that he was a turning me inside out, that my starn would be ahead of my nose afore I went five feet, and that the bee martins [11] would build in my har afore I lit. I *be* durn'd if I was sure I ever would lite at all.—Oh! durn his eternal picter, I say. But them *war* our cheers, and if I warn't feard of being kicked into kingdom cum, I'd hev em—I *be* gaul durn'd if I didn't."

It is almost needless to add, that in a few moments after the fracas the old chairs were hurled over the balustrade, and converted into kindling stuff in less than no time.

11. Kingbirds, a species of eastern United States.

HOW TO MARRY

A FEW years ago I made one of the seventy-nine passengers on
board the fast steamer Emily Barton,[1] bound up the Tennessee. A pleasant, intelligent, go ahead captain, a good steward,
and social refined company, made the trip one of pleasure; indeed, long shall I remember the saucy Emily Barton and her
superb living freight. One lovely summer afternoon it was whispered that we were to have a wedding before the boat reached
her destination, said whisper starting first soft and low near the
stern, somewhere in the vicinity of the ladies' cabin, and speedily
making its way to the hall, the boiler deck, and even to the main;
like the snowball down the mountain, gathering size, form, and
momentum, as it rolled *forward*, until the principals in the interesting scene were not only pointed out, but the parson—some
scraps of the history of each, fiction, fact, and surmise, all
hashed up ingeniously, leaving you in the half pleasant half
painful suspense and doubt that opens the eyes so wide and
strains the drum of the ear so tight to all transpiring around you.
Well, we landed to wood at a magnificent beech bottom, the tall
heavily leaved trees with their silver grey trunks making a deep
cool shade, while they, with the grassy green bank that bore
them, were imaged in the glassy river so clear, so true, that
inversion only pointed the false from the real; cutting this
charming spot in twain came a murmuring crystal spring brook,
scarce four spans wide, to lose itself in the mass of Tennessee
waters, they in turn to be alike lost in the boundless sea.

No sooner was the staging out than there emerged from the
ladies' cabin a fine manly looking fellow, dressed in faultless
taste, intellect beaming in every feature, while all over his face
perfect happiness shone like phosphorus on the sea, and leaning
on his arm was the most loveable woman it has ever been my lot

This story appeared in *Spirit of the Times*, XXIV (October 21, 1854),
422.

1. This may have been an actual packet, although no records have
been found to verify its existence.

to behold, her fine hazel eyes (tell tales that they were) speaking deep emotion, and her expressive lip quivering with suppressed excitement, while her step, dress, and grace, was that of a queen. "There they are!" "That's her!" "Oh, how handsome!" burst from many a lip as we instinctively made way to let them pass to the altar, and where *that* was we had about as clear an idea as a transcendentalist generally has of what he's thinking about. But one thing we all seemed to know, that there *was* fun ahead, and to fall in *their* wake was the way to see it. As the ladies passed a gallant arm was offered to each, and thus we marched out of the cabin, down the stairs, across the staging, and up the sloping bank. Some fifty yards up the brook the pair stopped, and joining hands they stood *with the clear water between them*—bridged it was with twining fingers and crossed by a stream of love as pure as itself. All was silent—still—until broken by the minister, reading in an impressive manner, "And of the rib which the Lord God had taken from man made he a woman and brought her to the man. And Adam said this is now bone of my bone and flesh of my flesh; she shall be called woman, because she was taken out of man. Therefore shall a man leave his father and his mother and shall cleave unto his wife, and they shall be one flesh." [2] He closed the book and offered a most touching and beautiful prayer; not a heart but seemed to feel that earnest appeal to the throne of grace. Then asking the usual questions he pronounced them husband and wife. The bride slowly sinking on her knees raised her beautiful face, all covered with tears, and her clasped hands, and in the most touchingly sweet voice, tremulous with deep emotion, said—"And now, oh merciful Father, grant that our two lives thus united may peacefully flow on in one, even as this rivulet, until we reach the river of death, and undivided in faith or conduct, be permitted to enjoy Thine eternal smiles in the land of the pure and blest." Every pulse seemed stilled, hoping, wishing for more of this beautiful drama. Not a word, not a movement from all that throng—all, all was happiness. Oh, lovely panorama, how deeply thou art graven on this heart! The happy man was in the act of imprinting a kiss on the smiling lips of his magnificent wife, when the clear tones of a manly voice startled all from their pleasing reverie; universal gaze rested on a handsome, tall Tennessean, whose eagle eye

2. Genesis 2:22–24.

spoke *the man*—a fit representative he was of the State where sleeps a Jackson.[3]

"I can't stand this any longer, I can't by ——. Pardon, ladies, pardon; I have a proposition to make in the good faith of a man who never lies or trifles. I *must* make it or *die*—so here goes. Now I will marry on *this spot* any lady in the crowd who has the nerve to face such music; look at me, and if you can love me as *she* loves (pointing full at the bride) I'll promise to be a husband to you, such a husband as *she* deserves, and such a husband as a true hearted man will make to the woman who comes trembling under his wing. I further say that no spot or shame attaches to my name, nor ever shall; and his arm will support and protect the one who can trust it. Who'll take me?" and his eye ran slowly and steadily over the crowd of handsome women around him; his earnest manner and novel speech had aroused an intense feeling; all was surprise and deep sympathy with the fearless excited orator, when, to the astonishment and delight of every one, a fawn-like, blue-eyed girl, from the flowery banks of the Alabama, stepped to his side, and looking confidingly up into his eyes, with her hands on his arm, said—"I'll trust you, and God giving me strength will be as true and loving to you as you *can* be to me—I am thine!" By this time his arm was around her waist, and parting her curls (black as the raven's wing at midnight) looked steadfastly in her face for a moment, and "signed the contract" with a kiss that all the married ladies afterwards pronounced of the genuine sort—perfect, satisfactory. Raising his flashing eyes with a triumphant expression from the pleasant job just mentioned, he said—"Where is that parson? send him *right here*—on this spot we met and on this spot we'll be made one. I never let such luck as *this* pass *me* by waiting a minute, so go ahead—all's ready!" And the parson did "go ahead," and on that spot where they first met were they solemnly united forever. When the words "what God hath joined together let no man put asunder" died away, a shout went up that awoke the echo for miles; every hand was extended to the happy, lucky, venturesome fellow, and every lady in that crowd pressed the lips of his trusting and handsome wife (for a moment I wished *I* were her, but I instantly recovered my self-possession and thrust the weakness from me; women kissing each other always seemed a waste

3. Andrew Jackson, seventh President of the United States, died nine years previous to the writing of this story.

of sweetness to me, but they know best), laughing, shouting, happy, we all returned on board. Our generous captain set a splendid supper; the clerk made out two marriage certificates —they were signed by the parson and seventy-*four* witnesses (*five* more made the nine, you know,) men and women all told —everybody signed. Then we danced, we laughed, we made children of ourselves—yes, I am afraid we made fools of ourselves. But be that as it may, when the watch changed at the noon of night the bluffs on the dark shores of the river returned only and unbroken the echo of the hoarse coughing of the Emily Barton's engines, for we slept, and our dreams vainly tried to vie with the lovely reality of the evening.

As I wrote I often thought of your "New Correspondent."[4]

4. The pen name of Mrs. Harriet Marion Stephens (1823–1858) of Boston, one of Porter's few female correspondents, and a writer for whom Harris seems to have had some admiration. A woman who would dare to make an appearance in the all-male world of the *Spirit of the Times* possessed the kind of unconventional, fun-loving spirit Harris would later have Sut Lovingood admire in females. Earlier in her career, Mrs. Stephens was an actress who used the stage name of Rosalie Summers (or Somers). After she was married to Richard Stephens, a comedian, she began to write and in 1850 left the stage entirely for her literary endeavors. She first had published sketches and poems in the Boston *American Union* (under the signature of "Gay Spanker") and other newspapers and periodicals (also using the pseudonym of "Marion Ward"). She wrote one novel about miscegenation called *Hagar the Martyr; or, Passion and Reality, A Tale of the North and South* (1854), published a collection of stories and poems entitled *Home Scenes and Sounds; or, the World From My Window* (1854), and adapted for the stage a number of Dickens' stories. Her first contribution to William T. Porter appeared in the *Spirit of the Times*, XX (November 2, 1850), 434, and through 1856 she remained a regular contributor of letters about Boston drama, fashions, racing, and other cultural, social, and political activities. Speaking of herself in the *Spirit of the Times*, XXIV (February 18, 1854), 1, she noted that her disposition "to write of things as they exist" won for her "many a hard rap, from censors who think a sugar coating necessary for every objectionable subject." Writing about how they made folks where she came from, she stated, "They give them a little egotism, a little self-esteem, a little sauciness, a good deal of independence, any amount of mischief, a cart load of 'don't care,' ditto affection, and let them slide to take their chances with the rest of the world!" Her career was cut short by her death of consumption on August 26, 1858, at the age of thirty-five. Her biographical remains consist of a few brief lines in Francis S. Drake, *Dictionary of American Biography*, p. 865; *Appleton's Cyclopaedia of American Biography*, V, 666; and *Herringshaw's Encyclopedia of American Biography of the Nineteenth*

Would that she had been there; how her true woman's heart would have went out in deep sympathy towards the loving, daring, trusting ones; and how her enlarged and liberal soul could revel in such an example of earnest and true feeling. *She* could understand the heart's workings that cast off all conventional trammels and *dared* procure happiness at the expense of the usual and oftentimes silly restraints thrown around women. But don't tell her, for she says "she *can* get mad," and although a thousand miles separate us, and in all human probability we may never meet, yet I would not invoke the anger of one who is far *above* and beyond her day and sex in all that makes the *true* woman.

Century, p. 886. For fuller details, see James Oakes' obituary, "The Late Harriet Marion Stephens," *Spirit of the Times,* XXVIII (September 18, 1858), 381, and "Our New Correspondent," *Spirit of the Times,* XXIV (June 3, 1854), 188.

THE COCKNEY'S BAGGAGE

SUT Lovingood sends the following to an exchange. A full-blooded Cockney who is now taking notes on the United States, chanced to be on one of our southern trains when a "run-off" [1] took place, and a general mixing up of things was the consequence. Cockney's first act after straightening out his collapsed hat, was to raise a terrible hubbub about 'is baggage, and among other things wanted to know "Hif railroads in Hamerica wasn't responsible for baggage stolen, smashed, or missing."

"Well, yes," said the Tennessean addressed, "but it is a deuce of a job to get your pay."

"Why so?"

"They will perhaps admit your claim, but then they offer to fight you for it; that's a standing American rule. There is the man employed by this road to fight for the baggage," pointing to a huge bewhiskered train-hand, who stood by with his sleeves rolled up, "I think, if my memory serves me, he has fought for sixty-nine lots, an' blamed if he hain't won 'em all. They give him the empty trunks for his pay, and he is making a hundred dollars a month in selling trunks, valises, carpet bags, and satchels. Have you lost any baggage?"

"No, no, not at hall. Hi just asked to learn your custom in case hi did loose hany. Hi don't think hi'll loose mine, 'owever."

Here train-hand, who overheard the talk, stepped up and inquired, "Have you lost anything?"

"Ho no! ho no!" replied Cockney, with unusual energy.

"Can't I sell you a trunk?"

"Thank you, sir. No, I think I have a supply."

This story appeared in New York *Picayune*, XI (February 26, 1858), 70. The "exchange" or periodical in which this piece first appeared is unknown. It may be an excerpt from a longer sketch carelessly reproduced. Harris became known popularly by the name of his fictional creation, hence the use of Sut's name.

1. The derailment of a locomotive or railway car.

"Well, if you do either lose baggage or wan't to buy a trunk, already marked, deuced if I ain't the man to call on!"

It is needless to say that instead of raising Cain generally as Cockney had been doing, he betook himself to zealously writing notes on American customs during the remainder of the delay. Probably he indited something fully equal to the London *Times* Georgia railroad story.[2]

2. This story has not been located. The *Times* did not usually publish humorous sketches.

LETTER FROM SUT LOVINGOOD OF TENNESSEE

Knoxville, June 12, 1858

T HE *Union* last received makes me irate, exceedingly. "Fish story!" Indeed! Very well, Mr. E., take care lest you sunder the ties which have grown with our growth and strengthened with our strength,[1] for lo! these very many years.

A veritable historical fact is tinged with a light shade of improbability, by his willful omission of a point stamping the whole as an indisputable truth. I distinctly explained to the incorrigible E. that a cartilaginous handle boldly sprang from between the eyes of the incarcerated, jug-bound cat-fish. Instantly assuming the regular jug-handle curve, it attached itself again to the back, aft the gills.—Further, that upon dissection the roe of the doomed fish was found to contain, instead of the

This letter appeared in Nashville *Union and American*, XXIX (June 16, 1858), 2. It was written in response to the following notice published by editor E. G. Eastman in the *Union and American*, XXIX (June 10, 1858), 3:

"A FISH STORY—When over in East Tennessee lately, GEORGE HARRIS told us a story that we don't believe. It ran thus: A man in Greene county was fond of whisky. He went to the still house in his neighborhood and had his jug filled with the critter. Between his residence and the still house a millpond 'intervened,' which, of course, he had to cross. Before reaching the pond, he had exhausted the jug; and was—well, say, *tight*. He held on to the jug, however. In crossing the pond, he fell in, jug and all. He got out, but the jug sank in the pond. In course of time the man joined the temperance society. One day he went to the same pond to fish. Soon he found his hook fast. After much effort, he drew the attachment to shore and it was *his jug*. Still more wonderful to tell, *a cat-fish* filled the jug. GEORGE HARRIS thinks that the cat-fish had entered the jug and could not get out. He grew till he filled the jug, and grew its exact shape, square stern and all! We told HARRIS that we didn't believe this story, and he offered to produce the broken pieces of the jug, provided we would go with him to Greene county, which we declined."

1. Cf. Alexander Pope, "Essay on Man," Epistle II, lines 135–136:
   The young disease, that must subdue at length,
   Grows with his growth, and strengthens with his strength.

ordinary eggs, about a pint of regular Greene county jugs, no larger than a grain of wheat. These seed of jugs have been planted in a crawfish clay soil, and have "come up;" and the only question now agitating the jug region is, whether the plants will bear catfish or jugs? and, if catfish, will they contain jugs? or, if jugs, will they contain whisky? I believe in the catfish theory decidedly, somewhat influenced by the temperance prestige of that ilk. Be this as it may, I am greatly exercised and much refreshed by the perfect coolness which E. assumes in his disbelief of the story, and that, too, after offering to fully believe the whole thing, from the falling off the log to planting the jug seed, for a consideration, viz: one pair of WILL LOWRY'S [2] three dollar boots. Such is the lever moving a world. Agassiz [3] will believe it *without the boots*—see if he don't! I may here add that, if the crop proves to be catfish, the proprietor of the Massasoit House [4] "takes 'em all;" if jugs, they are sold to PRENTICE of the Louisville *Journal,* [5] with the right to use.

Read the following verbatim copy of an order presented to our patient Postmaster [6] the other day:

Mynheer Pos offis

you no gives the letter for Jacob Stultz to he but you gits I to save um he no git him never soon I git bof evry one, nor eny bodyelse

2. This person has not been identified.

3. Jean Louis Rodolphe Agassiz (1807–1873), Swiss–U.S. naturalist, was a prominent nineteenth-century researcher in ichthyology. He came to America in 1846, later accepted a professorship of zoology at Harvard, and wrote several studies of natural history, especially on the fishes of America. See James D. Teller, *Louis Agassiz, Scientist and Teacher.*

4. Presumably a hotel or restaurant the existence of which has not been verified.

5. George D. Prentice (1802–1870), journalist, poet, and humorist, came to Kentucky in 1830, after abandoning law for journalism, to write a biography of Henry Clay calculated to bring the retired statesman back into political prominence. He was offered the editorship of a Whig newspaper, the Louisville *Daily Journal,* which began publication November 24, 1830, and under his imaginative and powerful management, it became the most famed and influential Whig paper in the South and West and earned for Prentice a reputation as one of the great nineteenth-century editors. See *Dictionary of American Biography,* XV, 186–187; Lewis Collins, *History of Kentucky,* pp. 389–391; Thomas D. Clark, *A History of Kentucky,* pp. 340–344.

6. Harris was postmaster himself at Knoxville from July 27, 1857, to February 10, 1858. Donald Day, "The Life of George Washington Harris," *Tennessee Historical Quarterly,* VI (March, 1947), 26.

What heve letter, he here I gone so I save letter in lock you know
I—I is goot so save him to me you pays Jacob postage soon I say
PETER VON DYKEN

After three careful readings—first upside down, then cross-wise, and last diagonally—the P.M. declined any action in the matter, simply remarking that he did not believe any such accident ever happened, and insinuated somewhat against the teutonic theory that lager beer cannot intoxicate.

Whereupon *Von Dyken,* indignant, started after Stultz, that he might "verify." He steamed away at a gait indicating hurry, and, if all his motions had been directed to one direct course, his rate must have reached twenty miles per hour. However, soon two indignant round hairy faces filled the window—the Stultz face inflated with much wrath, and fearful to behold, while streams of lager beer, mixed with chewed sour crout, trickled down the ravines heading at each corner of his mouth. He gave one huge onion-flavored blast, slightly reducing the facial inflation, and then he spake:

"You pos offis, cot-am, he git letter all heap, mine to he I gone, he here give im everybody's pay me guilders all goot, cot-am, nix-fursta—hey."

The bewildered, bedeviled P.M. closed the shutters in their faces, and started in hot pursuit of a special agent to consult on the alternatives of resigning the thundering office or drowning himself. The special suggested the propriety of his doing both, in view of his great provocation. It is thought by some that the document might have been an order for Von Dyken to get Stultz's letters in his absence.

Truly yours, S——— L——————, of Tenn.

LETTER FROM SUT LOVINGOOD OF TENNESSEE

Knoxville, June 19, 1858

D O not the belligerent demonstrations among our prominent men (?), in these latter lays, strike you as savoring somewhat of the ridiculous—rather of the Bombastes Furioso [1] school. The lie "passes" back and forth for some indefinite period of time (always before a full audience); then a call for friends; then a labored set of carefully worded and dated notes; then— *smoke;* an Indian would say "heap of smoke." Meantime all the news mediums, viz: loafers, gossips, telegraphs, editors, and old women, exert their powers lauding or decrying the animals whose trenchant horns are so soon to lock for life or death; when, lo! after all the supposed notoriety for "game" has been obtained, at vast expense of tongue and ink and shaky nerves, here stoops the mediating angel in a staid, Methodistic "cool" old man, "whose courage has never been doubted," because no sensible person ever thought it worthy of a test—or the pleading tears of well soared beauty drop like rain in the gladiatorial arena. Presto, change!—a healing balm, written on gilt-edged paper, called an explanation, for which all parties looked as they did for their mint-juleps, comes dove-like amid the savage sanguinary crowd, and all's over; each principal struts, as well he may strut, under his cheaply earned honors! [2]

This letter appeared in Nashville *Union and American*, XIX (June 24, 1858), 2.

1. Bombastes Furioso is the hero in a burlesque comic opera of that name by William Barnes Rhodes produced in England in 1810 in parody of Ariosto's Italian epic *Orlando Furioso*. The name was applied to anyone who talked or bragged in a bombastic manner.

2. The particular incident which has stirred Harris's vituperation in this first paragraph is alluded to in the second. During this time and earlier, American politicians sometimes were given to quick-tempered violence as a means of resolving personal conflicts with their colleagues. But when physical combat was imminent, many saw discretion as the better part of valor and retreated. Henry Wilson (1812–1875), Senator

Take an example: Here's the redoubtable prize ox in the human cattle show. Wilson, of Mass., reveling in animal strength, filling the eye with a redundancy of muscle, yet the veriest coward that ever truckled to an inferior foe—sows his insults broadcast, and then simply acts the poltroon.[3] A four year

from Massachusetts, later Vice-President of the U.S., and a zealous opponent of slavery, had several opportunities to prove himself of this stripe.

The first occurred after the attack on Charles Sumner, Senator from Massachusetts, during May of 1856 on the floor of the Senate chamber. Two days previous, Sumner had delivered a two-day tirade against the "harlot slavery," during a speech on a bill for the admission of Kansas to the Union, aiming choice epithets against Senator Andrew P. Butler of South Carolina. Butler's nephew, Preston Brooks, Representative from South Carolina, retaliated by striking Sumner over the head with a cane as he sat at his desk. On May 27, Wilson angrily rose during a discussion of the events to characterize the attack as "brutal, murderous, and cowardly." Brooks issued on May 29 a challenge to Wilson to a duel, which Wilson answered discreetly with a message in which he refused to retract his statements but offered an explanation for refusing to meet him on the field of honor: "I have always regarded dueling as the lingering relic of a barbarous civilization, which the law of the country has branded as a crime. While, therefore, I religiously believe in the right of self-defence in its broadest sense, the law of my country and the mature civilization of my whole life alike forbid me to meet you for the purpose indicated in your letter." *The Congressional Globe*, First and Second Sessions, Thirty-fourth Congress, 1856, pp. 1279, 1306; Elias Nason and Thomas Russell, *The Life and Public Services of Henry Wilson*, pp. 187–188.

3. Harris here refers specifically to the events of several days before when Wilson repeated his earlier actions. According to the newspaper reports which Harris read in issues of the Nashville *Union and American* (which are not fully verified, however, by the transcripts of the session in *The Congressional Globe*, First Session, Thirty-fifth Congress, 1858, pp. 2896–2902), on June 10, 1858, while debating a bill under consideration of the U.S. Senate, Senator William M. Gwin of California imputed unworthy motives to Wilson. In reply, Wilson noted that "The State of California always had her hands in the treasury up to her elbows," and he "would rather be a demagogue than a thief." Gwin retaliated by calling Wilson "a slanderer, a calumniator, and a coward," and the next morning invited him "to visit some point beyond the District of Columbia for the purpose of accomplishing a settlement." Wilson's reaction was as expected. He replied in a letter, "I cannot mistake the intention and purport of your note, and I reply to it as I replied to a similar one on a similar occasion two years ago," and he repeated almost word for word his earlier statement to Brooks on dueling. Wilson offered to permit any three members of the Senate to arbitrate the difference and abide by their decision as to who was in the wrong. John Jordan Crittenden, William H. Seward, and Jefferson Davis were selected and they issued a joint explanation of the circumstances

old, well preserved hickory,[4] in the hands of a brother blacksmith [5] born south of Mason and Dixon's line, is the true antidote for his grog-house poison.

All this reminds me of an occurrence of the olden time, whereat I have laughed, and perhaps you may: Todkins was delivering himself of some rather pungent remarks, addressed point blank to Bynum (you well remember him), which were rounded off somewhat in this style: "And now you d – – d villain, you sneaking dog-ear'd puppy, I mean to *grind up* my foot and make a scabbard for it in your loathsome carcass." Bynum, who had listened with an air of bewildered astonishment to the whole invective, without once looking at the inveigher, took my arm, and, after walking some distance in silence, remarked: "I am a *very* excitable man, and, when roused, very exceedingly dangerous. I do not wish to trust my judgment in this matter, and having full confidence in yours, I'd like to obtain your deliberate

leading to the altercation, concluding that although Gwin's implications were "objectionable . . . they by no means justified or warranted Mr. Wilson in using the very opprobrious epithet with which he retaliated." Both Gwin and Wilson were requested to withdraw their statements, to which request both conceded. The *Union and American* commented, "Wilson acknowledged himself a non combatant in the Brooks affair, though a falsifier and a blackguard; and Gwyn [sic], perhaps, knew there was no danger when he challenged him." Nashville *Union and American*, XXIX (June 13, 1858), 3; (June 16, 1858), 2; (June 17, 1858), 3; Nason and Russell, pp. 247–249.

4. Harris could be alluding here to two possible events concerning the use of hickory canes as weapons. On April 13, 1832, after Ohio congressman William Stanberry had publicly reflected on his character, Sam Houston (much admired in Tennessee) attacked him on the streets of Washington with a stout hickory cane made from a sapling cut by Houston on the grounds of Andrew Jackson's home in Nashville, the Hermitage. The second possibility is an action of Wilson's which Harris could be turning against him. At the first Republican national convention in Philadelphia on June 17, 1856, in anticipation of a possible assault, Wilson appeared upon the platform with a hickory cane in hand and shouted to the cheering audience, "Gentlemen, I beg you to dismiss your fears. Your public servants . . . know how to defend their persons, whenever, however, by whomsoever, attacked," a boast he seldom lived up to. Marquis James, *The Raven, A Biography of Sam Houston*, pp. 162–165; Nason and Russell, p. 449.

5. Wilson began his career as a shoemaker (the human counterpart to a blacksmith) in Natick, Massachusetts, and he was always popularly known as the "Natick cobbler." *Dictionary of American Biography*, XX, 323.

opinion. Do—you—not—think the general tenor of Todkins' remarks, as addressed to me, were tinged (perhaps slightly so) with
—with—something savoring of personality?" I gravely replied,
most decidedly not; that I viewed them as the most guardedly
general remarks I had ever heard, and most particularly the concluding climax. Bynum was magnanimously disposed to accept
my interpretation, and proceeded towards dinner—*a continuation* of our walk. The next tableau was said B., "under steam,"
with Todkins in furious chase, armed with an old buggy shaft,
which he was industriously "grinding up" to a sharp point with a
dinner knife. Mem.: *he didn't catch him.*[6]

Anent these popular belligerent whirlpools in life's stream,
have you read the edition of *Register's* (a paper in our city) reply
to a very remarkable article claiming the paternity of the
publisher?[7] Has not the editor got the "law and the facts?" and is
not he "usin' 'em" both?

> "*Coon may choose to skin coon,*
> *Yet the eagle bides his time.*"

But it nevertheless brightens memory's glass, in which I think I
see a reflection of the interesting passage at arms.

6. Neither Todkins nor Bynum have been identified. Donald Day offers
in interesting interpretation of this tale: "A good idea of Harris' attitude
toward the North, which is probably a fairly accurate statement of the
general prejudice in the South, emerges from this anecdote. . . . actually,
Todkins [the South] does catch Bynum [the North] and a 'right smart
fracas' ensues." "The Political Satires of George W. Harris," *Tennessee
Historical Quarterly,* IV (December, 1945), 325.

7. Harris is referring to a local altercation between Charles A. Rice,
publisher of the Knoxville *Register,* and James M. Fleming, editor. Rice
took advantage of the absence of the editor to use the *Register's* editorial
columns to voice a political disagreement with him. As publisher of three
newspapers in the city, each of which was supporting a separate candidate
for Congress, Rice noted, "I have resolved on pursuing a more *consistent*
course as a Publisher, even if I have to conduct one of these papers
without an Editor." Fleming had been warned several times to cease
criticizing the candidate Rice favored. Upon return from a trip to Virginia,
Fleming published a sharply worded reply in which he characterized the
publisher's action as remarkable—"remarkable alike for its imbecility and
impertinence." He carefully defined the rights of the publisher and the
editor, and justly felt that his rights had been "grossly violated." Fleming
concluded, "Hence, I am no longer Editor of the Knoxville Register."
Knoxville *Register,* XLII (June 10, 1858), 2; (June 17, 1858), 2.

A green cockney,[8] city bred—a "posted"[9] one—who deemed everything he didn't know as not worth knowing, visited the country to recuperate, which laudable intention he most fully accomplished thus: In a "rewwal wramble"[10] he discovered, attached to a tree limb, some unknown kind of fruit, done up in grey paper, which he incontinently knocked down with a hoop-pole.[11] It *might* have been a muskmelon, but it *was* a hornet colony, as he afterwards learned, partly by inquiry. I visited the sufferer in the zenith of his inflation, all cream-covered, oil-anointed, and dropsical in the extreme—when he thus testified: "I *did* knock the 'article' down through mistake;" and, opening one eye as wide as the swelling permitted, he added, "I would not have done it had I known it were full of *red hot dirks*, in the breeches seats of a pack of little winged devils dressed in *Rochester stripes crosswise*." I never heard a more penitent and probable confession. *There is no moral to this tale.*

You have often heard, but perhaps never ventured to publish, a good yarn on Dr. Thompson,[12] of Atlanta, a generous, good man, and a tip-top landlord and wit; but he certainly caught it once: A traveler called very late for breakfast; the meal was hurriedly prepared. Thompson, feeling that the "feed" was not quite up to the mark, made all sorts of apologies all round the *eater*, who worked on in silence, never raising his head beyond

8. An affected, effeminate person.
9. Well informed.
10. "Rural ramble."
11. A smooth, straight pole out of which hoops are made.
12. Dr. Joseph Thompson (1798–1885) came to Atlanta around 1845 and erected the famed Atlanta Hotel, both the first hotel and the first brick building in the city. He previously had a successful medical practice in Decatur, Georgia, until a rheumatic illness forced him to give it up for less arduous work. For years, Dr. Thompson's hotel was the one bright spot in Atlanta, and any visitor of note, such as President Millard Fillmore or Alexander H. Stephens (Vice-President of the Confederacy), was escorted and quartered there. The hotel was destroyed in 1864 by Sherman's forces. An unknown biographer wrote of Thompson: "During his hotel career he entertained magnificently, and his fame as a host extended into many states. He was jovial and good humored, and the weary traveler was ever eager to reach Atlanta hotel, where he would be refreshed and entertained in the most delightful manner." See *Pioneer Citizens' History of Atlanta, 1833–1902*, pp. 24, 27, 125–126, 178, 217, 343–345; "Federal Census of Atlanta, 1850," *The Atlanta Historical Bulletin*, VII (January, April, 1942), 64; Elizabeth Hamleiter McCallie, "Atlanta in the 1850's," *The Atlanta Historical Bulletin*, VIII (October, 1948), 104–105.

the affinative influence of his fork, or by any act acknowledging even the presence of mine host. This sulky demeanor rather "flea'd" [13] the Doctor, who, changing the range of his battery, stuck his thumbs in his vest arm holes, expanded his chest by robbing the room of half its air, and said: "Now, Mister, dod durn me if I haint made all the apology necessary, an' more too, considering the breakfast and who gets it, and now I tell you, I have seen dirtier, worse cooked, worse tasted, worse looking, and a h – – l of a sight smaller breakfasts than this is *several* times." The weary, hungry one meekly laid down his tools, swallowed the bite in transitu, placed the palms of his hands together, and modestly looking up at the vexed and fuming landlord, shot him dead with the words following, viz: "Is— what—you—say—true?" "Yes, SIR," came with a vindictive promptness. "Well, then, I'll be d – – d, hoss, if you haint OUT TRAVELED ME." There was posted in the front door a small nigger, especially to tell the way faring man "dat he didn't owe nuffin *dar*, sartin sure." After he was fairly under way, Thompson was observed creening [14] from an attic window, taking a pro- longed rear view of the steed and his rider with a four foot tele- scope. It has been intimated that the Doctor hesitated many seconds between the choice of the glass and a double-barreled shot gun.[15]

Truly yours,
S – – – – L, of Tenn.

13. Flayed.

14. Fretting; or craning.

15. This anecdote about Dr. Thompson was excerpted and reprinted with minor editorial revision and slight condensation in the Sioux City (Iowa) *Register* of January 13, 1859.

NOTE FROM SUT LOVINGOOD

S UT expresses his sorrow that he is unable to throw more light on the "fish business"—would be more than happy to enlighten your enquiring Georgia correspondent. But can only reiterate the main *fact* of the story, viz: that the fish was covered by a jug, but why should that particular fish, therefore, contain "the small jug" is more than any "nateral-born durned fool" can account for. He expresses a perfect willingness, however, to send your correspondent a piece of the original jug, in the hope that thereby she may be able to judge of its gender.

S—— L., of Tenn.

This brief letter appeared in the Nashville *Union and American*, XXIX (June 27, 1858), 2, and is a reply to the following correspondence received by E. G. Eastman with reference to Harris's "Fish Story" (see "Letter From Sut Lovingood of Tennessee," June 12, 1858) and published in the *Union and American*, XXIX (June 20, 1858), 2:

That Fish Story Again

Our friend Sut has fallen into the hands of a scientific lady of the "Teutonic persuasion." We don't believe our correspondent is altogether what *she* (?) pretends to be; but we know that *Sut* is willing to gratify even the semblance of a female, and we expect a prompt answer:

STATE OF GEORGIA,
CALHOUN, June 16, 1858

Editors Union and American—

GENTLEMEN: I see in your good paper an expose of a fish growing in a *jug*. I decide, from Mr. Webster, this to be "a vessel containing liquid." This development is very remarkable. Natural history is *my passion*. Please excuse my effrontery—I have plead [sic] my excuse in exposing my passion (natural history). I wish to know from your friend S—— L———————— of Tenn., how he reasons for the "small 'jug' in the fish." I will take it very kindly if you ask him, and transfer his answer to me in your paper. This proves to me the theory of "natural progression." I would much love to have his facts, and how he reasons. You disbelieve, I inquire. "Truth lies at the bottom of the well."

I gratefully remember your favor.

FREDREICA MULLER.

N.B.—I watch for an exposition in your paper.

LETTER FROM S----L, OF TENNESSEE

Knoxville, July 3d, 1858

JIM H――― tells a good yarn about one of our "shell bark lawyers." [1] His client was up on two small charges, "frivolous
charges," as shell bark designated them, (forging a note of hand
and stealing a horse.) On running his eye over the jury, he didn't
like their looks, so he prepared an affidavit for continuance,
setting forth the absence in Alabama of a principal witness. He
read it in a whisper to the prisoner, who, shaking his head, said,
"Squire, I can't swar tu that ar dockymint." "Why?" "Kase *hit
haint true*." Old shell inflated and exploded loud enough to be
heard throughout the room. "What! forge a note, an steal a hoss,
an can't swar to a lie! D――n sich a sqeamish stumick es that!
I'm done with all sich infernal fools." And he left the conscien-
tious one to his fate.

I heard a "scrimmage" lately between one of our most popular Railroad conductors and a very fast lady! something about
fare or change. The conductor wore a long, roomy, white linen
sack coat, with a standing collar, and buttoned up to the chain.
The lady won the victory most gloriously by the following brilliant and awfully destructive charge. "You are a purty fellow,
aint you? You are the fust conductor I ever seed a gwine about
among a passel ove decent wimmen folks *in his shuttail. Aint*
you *shamed* ove yersef." I think he was, for he left that car quickly
and unbuttoned the shuttail coat.

Now for old SHELL BARK again. Showing what an unex-
pected course a "law case" can take when it tries itself. JIM
THOMASON was "hed up" [2] for tearing down a house, breaking

This letter appeared in Nashville *Union and American*, XXIX (July 7,
1858), 2.

1. "Shell bark" refers either to a species of tree, such as the scaly-bark
hickory, or to any tree bark that is scaly or flaky. Presumably, a "shell bark
lawyer," therefore, would be a sly, untrustworthy, questionable member of
the profession, one who today might be called a "shyster."

2. Had up, or brought to trial.

the delf, and "flingin, an oman into a mill pond." The case came up before two Justices of the Peace for a mountain district. Court was to be held in a small log school house in July. There was a cloud of witnesses and no cloud over the sun; while the prisoner's guilt was quite clear, and old Shell very cool. After soft soaping the two old spectacled gourd heads about their intelligence and profound legal ability, he drew from his saddle bags a greasy copy of "Cobb," [3] and read therefrom that "whar an emergency arose requiring the temporary absence of the *defendant's* counsel, not gwine beyant four hours and fourteen minits, that said counsel mout *demand* (to further the ainds ov justice) that all parties to the case should be put onder rule waitin his return, en ef he staid beyant his time a verdick wus tu be given again his client by the court while onder rule." Whereupon he claimed to have forgotten a book—would be back in two hours—and demanded the operation of the rule as to the court, witnesses, and spectators. One of the court said "twoud be powerful hot in the house." "Very well," said old Shell, "we will go out into the dog fennel in the field;" and ordered the court to the shade of a persimmon tree; the witnesses under a clump of pines, the spectators to the shadeward of a blackberry thicket, the prisoner on a stump, and the constable mounted a mound in general charge of the motley crowd, each lot separated about forty yards from the other. Old Shell mounted his horse, and as he passed the stump he remarked to the prisoner: "Jist es soon es the top of my hat sinks behind yan hill, du you jist run like hounds wer arter you, an mix yerself in that ar thicket an never be seed in these parts agin," which order was fully obeyed. The constable started in chase, but bethought himself that the prisoner was but one party

3. The most likely legal work to which Harris is referring is John Haywood and Robert L. Cobbs, *The Statute Laws of the State of Tennessee, of a Public and General Nature* in two volumes, although no rule of procedure as outlined below appears therein. Joshua W. Caldwell, in *Sketches of the Bench and Bar of Tennessee*, p. 34, notes that the book was popularly known as "Haywood and Cobbs." It is conceivable that some shortened it to "Cobbs," or simply "Cobb." One authority in Tennessee legal history does incorrectly cite the name as R. L. Cobb: Samuel C. Williams, *Phases of the History of the Supreme Court of Tennessee*, p. 36. Another possibility is that the story was meant to be set in nearby Georgia, in which case the lawyer could have been referring to Howell Cobb, *Analysis of the Statutes of Georgia, in General Use*, although it likewise contains no such rule of procedure. Quite likely the attorney is only bluffing anyway.

out of the four, so he returned to stand guard over the remaining three. After a while the spectators broke in a crowd; still it was two to one, and he remained with the "court," and the witnesses, and the last Old Shell heard from there he was still in charge, the "court" exhorting him to "stand square up tu his duty ef hit lasted till Gabriel blow'd his horn." It is needless to add that old Shell has not practiced before that court since, nor has he been on that circuit. Old Shell is prudent as well as sagacious.

I have a story of the trials of an M.D. in collecting a medical bill from a county court against a pauper, which I will send by the first safe conveyance.[4]

Yours truly,
S————L, of Tenn.

4. See the story "The Doctor's Bill."

THE DOCTOR'S BILL

IN 1828, let's see, that's thirty years ago—how time flies!— the following most amusing occurrence took place. Among the few of that day who yet tread life's stage is Doctor ____ well, Blank let it be; who, in his calm, inimitable manner, sometimes in a circle of friends (and he has many of them) tells the story. Prefatory, I must say that in those good old days the title of M.D. meant something more than an assumption of the affix with a corresponding prefix as a balance-weight, composed too often of impudence and empiricism. Doct. Blank was well educated, a Bachelor of Arts long before he took up the Materia Medica, spoke and read the ancient languages with facility,[1] a matriculant of the University of Pennsylvania—became a M.D. under Doct. S.,[2] a gentleman of the old school, who, though in the

This story appeared in Nashville *Union and American*, XXIX (July 10, 1858), 1. From all evidence, it was based on a tale told about himself by Dr. James Gettys McGready Ramsey (1797–1884), distinguished Knoxville physician, historian, and civic leader. He was graduated from Washington College in 1816, studied medicine under Dr. Joseph C. Strong in Knoxville, and then entered the University of Pennsylvania to study medicine for a year. Ramsey began his practice in Knoxville in 1821, and in 1831 the Medical College of South Carolina awarded him an honorary M.D. degree. Besides maintaining his medical practice, Ramsey also completed an important history of the state of Tennessee and displayed an active interest in education, banking, railroad construction, and civic improvement. See Dr. J. G. M. Ramsey, *Autobiography and Letters*, ed. William B. Hesseltine.

1. Ramsey began the study of Latin under a private tutor before the age of eleven and continued studying classical languages later under the theologian James Houston at Ebenezer Academy conducted by his uncle, Rev. S. G. Ramsey. Dr. J. G. M. Ramsey, *Autobiography and Letters*, p. 13.

2. Dr. Joseph Churchill Strong (1775–1844), physician, surgeon, and civic leader, came to Knoxville to practice in 1804, following service as assistant surgeon with the United States Navy and practice at Sunbury, Georgia. He also sold drugs and medical books, and taught medical students. His best known scholar, Dr. Ramsey, described him as "an excellent teacher of medicine," whose "practical remarks had always the validity of medical axioms." Mary U. Rothrock, ed., *The French Broad–Holston Country*, pp. 492–493.

presence of his patients he spoke in the vernacular, yet before
his students and his brother practitioners kept his right ear for
the learned languages and the pure technicalities of his profession. Preceptor and pupil were both legitimate sons of Aescula-
pius.[3] Their recipes and formulas were always written in good
Latin on their Day Books and Ledgers, and each medical service
and each article of medicine charged against a patient was put
down with learned precision and accuracy in that language in
which the fathers of the science first wrote the able and elaborate volumes which are to this day considered the foundation of
the Divine Art of healing. To charge a dose of *castor oil* was
outrageously vulgar and not to be thought of. The entry would
run thus: "Ol ricini ℥ j." [4] To say on his account "to pulling a
tooth," was unprofessional and implied danger to the patient's
jawbone. Doct. Blank would put it down: "Ext Dentis;" [5] and so
through the whole vocabulary of medical terms. At least one half
of Doct. Blank's practice then was given away, and in later days I
know he has not mended his habits. No one unable to pay has
ever been asked for it, and I hazard the assertion that in a large
and successful practice of nearly forty years, during which he
has built up a name not only as a very successful practitioner of
medicine, but a statesman, antiquarian, historian, and best of
all, a MAN, but few can show as long a list of gratuitous services
as he. Yet one time he *did* charge a distant pauper at the cost of
the county, justly feeling that the county needed no charity from
one who was single-handed striving for competency, while half
his time and his best ability were given to her citizens.[6] Hence
the following bill and its laughable sequence:

"Knox County, Tenn.,

"Dr.[7] to Doct. Blank

3. The mythological god of medicine and healing.
4. *Oleum ricini:* oil of ricin, or castor oil; ℥: apothecaries' symbol for
ounce; j: Roman numeral for the number one. Hence, one ounce of castor
oil.
5. *Extracti dentis* (*causa*): for the extraction of a tooth.
6. Although the following tale may have been related by Dr. Ramsey as
an actual occurence, it has no basis in fact. At least the preserved
"Minutes of the County Court of Knox County" (available in typescript at
the Tennessee State Library and Archives) for the years 1824 to 1830
contain no evidence that such legal events took place, although the principals involved in the story do frequently appear in the pages of the records.
Ramsey's *Autobiography* also contains no mention of such an incident.
7. Debtor.

"For visits, medical services and sundry medicines, &c., for David Dunkin,[8] a pauper of said county.

Total amount, $12 50"

This account was handed to the clerk, to be by him presented to the august "court," at its July session, that it might be audited and paid, upon which presentment the fun began. Esq. MOUNT [9] had promised Doct. BLANK to take the weighty responsibility of seeing the bill through the court successfully, as DAVID DUNKIN lived in his "deestrick," and the Doct. was popular, in fact, he took both the M.D. and his bill and the consequences under his patronage, hoping thereby to make all parties not only bow to his great influence, but feel indebted for all time to come for rare service rendered and vast ability employed. Well, with the permission of the sapient Squire Mount, we will "call court," and "perseed to biznis."

Major S———,[10] the then deputy clerk, in his quiet and smiling way, presented the account, and it was on the verge of passage, when a member at the west end of the bench craned forward and wanted "items." He said "he wanted tu know what the people's money wer agwine fur; spected hit wer all right, as Squire Mount sed so, but as he wer thar tu take keer ove the

8. David Duncan was one of Knoxville's best known paupers. In the minutes for the July court sessions of 1824 appears the following entry: "Ordered by the Court that forty dollars be allowed and paid by the trustee out of the County Money to John Doyle for keeping David Duncan a poor man One year payable Quarterly commencing the first of July 1824—" Similar entries concerning David's upkeep are found in the minutes for the July sessions, 1825, the October sessions, 1828, the April sessions, 1829, and the July sessions, 1830. "Minutes of the County Court of Knox County," Book No. 13, 1824–1826, pp. 34, 146; Book No. 14, 1826–1830, pp. 178, 230, 358 (page numbers refer to the typescripts in the Tennessee State Library and Archives prepared under the Work Projects Administration). David Duncan's name is spelled correctly by Harris at a later point in the story.

9. The names of Squires Mount, Raccoon M., Ollfat, Boggis, Hardshell, Maulit, Saveall, and Roundhead, naturally, do not appear in the court records. They obviously were created by Harris as indicative of the respective personalities or characteristics of people involved in the Knox county trials, but they can no longer be identified.

10. The county Court Clerk at the time actually was Charles McClung, but between 1836 and 1844, a Moses M. Swan did serve in that capacity. Rothrock, p. 536.

people, he'd be glad tu see a *few* itims, *his* people loved itims, an in fac, he'd never seed any harm dun by itims yet. He loved a few itims his self." Then he rubbed his knees with his hands, and wound up by scratching his head behind the ears on both sides; affected thereto perhaps by more "itims." Now was the golden moment for Squire Mount to impress his protege, the Doctor, with his power and influence. "He knew Doct. Blank well, a monsous knowing Doctor—he'd cured poor Davy Dunkin —knowed him too—lived in the deestrick—a onist man ef he was a pauper—all right—vote the amount and lets be doing sumthin else." But no; "this court" decided that "hit wur on-constitutional to pay any bill in the *lump*," and the "itim" man at the west end of the bench gained a victory, while the bill was "throwed outen court" until the October term, when if the Doctor pleased he might present it again in detail.

Well, he went to work and prepared it in full form, in good Latin, according to regular usage. Much fearing that it might fail for want of detail, he took pains, and a more unexceptionable or orthodox bill never appeared in court. Now mark how it was served.

In October, 1828, court met. Squire Mount seeing Doct. Blank in the room motioned him up with dignity. "Hev yer got that ar account now with itims!" "Yes." "Well, I'll hev it passed ur bust this court plum open. I did my dirtiest fur you last time, but them ar itims wurnt thar, (here he looked inquiringly at the Dr.). Does the itims make the account eny bigger?" "Oh no." "How meny ove em did you gin Davy?" "Oh, only a few." "They worked on his bowels powful, didn't they?" "Oh no, not at all." "Puked him orful, then?" "No." "Well, what in the H－－l good did they do Davy?" "Cured him." "Oh, I see. I allers sed you wer a hoss ov a doctor; you cured Davy with itims what dont either puke or purge. That bill shall pass." And he gave the Doct. a patronizing wink, three benevolent nods, and a lengthened approving smile.

Major S. held up the bill and announced its purport to the court, while one of his best benevolent, yet malicious, smiles flitted over his face. Silence profound reigned for a space along that august *long* bench of dignitaries, to be broken by Squire Mount, the patron of the bill and of the Doctor. Authoritatively he spoke: "That ar bill hes been *de*gested by Dr. Blank; he cured

Davy Dunkin, pauper, with *new* medecine, an now, for the second time, he axes for pay. I *know* the facs, and let us order pay and be done with hit."

"Is that the account we throw'd outen court last time?" said old Raccoon—M. "Send the 'papers' down to this aind of the bench an *we'll* zamine em." At this critical moment, the "papers" were held in trembling grasp by Squire Mount himself (the chairman of the court,) looking ever and anon over his glasses in search of the Doctor; failing to "spot" him, he despondingly passed the document along the line. A glance sufficed the more modest ones, and the troubled paper was "passed furder," now it stops; a huge pair of copper bound specks is leisurely drawn from the groin of a pair of flax and cotton breeches, and most carefully planted astraddle of a huge copper nose; the hand is moved near and far before them; a sweeping look around the room is taken to see if the focus is not changed, and then the paper is lifted for investigation. After a pause, "copper nose," after many scratchings and shakings of head, thrusting back his specks to their abiding place, the "groin," and starting the outlandish paper towards the clerk, thus addressed the court. "That ar dockymint aint 'cordin to law; hit's writ in Cherokee in part, and the ballance in nigger, to mistify *this court.* I onderstands part ove hit, an I think he's been a doctorin sum body else besides Davy Dunkin, an wants to *club his pay.*"

The mischievous clerk, scenting more fun, handed the bill to Mynatt,[11] the attorney, who read gravely, *seriatim,*[12] as follows: "May 3d, 1828. To visit—Arteriotomy"[13]— placing a malicious and undue emphasis on the last two syllables. "Tommy!" said Squire Ollfat, "I tho't hit wer *Davy* he wer a doctorin. Is Tommy Duncan a pauper too?" Squire Mount: "No, no, hits Davy. Tommy haint been sick at all; he pulled fodder fur me last week, an wer a cussin an a cavortin round yesterday at the still house, arter makin a fust rate crap.[14] He never *was* sick. I sees bof on em every day. Gentle*men,* I dont *on*derstand that ar charge," and Squire Mount shook his head doubtfully. The other members of the court now begun to crowd around the centre of attraction.

11. William C. Mynatt, attorney, appeared frequently in the Knox county court room on behalf of various clients, as the minutes indicate.
12. In a series; one after another.
13. Bloodletting from an artery.
14. After bringing to maturity a growing crop.

Searching investigation being now the order of the day Dr. Blank's claim was under a cloud. "Read the next line," said one. "Not ef hits for Tommy," said Raccoon M. Here Atto. Mynatt handed the "orful" paper back to the chairman, who boldly attacked the next line: "Man. & Sen. opt ℥ j." [15] "I can't make hit out," said he, "Squire Boggis, you'se good at figgers; cifer that out." Squire B. majestically and promptly reads: "Man sin often; but thar's a double izzard and a Y with dots over hit; what dus *that* mean? Raccoon is hit Cherrokee ur Nigger?" "Oh, durn'd ef I know ur care," said Raccoon, leaning back on the bench, and thrusting his hands deep in his pockets, while he crossed his legs with a slam, and then looked at his toes, indifferent to all things coming. Squire Hardshell here interposed, in deep voice, clasped hands, and solemn mien; (he believed in 'dippin and drams').[16] "I knows man sin often; I sin, the Doctor sins, Davy sins, and Tommy sins; but ef evry thing whatsoever crawl'd sin'd, is that any reason *Knox county should pay fur hit*? I'm agin the extortionate claim; the county paying fur men's sins, hits monsous, an a payin ove hit tu the Doctor at that, instead ove the church." Here the disgusting paper found its way back to the clerk's box, whose wicked occupant finished out the line, "Sal. Eps. ℥ ij." [17]

"Sall Epps, did you say, Mr. Clerk? How dus *her* name cum in Davy Dunkin's account agin this ere court, and through hit, agin the county," asked Squire Maulit, ('old broken specks,' he was called). "That won't begin to do. I know her well." "Not as Adem did Eve," said the incorrigible Mynatt. "I knows her better; *she won't sample*," replied the unconscious broken specks. "She's an orful caractere." Squire Sample (spelled with an *a*) [18] took up the thread. "Why, she's the durnd'st wust —— what ever knit a stitch in Tuckahoe,[19] *an I knows hit*."

Here Mynatt took the account from the hands of the clerk,

15. These are not recognizable abbreviations for any known drugs. Harris may be using his imagination to increase the potential humor of the situation.

16. "Dipping" could refer to either baptism by immersion, or the use of snuff by taking it into the mouth by means of a moistened brush. A "dram" is a small drink of whisky.

17. Epsom salt; ij: two. Hence, two ounces of Epsom salt.

18. A Samuel Samples frequently served among the magistrates during the eighteen-twenties.

19. The area east of Knoxville near Tuckahoe Creek, a tributary of the French Broad River.

observing that he would read the balance, as he wished to make a few remarks on the most extraordinary claim ever presented to any assemblage of reasoning, sensible men; and as the Attorney for the county, he meant to fight the swindle to the death. Thereupon, he read the next line. "May 7th, Spirits Turpentine, ℥ ij." Squire Saveall: "The turpentine mout do tu pay for, but I'm sot agin the sperits. Put me down NO." "Did Sall Epps ur Davy git the turpentine?" asked a lean, say nothing, modest Squire. "Don't know," said Mynatt. "Why, Sall got *hit* ef any body did," replied Sample. "Who, then, got the sperrets?" "Davy, I reckon," responded the iron-faced Mynatt. "Read on," from the now wavering Chairman. "Spts. Nit Dul ℥ ij." [20] "Thar's a heap ove sperrets charged in that ar bill," says one. "An a heap ove people, too," says another. "May 8th. Visit—Sal. Eps—nocte." "Read that agin, Mynatt." The infernal quiz, Mynatt, turned to the persecuted Doctor, and cooly asked, "What do you mean by 'nocte?' Doctor Blank." Dr. B., pale, but still courteous and polite, with a bow, "*nocte*—by night—night service, sir." Mynatt, to the Court: "Did you hear that brazenfaced reply?" A stupid, blank sort of look was at this moment common to the whole Court. "Doctor Blank charges the good county of Knox with a visit and service *at night,* to Sall Epps—he being the beneficiary, and Davy, poor Davy Duncan—the pauper—he wants to make his scape goat. A-w-f-u-l audacity." (About this time the temperature of the room was rather torrid, the young Doctor thought.)

"I don't onderstand," said Ollfat, "adzactly. Was hit Davy or the Doctor at Sall Epps's on the night of May 8th?" "Goodness only knows, (said Mynatt,) I don't. But one thing I do know; this county *shant pay the fiddler while they do the dancing.*"

The Doct. and other intelligent bystanders were in convulsions at this ludicrous scene. A ferret eyed Squire caught Dr. Blank in his merriment, silent as it was. "See," said he, "he's a larfin at his shame rite afore this yere court." The chairman sternly ordered the delinquent *"tu bring his face home,* least he mout hev to tote hit tu jail." *And from that moment he was dead set against the claim.*

"Read on, Major Mynatt," from a member of the court. "May 9th, Spts Mendeneri and Phl." [21] "More spirits! Davy must love

20. *Spiritus* (?) *dulcamara:* spirits of (?) dulcamara. Dulcamara is a drug employed in the treatment of cutaneous diseases.

21. *Spiritus* (?) and *phenol:* spirits of (?) and phenol. Phenol is an antiseptic and disinfectant.

spirits," said one. "An the doctor too," said another. "Go on with the rascally thing."

"May 10th. Ol. ri, and phl ℥ ij"; [22] "oil-of-R-y-e, did you say, Major? Wornt he rather choise in his liquors tu be a pauper?" "I think so," said Mynatt. "Didn't they both have a good time?" "Yes, I think they mout a had," from most of the court; Squire Hardshell not assenting.

"May 11th, ol, cornui cervini ℥ ij"; [23] "oil of corn, does hit read? Why he gets a new kind every day."

"Read straight along, Mynatt; hits got beyant the power ur will ove *this* court, long ago, so let's hear the balance fur infurmashun."

"May 12th. Visit nocte Sal eps and Mag Alb ℥ ij ae—ae." [24] "How is that? Major, ain't you mistakend? Sall Epps and Mag both the same night? Hits onpossible!" said Raccoon M. "I'se too good a judge ove human furbearance an moral capacity tu believe that. Onless the Doct'r tuck Davy with him." Here the Baptist "stood up." "May I ask, Maj. Mynatt, what that double izzard an two dotted ys an two twin E. A's mean at the aind ove that ar line." "O!" said M., "that jist means hurra—we are hosses —all right—weeded our row through—or something of that sort. It wont cost the county anything, however." The water craft anchored; when a huge, oleaginous squire, hitherto silent, arose, slowly sorting something in his pockets, and humbly "begged that the readin mout go on slowly."

"May 13th," says the inveterate wag, Mynatt. "Ex. dentium duorum." [25] "What's that?" M. gravely read: "do-owe-rum; which might be more plainly written: *you do owe for rum;* and being in this account, it must have been obtained for Davy, the Doctor, Sall Epps, or Mag; and I swear I don't think Davy or Mag drinks." "That's more nor I'd swar for Sall or the Doctor," said Raccoon M. Esquire Roundhead, hitherto silent: "Gentle *men,* I've been sat on this bench ni ontu twenty years, and in all my legal sperience I never yet seed jist sich a sensible bill es that. Ile ove corn; ile ove rye; rum, Sall Epps, and Mag. I mean tu vote fur hit, an Doctor Blank shell be my phisicker es long es he lives."

22. *Oleum* (?) and *phenol:* oil of (?) and phenol.
23. *Oleum, cornu cervi:* oil, hartshorn (ammonia water).
24. *Magnesia alba:* magnesium carbonate; *ae.:* aged.
25. *Extractorum dentium duorum (causa):* for the extraction of two teeth.

At this point Esquire Robt. Houston [26] came in, and in his calm, sensible, matter-of-fact way soon set all to rights. The claim was allowed, but it took years to regain the full confidence of "the court." Still the persevering and manly Doctor won them over. But to this good day, when he writes Latin he is sure who is to read it, and when he speaks it he looks first to see if any member of "the court" is even in sight.

S——L., of Tennessee

26. Robert Houston (1765–1834), first sheriff of Knox county, also served as tax assessor, justice of the peace, county trustee, Secretary of State of Tennessee, and state senator. Rothrock, pp. 430–431.

SUT LOVINGOOD'S HARK FROM THE TOMBS STORY

THIS good yarn, for the truth of which "Sut" vouches, that is, "in the main like a man takes a wife" as he phrases it, has appeared in several papers lately in an incomplete form. He has therefore in justice to all parties prepared a correct version for "THE AMERICAN UNION," well knowing that the Major will laugh as heartily as any one. The truth is, it is highly characteristic of the man; no one can more readily read through a rough exterior, or measure worth correctly with disadvantageous surroundings than himself. This is one of the secrets of his wonderful success as a railroad manager and his popularity personally, but to the story.

Anyone acquainted with Major Campbell Wallace,[1] the present able superintendent of the Western and Atlantic Railroad, will not fail to enjoy the following "owre true tale."

Many years ago, while President of the East Tennessee and Georgia Railroad, he chanced to be traveling over the line in a car where there were but few passengers, seated opposite the stove, wrapped up in his shawl and meditations connected with the gigantic job, which he had undertaken (building a railroad without money,) when night came on. Presently in bounded a brakeman, loudly slamming the door behind him—one of those country geniuses, who with a laudable ambition, had a day or two agone, abandoned the girls, the fiddle, and the plowtail, to

This story appeared in Chattanooga *Daily American Union* (March 17, 1868), 1.

Knoxville *Press and Messenger*, III (March 27, 1868), 1. Reprinted without editorial revision.

1. Campbell Wallace, born in Sevier county, Tennessee, in 1806, became president of the East Tennessee and Georgia Railroad in 1853, and rehabilitated and completed it from Cleveland to Chattanooga and Knoxville by June, 1855. As a railroad superintendent and commissioner, he devoted his life to developing the South's railway systems before and after the Civil War. *The National Cyclopaedia of American Biography*, II, 35–36; Philip M. Hamer, ed., *Tennessee: A History 1673–1932*, I, 448–449.

"climb in the world," to become a brakeman. He had been the king-bee at all the neighborhood frolics, at the house raisings, at the corn shuckings, and at the cross road's doggery fighting ground, and now he felt that he was a king-bee on railroads. Strutting up to the stove he slammed down his lantern, kicked the mud from his huge boots, on the foot board of the seat, spit tobacco juice copiously and noisily on the hissing stove, crossed his muscular thighs, took a survey of the aforesaid boots, with harness leather straps, and he bethought himself of the "customer" sitting opposite, on whom he proceeded to bestow a lengthened critical and saucy look, as though he doubted the "customer's" right to be in the coach at all. At length he sought the knowledge.

"Whar ar you gwine, Mister?"

"To Dalton,[2] sir," responded the Major quietly.

"Preacher, aint you?"

"No, sir: I am not, but why do you ask?"

"Oh! nothing only by——I thought I saw 'Hark from the tombs,'[3] stickin' out, all over you like measils. You know ME I recon?"

"I am sorry to say that I do not."

"Well, I'll jist be dam; why whar the devil wer you raised?"

"At Maryville,[4] East Tennessee."

"Oh! that excuses you, for if ever I hearn ove that settlement afore, I wish I may be durned, and I know *every* place, I dus."

"You seem to be well acquainted with the place you are *now* occupying," remarked the Major, almost choking with efforts to suppress his laughter.

"What place do you mean, Mister. This yere red bainch kivered with the dried skins off cow's tongues, or *my office*.

"I alluded to your office and by the way, what *is* your position on this road?"

"BRAKEMAN, by the jumpin' geminy. I tho't every body

2. An industrial city in Whitfield county, northwestern Georgia, thirty-eight miles north of Rome.

3. "Hark, From the Tombs a Doleful Sound," a hymn for burial services by the British hymnologist Isaac Watts (1678–1748), first published in his *Hymns and Sacred Songs* (1707) and entitled "A Farewell Thought." Its use has been mainly confined to America. John Julian, ed., *A Dictionary of Hymnology*, p. 486.

4. A city in Blount County, fifteen miles south of Knoxville.

know'd that, brakeman ove the Yeast Tennessey *and* Georgy Railroad."

"Unfortunately I did not know it," responded the Major.

"Well, you'd a dam soon foun' the fac' out, if you'd a cut up any shines roun' yere, huggin wimmen, or cussin, or tryin' to steal any body's carpet bag, or talkin sassy to the conductor or sich. Why I'd a chuck'd you butt foremos' thru that winder, like dartin' clapboards thru the cracks ove a barn, for I means to run this yere train on high moril principles, I dus. An' you dident know I was the brakeman ove this yere railroad?"

"Indeed, sir, I did not."

"Well, old Slideeasy, all I hes got to say is, *that for a man ove your looks, you know less than any body I ever saw.* How *do* you manage to make a livin', enyhow?"

"I receive a salary, I am President of this road; Wallace is my name. But I have not the pleasure of knowing yours; will you be kind enough to inform me?"

All symptoms of "kingbee" disappeared at this thunderbolt announcement, and in their stead, timid humility, crushed pride of place, a strong "get-away" desire, and a most confounded hang dog look.

"Now, please don't, Mister Wal————, Mister President, *don't* reach for my name; hits no use, for you'll never see me again; needent waste eny time a tryin' ove me for my sass, or in countin' up wages; I can't wait for either ove 'em. Daddy's sick, mam's reumattey,[5] an' I *mus'* go home right now."

Here he made a sneaking cautious reach for his lantern, when the Major's hand was laid on his shoulder with, "Be seated, young man; I wish to talk with you."

Then followed one of those mild, kind, terse lectures, by which he has made many efficient men from even more unpromising material than "Boots" was. The President on this occasion certainly exhibited in a signal manner that fine judgement of human nature for which he is pre-eminent, for this same rough hewn stick, became a most competent and trusty employee. He often says frankly that what he is, he owes to the forbearance and kind advice of Campbell Wallace, and vows that he never can forget the night when he mistook one of the ablest railroad men of his day for a preacher. He generally winds up his account

5. Rheumatic.

of the affair somewhat in this manner. "Boys, haven't you dreamed of climbing a perpendicular bluff ove rocks, and when you got almost to the top, was holdin to a root restin', for the last lunge, when the root tore out, and after fallin' some five thousan' feet you waked up, still a fallin?"

"Yes, often."

"Well, in a mild reduced way, you have an outline idea of the fall Wallace gave me that night. But he made a man of me,—Say fellers, there is *one* thing you've all got to quit, in tellin' this story on me."

"What's that, mate?"

"Why I never called the Major, 'Old Slideeasy.' Jim Bridges, or George Brocins, put that to it, like the truth wasn't bad enough, durn 'em. Thank God, I have never spoke a disrespectful word ove him since I found him out, and no body else can justly, or shall where I am. No, no; that Slideeasy part, is an infernal lie."

Sut Lovingood's Yarns

Between the time that Sut Lovingood first appeared in the pages of the *Spirit of the Times* in November 1854 and the outbreak of the Civil War in April 1861, Harris contributed to newspapers and periodicals in Tennessee and elsewhere a quantity of stories about Sut Lovingood. Of those which were published during the seven-year period and survive in fragmentary or complete form, eleven are humorous yarns and three are political satires (two of which appeared in several installments). The two types of stories indicate the double function Sut was made to perform throughout Harris's career—a literary figure living partially in a world of reality and mostly in a world of his own making, and an ironical and literal mouthpiece for Harris's political opinions and satirical attacks. The second time Harris wrote about Sut, in fact, was in the latter vein. This was "Playing Old Sledge for the Presidency," presenting his views on the 1856 presidential race between Buchanan, Fillmore, and Frémont. After the war years, Harris continued to write about Sut until his death, and of what he produced between 1865 and 1869 we have in all twenty-six humorous tales (including the sixteen that appeared in the collected *Yarns* for the first time) and six political satires (one of which was published in four installments).

The uncollected yarns of Sut Lovingood add to the Harris canon a considerable number of new adventures on the part of the Tennessee mountaineer and provide new insights into Harris's mind and art. They also display the consistency of his technical standards despite the intervention during the height of his literary career of the Civil War, a conflict that would deepen his cynicism considerably and in his political satires unleash an uncontrolled vituperation.

Two of the stories have not survived in complete texts. "Sut Lovingood and the Locomotive" is no more than a brief anecdote that went the rounds of the journals. And since this is the only incidence of an anecdote by Harris, it may be assumed that it is actually a surviving excerpt from a longer story now lost. The subject, what happened when Sut first saw a locomotive, displays the typical reaction of the inexperienced country dweller to the product of modern technology and progress. To force this new invention into the narrow framework of his traditional experience, Sut animalizes the machine as a "beastes" whose steam blast is a nicker for her colt. The second piece, "Saul Spradlin's Ghost," does not exist in a full text simply because no copy of the issue of the Chattanooga *Daily American Union* containing the second installment has survived. All that we have is the tantalizing lead into a story in which Sut has been sent to bring Parson Small to widow Hunter's house in order to exorcise the spirit of Saul Spradlin. Only by mentioning the fact that food will be available, and that the widow has a more than spiritual interest in the parson, can he be persuaded to go. As a hint of what is to come, Sut tells George, "Instid of layin hit as we aim'd tu do, we misfortinatly made a mistake in the cungerin an' raised the devil."

Among the complete texts, "Sut Lovingood's Chest Story" is one of the best. This yarn completes the cycle of stories dealing with the Burns family—Sicily, who originally perpetrated the "love powder" trick on Sut in "Blown Up with Soda," and her father who is sent on a wild bull ride as a result of Sut's revenge in "Sicily Burns's Wedding" and "Old Burns's Bull Ride." All three of these were collected in *Sut Lovingood, Yarns,* and Harris must have intended to include the "Chest Story," since in the "Preface" he mentions the central victim, Doc Fabin, as one of the "misfortinit pussons menshun'd inside yere." As a continuation of Sut's revenge on Sicily, Harris has him fulfill the role of minister of justice once more. Sicily has proven unfaithful to her new husband, Clapshaw the former circuit rider, by finding her "affinity" in Doctor Gus Fabin ("the boys called him Gut Fatty fur short"), "a man powfull with pills and squts." Sut describes him with typical color and exaggeration:

He wer jist four foot fourteen inches high, an wer taller a lyin down than when he wer standin up. His eyes wer like ontu two huckelberrys es tu color and size, stuck deep inter a big ball ove red putty. If he'd been killed and biled in a hogshead ove lye, he'd a made soap enuf tu a washed away the sins ove a whole know-nothin congressional deestrict—congressman, lawyers, wimmen an all.

Sut catches the couple during an adulterous act while Clapshaw
is over the mountain collecting store debts. The doctor hides in a
trunk, which Sut attaches to a scared horse, and he is then sent
bumping half way across the county. In one passage, Harris uses
the medieval concept that heavenly portents foretell dreadful
events about to occur on earth as a basis for some vividly imaginative imagery. Before the wild trip, Sut sneaks up to the trunk
in which the trembling victim is hiding, and pretends he is
Sicily:

"sumthin arfuls agwine tu happen imedjuntly; thar's signs an
wunders in the ar; ni ontu twenty full moons am a hangin in the ar
abov the comb of the mountin, an they all hes eyes an noses like
mister Clapshaw's, an they's a makin dredfull mouths et me, en thar's
a 'thousand laig' wum ontu the fence es long es a close line, hits
body is red an streaks ove sheet litenin is a playin amung hits scales,
an hit hev two imiges ove peple in hits mouf, like ontu you an me.
I kin see my har a hangin most tu the yeath, an now an then hit gins
a shake an great big drops ove fat comes outen you, an afore they
drops tu the groun they ketches fire and burns like turpentine.
. . . thars vexashun ove sperit an bodily tribulashun ahead fur us
bof."

Harris sends Sut out to see the world in "Sut Lovingood
Escapes Assassination," "Sut Lovingood's Adventures in New
York," and "Sut Lovingood at Bull's Gap." In the first, Sut is
brought into direct confrontation with the stock speculators on
Wall Street, visits one of New York's popular hotel restaurants,
and is noticed by P. T. Barnum who wants to stuff him as an
exhibit for his famed museum. He is finally put to flight by a
photographer whose equipment Sut mistakes for a weapon.

Harris's treatment in the second New York piece of the Fifth
Avenue dandy, in view of the time he was writing, is rather bold
in its explicit detail about the dandy's femininity and lack of
sexual virility:

"No'th Ca'lina am noted fur pole cats, Georgia fur groun-hogs, an'
Tennessee for coons; I knows this frum 'sperience; an' now I kin say
that New York am noted in the same line fur dandys, (do you know
the varmint?) an' I'd a durn'd site rather mix with the stink ove the
pole cat, the rascality ove the coon, an' the dirty ways ove the groun'
hog, then jest tu see one ove these cussed infunel spider laig'd wuthless fixin's. They haint neither man nur 'oman, 'caze they can't talk
good nor fight like wun, or kiss ur scratch feelin'ly like t'uther. They
seems sorter like a strange wether what had seen a heap ove tribulashun among an ekal number ove rams an' yews—they's butted

about permiskusly by the one, an' is snifft at by t'uther; and as they can't fill or feel the instink ove a man, nur do the juty ove a 'oman, they jest settles on a cross fence atween the two' an' turns inter the wust kind ove fool monkeys despised by wun, an' larft at by t'uther, and the most human view you gits ove 'em, is when they is above you a climbin' up. . . . S'pose a expectashun towards him wer a cumin' from a tarin wild school gal what had seed snow say about sixteen times, an' flowers an' leaves es often, wou'dn't she meet a disappintment? An' then she'd jest kill him with contem't, an' feed the ca'kus tu her daddy's work steer what is yoked with his bull, in the view ove hit bein' suitable feed fur one in his condishun."

Sut also encounters "the only man in New York what kin hold a candil for me tu act durn'd fool by," Horace Greeley. Using Greeley as a representative of modern progress and technology, Harris vents his hatred for things Greeley had championed by accusing the liberal reformer of carrying out some rather strange sexual experiments, equally graphic in their suggestive detail. Greeley has had a female friend "tu try a few small 'speriments with a steam rock drill, while he practices a while on a thirty ton locomotive, an' specks the consekenses will 'stonish the world." Such unnatural experimentation, Harris feels, will ultimately call down God's wrath: "he'll keep on till thunder striks him yet, see ef hit don't." Greeley accuses Sut himself of being "a livin' sample ove human progress an' free love atween a kangaroo an' a mowin' mershean."

Like "Tripetown: Twenty Minutes for Breakfast," in the collected *Sut Lovingood, Yarns*, "Sut Lovingood at Bull's Gap" is primarily a diatribe against the poor food and accommodations provided by nineteenth-century hostelry and inn keepers. Complaints about the food and sanitary arrangements at inns extend back in literature at least as far as Shakespeare, who provides in the scene so often noted for its rustic realism, Act II, Scene i, of *I Henry IV*, a group of travelers who complain of the inn at Rochester: "Peas and beans are as dank here as a dog, . . . I think this be the most villanous house in all London road for fleas. . . . Why, they will allow us ne'er a jordan, and then we leak in your chimney; and your chamber-lie breeds fleas like a loach."

Harris's tavern keeper is one who glories in his poor service and keeps the place only for the curses it brings down on him. His warmest memory is of the time a group of customers "cussed him pussonely, till his jackit buttons flew off an the ainds ove his har cotched fire; then they turned in ontu a stage agent an cussed him into a three weeks spell ove fits and diarrear, . . . an then finished off by cussin wun ove the stage waggins ontil hit run off inter the woods without eny hosses tu hit." The hyperbole is typical of the frontier braggard, but the coarse excremental detail, "diarrhea," is the kind of thing only Harris, among the frontier humorists, would put into print.

When Harris writes about the bullfrog, who saves himself from the rain waters by paddling away in an old over shoe with a spoon, "injun way," he is drawing upon the same pool of oral bullfrog stories that Twain used when he wrote "The Celebrated Jumping Frog of Calaveras County." Published seven years later than Harris's story in 1865, it is one of Twain's best contributions to the school of frontier humor where he received his literary training. One of Harris's most memorable minor characters also appears in the yarn, a "big-thunderin" Dutchman, the worst Sut has ever seen for "fat an unonderstandable lingo." He swallows chickens whole, punctuates ladles of sauerkraut with chunks of beef steak, gulps down imitation beer made with dish water, red pepper and "tanglelaig whisky," and pronounces it all "tam goot." During the night Sut awakes to find the Dutchman mounted on the foot of the bedstead, crowing like a rooster; then, he jumps down on the floor and imitates a bull. Sut discovers that he is sleep walking and in the process of awakening him causes him to split open his stomach. Sut sews him back up with some crude implements, and the Dutchman's only concern is that he might leak his lager beer. Fantastic as he may be, the Dutchman is Harris's contribution to the comic fat-man tradition, of which Falstaff is the prime example.

This story is also the source of Sut's famous dog story, an anecdote that was excerpted and widely reprinted during Harris's lifetime (the present editor has found five examples which appeared between 1859 and 1869, as indicated in the footnotes to the yarn). One wonders why this piece was so popular, since it depicts in cruel detail how Sut, when a boy, makes a firecracker out of some old meat and lets the dog, "a mangy, flea bitten, grey ole fox houn," swallow it. The dog is literally torn to pieces, and its entrails are vividly described as hanging "in links onter the cabin chimley, sept about a yard in mam's bussum." This is fairly distasteful even for the modern reader, and one is hard put to explain exactly why the nineteenth-century reader found it humorous.

"Sut Lovingood's Hog Ride," set in Nashville before the Civil War when that city was the most important dry goods market south of Philadelphia, treats the Jew as a comic figure in the traditional way of the time and age, although a modern reader might consider it almost anti-Semitic. But Harris might be defended in the same way that some scholars have excused the seeming anti-Semitism Chaucer displayed in his Prioress' Tale: there were few or no Jews living near either of them during their lifetimes. The supposition is that, had they known any, they might have realized that Jews were ordinary human beings and might not have treated them fictionally as diabolical abstractions.[1]

Fedora S. Frank has noted in her study of Nashville's Jewry that "An examination of contemporary writings proves most conclusively that the Jew was not only a rarity but an unknown quantity in Nashville history prior to 1840." [2] When the first Hebrew Benevolent Society was founded in 1851, it consisted of only five families and eight single men, and by 1860 there were no more than three congregations in the entire state of Tennessee.[3] It is very likely then that Harris never became acquainted with a Jew either in Nashville or Knoxville. But there is no reason to expect either Chaucer or Harris not to have accepted the common social superstitions and prejudices of their cultures or to have displayed any sort of liberal, open-minded humanitarianism toward Jews. Even Shakespeare's Shylock, despite his human touches, is heavily influenced by traditional treatments of the Jew in medieval literature as a merciless usurer.

Harris's use of Christian allusion is interesting. Sut calls the clothes dealer in the yarn a "Ch—–st killin . . . hoss"; the pants he loses are *cross* barred britches; a bystander (who, in fact, seems to be a carpenter) accounts for the hog's behavior by noting, "The devils in that swine"; a man struck down in the confusion surrounding Sut's hog ride lies in the street "wif his arms spread like he wer crucified dead," and besides other names, Sut calls the Jew "Pontshus Pilit." A modern critic with a bent for Chris-

1 See Marchette Chute, *Geoffrey Chaucer of England*, p. 296.
2. Fedora S. Frank, *Five Families and Eight Young Men*, p. 18.
3. *Ibid.*, p. 39.

tian symbolism might conceivably find some curious meanings in this tale.

Harris takes a few strong jabs at contemporary social customs in "Sut Lovingood's Big Dinner Story," a yarn which probably has more action in it within a closer area than most of the other stories. When the high-toned Mrs. Jarrold holds a big dinner to expose her "bud of promise" to a local lawyer of dubious reputation but proper social station, Sut intervenes to hide among all the dishes a variety of animals and "venemous reptiles, too numerus an' horrid to menshun." The wild scene that follows the uncovering of the dishes is extravagant, broad, and effective in capturing the minutest detail of action.

In the person of Mrs. Jarrold, Harris especially attacks filiopietism or ancestor worship. This kind of person, says Sut, "ginerily has a pedigree wif one aind tied to thar sturn, an' tother one a-soakin' in *Noah's* flood, an' they'l trace hit back for you, round the jails, onder the galluses, apast the soap works, an' over the kitchens, ove four thousin years, an' if you'l notice clost, hit makes some ove the shortest kind ove dodges, to miss 'em all, but by golly, hit does miss 'em, an' hits every durnd castil, an' throne, on the whole road." But Sut also dislikes her social pretensions, her big points of gentility being, among many cited, coiling up her nose at "low trash," hanging up fly paper to catch flies, keeping *The Pilgrim's Progress* on the candle-stand, and "thinks callin dung—dung, bad grammer."

The social convention of a planned marriage also is a direct target of Harris's satire. Mrs. Jarrold invites to the dinner "all the ugliest gals roun thar what cum up to her idears ove decent standin', so as to set off the 'bud ove promice' in the eye ove" the young lawyer. But among the girls invited is one Violet Watson, a representative of the kind of girl Sut most admired (and perhaps Harris himself), about whom he says, "not a purty gal, I know, but smart, neat an' as full ove mischief as a turtil is ove aigs in May. She had no sort ove fancy for Misses Jarrold's fool ways, an' valued Mister Gripes [the lawyer] about as she would any other peckerwood or pole cat." This unconventional, fun loving girl assists Sut in pulling off his pranks.

The subject matter of "Sut Lovingood Reports What Bob Dawson Said, After Marrying a Substitute," is most unusual in view of the Victorian attitudes of Harris's time. The central plot itself, the story of Bob Dawson's unfortunate marriage, is a nineteenth-century variation on an ancient theme in ribald humor, poetry and prose, one which has furnished the substance of many an oral barroom joke: an anxious and eager husband finds, on his wedding night, much to his dismay, that when his bride disrobes, most of her physical components are false. She removes the padding from around her hips and legs, two imitation breasts, her false teeth, a glasseye, a wig, and when she intimates that perhaps one other false object yet remains to be discarded, the husband bolts for the door and clears out of the state never to return.

Harris skillfully plays his version of the story for all its ribald possibilities, but the story also leads Sut into a dissertation on a contemporary custom among the women: that of rounding out certain parts of their anatomy with substitute fillers, especially around the bust line. In the slang of the period, what we now call "falsies" were called "palpitators," and Harris, indulging in none too subtle word play, calls them "palpititytators." Once again, it's the "unnaturalness" of these modern innovations that disturbs Harris. "Now jis' answer me one questin," says Sut, "what in the thunder an durnashun do you recon the comein generashun ove babies am to do for milk? That's what's a pesterin' me." Sut makes a vow: "If ever I interjuces, insinuates, or socks ary one ove these paws in atwix the silk callicker or gingham an' the bustez ove one ove the tother sort ove cats, onless I hes had a pufeckly fur sight afore han', I jis' wish hit may get bit off at the wrist."

The humor in "Sut Lovingood's Big Music Box Story" turns upon a typical prank of Sut's. He sicks his dad's dog, Boze, on a stranger who wanders accidentally onto the Lovingood property; the man climbs a tree, but fails to escape the jaws of Boze, who fastens himself to the seat of the victim's pants. Sut's "king fool" Dad gets involved, but the rumpus is soon broken up when a music box dropped by the stranger begins to play eerie music. Sut thinks either Dad or Boze is having the music mauled out of him. Boze takes off for the woods, and Dad departs down the road, "Feard ove his herearter bein' clost about." The story does provide some examples of the common physical crudities Harris might include without qualm. In the beginning Sut is sitting on a fence with his trousers' leg rolled up, "a saftenin' the holts of the dorgticks on my laigs with spittil." Sut can even philosophize on the subject: "tick bites am curious; they makes the sweetest scratchin' spots, for about a day, I ever had the scratchin' ove, an arter that the sorest bump, an' the blackest scab outside ove the small pox."

Returning to his adventures as a thirteen year old, in "Sut Lovingood, A Chapter from His Autobiography," Sut recalls some of his first attempts to discover "what his gif' am, his bes' pint, what game he's stronges' on." The sketch consists of six related anecdotes, two of which are notable. One describes a fight between Sut's mother and Sall Simmons, a local woman of loose morals who suckles "cum by chance childer," has no latch on her door, and greases the hinges. The actual basis for their argument, Sut reveals, goes back to "an ole grudge atwix 'em . . . sumfin 'bout dad," thus indicating that the old man is not only a "king fool" but an adulterer as well. The last anecdote in the piece is memorable as one of the funniest scenes in Harris's writings. To get back at a couple who have bemeaned Sut, he releases into their bed one night a bag full of black ants. The ensuing scene, in which the prudish husband tries to preserve the proper respect for his wife, as she is forced to discard her night gown and he rolls from one end of the room to the other, is told with just the right amount of restraint and controlled characterization. The couple eventually take off for the creek, both in the nude. Sut wryly concludes, "Folks do say, that him an' her dont agree very well, since they danced that Firginey reel naked, by moon light. But then folks do lie so, you know, George." Sut's revenge has a long-lasting, often permanent effect.

In "Bill Ainsworth's Quarter Race," Harris returns nostalgically to the "Old Times" in East Tennessee, around the year 1833, when he was only nineteen and the South was more interested in quarter racing and frolics than in modern progress and social advancements. With a keen eye for local color and character, and a much more advanced stylistic control, Harris returns to the subject matter of his early "Sporting Epistles," and describes through Sut the scenes before and during a characteristic Tennessee quarter race. Sut is in top form: "whisky warnt made to be drunk on the sly. Hit warnt intended no how for wimmen, passuns, nor hypocrits." Pretending to relate his difficulty at Bill Ainsworth's horse race, "about catching a flea, or a bug, off a young lady," instead Sut dwells on the physical beauties of the two race horses, Ariel and Kate ("Standin' side by side, they 'minded me ove a locomotive, with steam up, all brass, polish an' power"); the card playing among the men "for from a dime to fifty dollars"; the food prepared by "fat ole wimmen"; the young men winking at the young girls "lookin' soft an' sweet"; the music played by Claib Nance "like no other man ever has"; the old toothless men of another generation who fought in the Revolutionary War and under Andrew Jackson against the Creek Indians in Alabama and the British in New Orleans; the young Negroes wrestling "briches holts"; and dozens of other engaging activities seen and heard on such a pleasant occasion. So enrapt are Sut's listeners that they do not notice, until after he has finished describing the race, that he failed to tell the story he said he would. "You never intended to tell that story, you are *ashamed* of it," says George. But Sut is too sleepy to continue; "No, I aint sham'd—you be durn'd, I'l swear I'l tell hit—some time."

Although there is much in this story to commend, and it would have warmed the heart of William T. Porter during the days of the *Spirit of the Times* (both were now deceased), this sketch is a little too nostalgic to be humorous to the modern reader. But two critics have responded to it generously. Walter Blair called it "Harris's masterpiece, among all the stories I have seen," [4] and Donald Day wrote that it "gathers together the excellence of Harris, both in his selection of material and use of technique, mellows and softens his robustness without the loss of any of his strength, and perhaps, rests at a peak of attainment in American humor." [5] One hesitates to disagree with such authoritative critical praise. Most modern readers, however, will continue to prefer the livelier, more robust Sut stories.

Harris borders on the grotesque in his morbidly minded sketch of the death and burial of Sut's father, "Well! Dad's Dead." Using the burial journey as a structure, a theme found in legend and folklore since medieval times, Harris uses the same characters from some of Sut's most hilarious escapades, but this time handles them in a dry, macabre way so as to achieve an Edgar Allan Poe–like effect. It calls to mind the darker work of Ambrose Bierce, Mark Twain, and William Faulkner, especially

4. Walter Blair, *Native American Humor,* p. 99.

5. Donald Day, "The Humorous Works of George W. Harris," *American Literature,* XIV (January, 1943), 406.

the latter's novel *As I Lay Dying*.[6] Nowhere, except for the political satires, is the cynicism which possessed Harris after the Civil War more clearly evident than here. Hints of cynicism, of course, are to be found throughout Harris's work, even in such a pre–Civil War piece as "Sut Lovingood at Bull's Gap," where Harris has a drunken character set in to cursing the world and say that "hit were all vanity an vexashun ove spirit—a dam onmitigated humbug frum the center all round tu the sea." But here a nadir of consistent morbidness in tone and subject matter is reached.

Sut is glad to see the old man go: "Now, my Dad, put off doin his good thing, for an awful long time, but at last he did hit, like a white man. He died, by golly! . . . Aint you glad?" Sut's mother feels that General Washington himself never did a better thing in his whole life; "She only grumbles that he dident ketch the idear twenty years sooner." The body is wrapped in an old, black bedspread and placed on a shingle sled drawn by two stolen steers, but on the way to the grave the steers bolt at the smell of the corpse, throw all the mourners off, and when the sled flies over the grave Sut kicks the remains into it. The lack of respect Sut shows for his father doesn't disturb him because he is at least being consistent and not hypocritical; he has hated his father in life and death. He philosophizes:

Dad shave the hipocracy ove fixin a dead man away nice, arter lettin' him starve. Many, many a time, has people spent enough in plantin' a corpse, that if they had ever a loan'd the half ove hit to the mortul a livin', hit would a put off a funeral. But then the cuss wudent a went, when his time had come. Thars the devil ove hit—flustratin' doctrines so bad, you know.

It is ironic that Harris was writing about this subject just a year before his own untimely death.

Donald Day reads this story on an allegorical level, considering it among Harris's political satires. Harris, according to Day, "equates Sut's worthless old Dad with the decaying and dying

---

6. The similarity in plot structure between Faulkner's novel and Harris's sketch was first noticed by Brom Weber, ed., *Sut Lovingood* by George Washington Harris, pp. xiii–xiv. For a full exploration of similarities and possible influence, see M. Thomas Inge, "William Faulkner and George Washington Harris: In the Tradition of Southwestern Humor," *Tennessee Studies in Literature*, VII (1962), 54–57.

remnant of the Old South, which, for the best interest of all concerned should take its last gasp and pass on." [7] But Harris does not make it clear that such a reading was intended, and in view of the consistency of his political belief all his life, it is not likely that Harris would suddenly reverse his stand at this point in his career. The story is, rather, one last cynical blast at a world in which Harris had experienced only frustration and defeat in his professional and political affairs, after a life that had left, in Mam's words, a "puckery taste" in his mouth.

The two remaining sketches, "Sut Lovingood On Young Gals and Old Ones," and "Sut Lovingood Sets Up with a Gal—One Pop Baily," are minor in importance and reminiscent in nature. In the first, Sut, in the role of the crackerbox philosopher, descants on the problems of raising a daughter (as Harris was doing himself at the time) and his feelings towards finicky old maids, always afraid of losing their virtue to some "big, hairy man," and sleeping with their feet locked together. In all justice, Sut must admit, however, that "the very bes' 'oman that I ever know'd, in my whole life, was a old maid, but then, you mus' bar in mine, she were my own mammy." The last sketch Harris wrote, a few months before his death, is also on the subject of women. This time, he describes Sut's opinions on kissing, and relates his adventures in this line with one Pop Baily, a local girl. Both of these last pieces are obviously efforts to revive Sut to his former, whisky drinking, hell-raising self, but after "Well! Dad's Dead," it is no wonder that these read like empty echoes of livelier times.

Although some of these fugitive stories, collected here for the first time, do not display Harris's talents at their best, most of them are equal to the best of the collected yarns and worthy of a wider reading. They are especially necessary if we are to view Sut Lovingood in his total development as a fictional character, and they give us besides a fuller view into Harris's basic thought. They reveal, for example, his feelings toward a number of contemporary ills: the undue worship of modern technology and progressivism as the means to a better society, the poor accommodations to be found in contemporary inns, the tendency of women to give mother nature some "unnatural" assistance in filling out their figures, or the social hypocrisy of pedigree hunt-

7. Donald Day, "The Political Satires of George W. Harris," *Tennessee Historical Quarterly*, IV (December, 1945), 336–338.

ers. And we can observe the development of a philosophical pessimism on the part of Harris, culminating in the strangely grotesque story of the death of Sut's Dad. But the bedrock of sane and healthy good humor counterbalances the cynicism, as it must in the work of any successful humorist, and for this reason above all others this material is worth preserving. It might also be noted that nowhere else in nineteenth-century American literature do we find such a wholesome and open-minded attitude towards sex and physical functions.

SUT LOVINGOOD'S CHEST
STORY

By S————L, of Tennessee

I TOLD you, George, that Sicily an her hoss, ole Clapshaw, warn't agwine ter pull well in the same yoke, as soon as I seed the orful misfortinate start they got. No man an oman could ever get as clost as man and wife should, arter sich a h——l ove a fuss an hurtin as tuck place at ole Burns' that day.[1]

Theyse all got a spite at me yet about that ar trubil, an I swar I warnt tu blame fur hit. "Ole Sock"[2] orter be made beef outen; he did hit all; and yet the cussed fools dont blame him a bit. He orter have his durned haslet cut outen him, an I'll du hit fur him ef ever I ketches him, fur gittin me inter trubil, arter he did all the devilment, while I has to bar the blame. Now aint hit hard that being a nateral born d——d fool es I *owns* I is, I has to bar the blame of the doins of a infunel stumpy hon'd, curly faced hole fool bull; an that, too, arter I'd dun him a kindness, puttin the baskit handil over his hons, so he could eat the corn while he war a travelin; fur I swar they'd a mauled him good ef they had kotch him a eatin ove hit. He's an ongrateful beast, an I'll do him wus than the bees an ole Mills bull did. I'll

---

This story appeared in Nashville *Union and American*, XXIX (June 30, 1858), 1.

1. The events mentioned in this and the next paragraph are references to occurrences in "Sicily Burns's Wedding," and "Old Burns's Bull Ride," included in *Sut Lovingood, Yarns Spun by a "Nat'ral Born Durn'd Fool,"* pp. 86–97 and 98–107. This story brings to completion Sut's revenge for the trick perpetrated on him by Sicily Burns, now married to Clapshaw the circuit rider, in "Blown Up With Soda," *ibid.,* pp. 75–85. Apparently Harris originally intended to include it in his collection since he mentions in the preface the central victim, Doc Fabin, as one of "three misfortinit pussons menshun'd inside yere," *ibid.,* p. x.

2. The bull that takes old Mr. Burns for a ride in the above mentioned stories.

wheel barrer him into Eternity, an ole Burns *tu,* mine ef I dont.

Es fur Sicily, ef I haint even with her, you may jist nail my tung to a tree an then skeer me till I reels my hole carcuss inter about a mile of tung, an thar'll be nothin left but my bones on tu the toe nails, an perhaps a scrimpshun of laigs, an a pile ove rags an har at the end of hit. *She dont owe me nuffin now;* an I'll tell you how I paid up—it wer about layin by corn time when she married that hard faced, meaty fisted, groanin ole cuss. At nex aignog time I begin to see that he wernt her "affinity" es a school teachin oman called hit, when she wanted to circumvent me so as tu get her wood cut an her mar curried. George, did you ever hev a strong minded oman git arter you—a rale he oman? "No." Well, ef ever wun does—jist you fight her like she wore whiskers or run like h––l; ef you dont, ef she dont turn you inter a kidney worm'd hog what cant raise his bristles in less nor a month, you ar more or les ove a man than I takes you to be. Ove all the varmints I ever seed Ise feardest of them. They aint human; theyse an ekal mixtry ove stud hoss, black snake, goose, peacock britches—an d––d raskil. They wants tu be a man; an es they cant, they fixes up thar case by bein devils. Take keer ove em: you'd better cum in contact with a comit ur a coal porter than wun ove em any time. They'll ondermine your constitution sure.

Well, matters rocked along, all hands doin es they pleased, an I a watchin ov em—fur I wur arter revenge—ontil about the time hosses begin tu squeal an tuckys tu gobble [3] I discivered her "affinity." She wur runnin an oppersishun line to the old chicken eater, in cahoote with a man powfull with pills and squts—Doctor Gus Fabin—an they wer makin fast time, all conections, an the male wer kerried pufectly fust rate. An I don't much wonder; she never did feel warm tu old Clapshaw; hit wus the suckit rider's charm what foch her agin her will. George, youse got a *heap* tu larn yit. There am three varmits what kin charm wimmin an birds—the suckit rider, the cat, and the black snake. They kin du hit, and nun ove em ever misses a chance. Ef I hed a pet mockinbird an a darter, I'd make war on all cats an sukit riders—I'd fill the beryin groun with wun, an the big sink hole with tuther; an I'd hev a barrel ful ove hyme books an claws es medals ove my skill in clost shootin. I seed a loaded shot gun

3. Spring, the mating season.

once lyin broadside ontu the counter ove Congdon's store,[4] and
thar wer a cat washin ove her face a top ove a hat box, an a sukit
rider wer a tryin tu git Congdon tu gin sumthin tu pay fur
"overcoats fur the pious Sepoys," [5] at tuther aind ove the room;
an durn'd ef hit didn't cock hitself, an then swung round like the
needle of a compus, fust towards one an then tuther. I duno *how
often,* an at last went off—killed the cat es ded es be d––d, and
tuther barrell tore off four squar yards ove the sukit rider's
overcoat tail. Thar's an instink in shot guns about this thing,
sartin; fur you never seed a sukit rider with one in his han, nur a
cat what loved the smell ove gunpowder.

Well, arter I larnt what road they run thar line over, an all
the pints ove the case, I went tu work tu gin both a skeer, an him
a little hurtin. Doct. Gus Fabin wer wun ove em; the boys call'd
him Gut Fatty fur short, an he call'd em "imperdent onedicated
d––d jackasses" fur long. He wer jist four foot fourteen inches
high, an wer taller a lyin down than when he wer standin up.
His eyes wer like ontu two huckelberrys es tu color and size,
stuck deep inter a big ball ove red putty. Ef he'd been killed an
biled in a hogshead ove lye, he'd a made soap enuf tu a washed
away the sins ove a whole know-nothin Congressional deestrict
—Congressman, lawyers, wimmen an all. He dress'd hissef *tu
kill,* an rid a monsous big black hoss, seventeen hans high, an ni
ontu seventeen feet long. When I got done with him his perporshuns wer changed—he wurnt over ten hans high, an es long
es one ove ole Bullin's sarmints.[6] I hed gethered an hid a fust rate

4. Samuel Congdon, a mining financier, owned until 1857 a commis-
sary at the Tennessee Mine in the Copper Basin in Polk county, Tennessee.
R. E. Barclay, *Ducktown Back in Raht's Time,* p. 81.

5. The Sepoy Rebellion (1857–1859), which resulted in the transfer of
the administration of India from the East India Company to the crown,
was presently underway in British India. The collection of money for such
unlikely causes by pious frauds constitutes a recurring theme among the
Southwestern humorists. In "Simon Suggs Attends a Camp-Meeting," chapter ten of *Some Adventures of Captain Simon Suggs* (1845), Johnson
Jones Hooper has his rascally hero collect money at a religious gathering
to found a church under his dubious ministry. Mark Twain's equally
rascally King collects money at the Pokeville camp-meeting for the conversion of the "poor pirates" in the Indian Ocean in chapter twenty of the
Adventures of Huckleberry Finn (1884).

6. Parson Bullen is the clerical victim of Sut's prank in "Parson John
Bullen's Lizards," *Sut Lovingood, Yarns,* pp. 48–59. Harris inconsistently
spelled the name as "Bullen" and other times as "Bullin."

lot ove fox fire, all reddy tu use. Well, one night I found this black king hoss hitched tu a swingin limb, in a "sink hole" not fur ahind ole Clapshaw's house, *an he wer over the mountin a collectin store debts;* so I tuck off the Doctor's squar bodied saddil bags an sarched em, an tuck all the docterin truck outen the vials an boxes, an poured hit inter his half-full big bottil ove whisky, shuck hit up good, an jist drenched the durned big dromedary hoss with the last spoonful. Hit wer the biggest mixtry ove a dost ever tuck by man ur beaste, septin ove my soda.[7] I stole a set ove plow geers outen the stable, an put on the ole black "patient," now laborin onder my perskripshun (warnt hit beyant common docterin?); then I tied lumps ove fox fire all over the harness, inter his mane, an onter his years. He looked—the ole black devil did—like onter a star lite night, ur a convention ove big litenin bugs mixed with a scattered camp fire. But his looks warn't nuthin tu his feelins afore he got dun with hit, ef I em eny judge ove medicine mixed with an orful skeer an a powful site ove good hoss hurtin. Then I spliced on tu the onder side ove his tail a big jint ove cane, pack full ove wet powder, with the open aind towards—his—his hed. Now, I meant tu lite hit, an start him on his travels with a tree top fast in the swingletree; but I thot I'd fust sneak up tu the house an see what wer a gwine on, an what I saw altered my plans mitely. I speck I must a made a nise; fur when I peeped through the crack in the door, thar wur Sicily a flingin out bed quilts outen a big chist, but she left in her skeer a baskit with two hundred aigs an a paper ove lamp black onder the till. In jumped Gut Fatty in his shut tail. She slam'd the lid, turned the key, an flung on her dress terrectly. I knocked a staggerin sorter onsartin lick an wur *so* drunk I cud scasely stand. I managed tu ax Sicily fur sum supper, an she wer mity willin an pleasin an broke out tu the kitchen tu git hit in the hopes that when I'd stuffd my carcuss I'd go tu sleep. When she lef, *so did I*, arter the ole thrashin mersheen kivered with hoss hide an fox fire. I foch him up clost tu the door, an tied a stout rope tu the handil ove the chist an tu the swingle tree. That wer a new conection fur Mister Doctor Gut Fatty's line. Now mind, he'd never seed me in all his bornd days, an praps never hearn ove me, so while I wer makin the hoss pufectly fast ontu the chist, he whispered, "Sicily, love, is *he* GONE?" Sez I, "yes, but

7. See "Blown Up With Soda," *Sut Lovingood, Yarns,* pp. 75–85.

du you keep still; sumthin orfuls agwine tu happen imedjutly; thar's signs an wunders in the ar; ni ontu twenty full moons am a hangin in the ar abov the comb [8] of the mountin, an they all hes eyes an noses like mister Clapshaw's, an they's a makin dredfull mouths et me, en thar's a 'thousand laig' wum ontu the fence es long es a close line, hits body is red an streaks ove sheet litenin is a playin amung hits scales, an hit hev two imiges ove peple in hits mouf, like ontu you an me. I kin see my har a hangin most tu the yeath, an now an then hit gins them a shake an great big drops ove fat comes outen you, an afore they draps tu the groun they ketches fire an burns like tupentine. Oh Lordy! Gus, love? we hev ruinated our sefs. You begin rite in the middle ove the biggest six hoss prayer you know—nun ove yer little "now I lay me down tu sleeps," but rale strong devil skurin prayr, an keep on at hit, fur thars vexashun ove sperit an bodily tribulashun ahead fur us bof." I hearn him groan an he trimbled till he shuck the chist, but he sot in tu prayin fur the heathen, an spread ove the gospil, like a hoss. I know'd that I hed planted a big skeer an that hit would bar fruit afore moon down, so I jist snatched up a chunk ove fire ofen the hath an toch off the powder onder the tail ove the ole hoss. Now I'll jist be continentally an espesially durnd ef that chist didn't go outen the door breast high, an the fus time hit struck the yeath wer forty feet down the hill; rite thar the fust ove the aigs got thur sefs busted; the nex time hit toch the yeath wer on tuther aind (an thar the ballance of Sicily's aigs gin up thar shells,) away below the stable; now the mixtry begun: aigs, lamp black, an OLE GUT FATTY. The chist tuck down the mountin; I seed hit's course by the lite ove the cane squib [9] an the fox fire, an every now an then the hoss fotch a yell—hit won't a squeal, ur a bray, but sorter between the two: a orful sound. I've never hearn eny live thing make jist that nise afore or sence, an I swar I dont want tu.

I thort I'd foller an see what went with the chist. Arter I'd went a mile ur so I hearn a voice up in the ar, say, "mister, you'd better not travel much furder that course. H——l's busted plumb open, an this yere mountain's full ove the devils. I wish I wer back in old North Calina, whar onest people ken sleep ove nites." I looked up sorter skeer'd, an thar sot astraddle ove a limb ove a big red Oak, a long bony speciment ove a regular herrin mer-

8. Combe: a narrow valley or deep hollow.
9. Firecracker.

sheen,[10] in his shuttail; his eyes shined like a mink's, an the bottoms ove his feet looked sorter like a tater patch in the weeds. Sez I, "hev yer got any liquor lef, or is yer drunk et all, ur only a durn'd fool?" "I ain't neither, (gin us a chaw terbacker.) I jist camped round the pint over thar with the ole oman on her litter, when we wus woke up by an arful yell, an here cum the devil a tarin es big es a corn crib, an he had *hellfire harness on,* an a knot on the aind ove his tail es big es a turpentine still, an he run over my hosses an upsot the waggin, en tuck thru my camp fire, makin the chunks, an sparks, an ashes fly es high es the trees, an out ove site in a minit. The ole hen an the chickens am scattered an I tuck this yere tree, an I'm gwine tu keep hit till mornin. (Gin us a chaw terbacker.) I'll tell you, mister, this yere Tennessee don't suit me. Sich sites ove nites, an sich mountains ove a day, will break down arry man ever foal'd, an no herrin, nor tar; [11] dam the place. I'm gwine back, do you hear my horn?" Sez I, "I speck you had best go back, and travel in the woods et that, for that warnt the devil you seed, but the fool killer [12] fur Polk county, an ef ever he sees you, you'll never see ole Noth Calina, nur yer tar kiln either, so you hed better mind.

I went on tu his camp, an thar sot Gut Fatty, squatted ontu his hunkers, all alone, an jist sich a site were never hilt up tu mortal eyes. He wer orfully swell'd, he'd a rolled wun way es well es tuther, an he wer every color ever invented. His shut wer stuck es tite tu him es my pasted one, an he wer peppered all over with broken aig shells, nara piece es big es a grain ove corn.

Here were a black streak aidged with yaller, thar a yaller one aidged with black, then a mixed splotch ove all cullurs, then a little blood oozing thru a sunflour calliker pattern on his belly ur his laigs, an his har looked like hit had been dipped in thunder an litenin and sky blue; he was no more like human than dad were like a hoss when he acted hit,[13] an he out stunk a buzzard's nest, fur sum ove the aigs were sorter spiled like an sum were almost ready to chirp. To look at him an smell ove him you

10. North Carolinians on the coast made fishing a profitable business; herring were especially plentiful at Cape Hatteras.

11. Natives of the pine barrens, especially North Carolina, have long been nicknamed "tarheels," because of the early production there of rosin, turpentine, and tar from the long-leaf pines.

12. See "Sut Lovingood Come to Life," note 3.

13. See "Sut Lovingood's Daddy, Acting Horse," *Sut Lovingood, Yarns,* pp. 19–28.

couldn't think he ever thought of an oman or that wun would let him cum inter the lot. I think his appertite fur them kind ove vittals are all gone. Sez I, "What er you?" "Do no." [14] "Ar you sum invenshun to skare wimmin an hosses?" "Do no." "Whar do you live." Now his senses seemed sorter to cum tu him, an he axed how fur hit wer to the Hiwassee copper mine.[15] Sez I, "I never hearn tell ove hit." "Well, hit's in Polk county, Tennessee." "You am jist about one hundred an fifty miles frum thar, on the noth side of the Tennessee river, in Jackson county, Alabama." [16] "Is that a fac, mister?" "Sartin," sez I. He fotched a big breath, "well, I've made the fastest time ever made by mortal man atween them pints. I'se jest been about four minutes a doin hit, but hit has ni onto killed me." "Now," sez I, "mister, ef that is so, dont you tell hit here, fur they'll take you fur the tellegraph what they've been watchin fur with guns fur a long time, an they'll hev your scalp a durned site quicker nor you made your fast trip; they dont believe in you ur the devil what invented you; so dont waste time in puttin another hundred miles ur so atween you an this yere place." I follered the hoss about seven miles by the Doctor's truck what I'd give him, but I couldent ketch up. I never seed him nor the chest nor Gut Fatty arter that nite, an *I dont care a durn ef I never do.* Wonder ef Sicily misses him much! Ole Clapshaw believes in "witches, an warlocks, an long nebbed [17] things" more than he does in Sicily an his "growin" skeer ov ghostes keeps him at home o' nights. I railly think he's gettin to be a pious man. Poor Sicily, she's warin thin, her eyes am growin bigger, an she has no roses on her cheeks. She *cant* laugh, an she *wont* cry. Haint hit orful to think ove? Say, George, dont sum feller up your way make whisky outen corn an not strike nine? [18] If thar is, send me wurd by the fust chance.

14. "Don't know."

15. During 1854 Harris surveyed the Hiwassee or Ducktown copper mines in Polk county, Tennessee. It was here that Harris may have met "Sut" (William S.) Miller, the corn farmer who served, it has been suggested, as a model for the creation of Sut Lovingood (Ben Harris McClary, "The Real Sut," *American Literature*, XXVII [March, 1955], 105–106).

16. Located in the northeast corner of the state.

17. Long-nosed.

18. Strychnine; strychnine whisky is a very inferior grade of whisky thought to be poisonous.

SUT LOVINGOOD ESCAPES ASSASSINATION

Sut visits New York—His opinion of the City and the Police—Visits
Wall street—His opinion of Stock Brokering—He takes a "Skeer"—
Views Trinity Church—Stops at Lovejoy's Hotel Restaurant—Sees
Barnum—Is entertained gratis—Escapes Assassination by a Daguer-
reotype Artist!

"WHY, Sut where have you been? You look like you have
suffered greatly." Yes, George, I hes suffered (shaking his
down-cast head) in body, laigs and speret. Ise been tu NEW
YORK, an' now I keers less for H––l nor ever I did; an' es fur dying, why, I aint half as feared ove hit es I was. I tell you, *now*, a
man what's been tu that ar place, New York, hes suffered all he'll
ever hev tu suffer, and larnt more nur wun man ortur know, tu
be comfortable, not tu speak ove the onecessary ware an' tar ove
his laigs; an' you know a good, holesum par ove laigs is the best
thing ever a man-body kerried, 'septing a full bott-il ove good, safe
whiskey. I'd like tu wore out the best par ove laigs (d'ye see
'em?) what ever grow'd tu the aind ove man, in thuty days, in
that cussed, n'isey, skary, strange-lookin' country—they calls
hit a city—a wuckin' ove myself outen scares an' scrapes. They
gin me too much tu do, an' no good groun' tu do hit on. I led a
mons'ous active life—I generally hed about two tarin', orful
scares, an' the aigs ove five or six scrapes a hatchin' at onst—an'

This story appeared in New York *Atlas*, XXI (July 11, 1858), 6. Earlier,
in the June 20 issue of the *Atlas*, the following announcement was made:
ANOTHER GREAT FEATURE FOR THE ATLAS!
The lion is caught! We have at length succeeded in securing, as a
regular contributor to the ATLAS, the author of the famous and
unapproachably humorous
"SUT LOVINGOOD LETTERS,"
which he will hereafter contribute exclusively to our columns. These
remarkable papers, so far as they have been already published in the
columns of the Nashville *Union*, have met with the most wonderful
success in all parts of the country, having been copied far and wide.
In these letters, "Sut" details his remarkable scrapes by flood, fire and
field, with a zest and humor perfectly irresistible, as all our readers

I never hed a pufectly far track tu run on while I wur thar. The roads ar tu full ove things warin' ove wheels. They *believes* in wheels es I dus in laigs, an' puts 'em onder a'most everything, 'septin' ove thar perlice; an' I now swar they needs 'em wus nur eny movin' things I ever seed. They is es slow es mud-turkils in aigin' time, onless you actuate 'em with a skeer, an' they takes on can bear witness, who have had their livers excited by his accounts of how his "Dad Played Hoss," the adventure with his "Shirt," "The Camp Meeting," etc.

"SUT LOVINGOOD," albeit, according to his own account, he is "a natral born durn'd fool," always getting into "scrapes," is no servile copyist or imitator of any one else. His rich, unctuous humor is his own, and it squeezes out of all his writings, which are as full of it as an orange is full of juice. He has ranged up and down the Mississippi and Missouri, and hunted "bar-meat" from Kaintuck to the Rocky "Mountings," and what he cannot relate in the way of adventure, "ain't worth telling." He promises us to tip his coon-skin in New York shortly, and if he does, he would be a greater card for Barnum than ever was Tom Thumb or Jenny Lind. But we have secured him exclusively, and the "keard" is ours.

SUT LOVINGOOD,

for the future, will write

EXCLUSIVELY FOR THE ATLAS,

and thus will present to our readers and the public

THE GREATEST LITERARY FEATURE OF THE DAY!

Others have tried to cage this lion, but we alone have had the good fortune to secure him. So look out, next week, or the week after, for the first of the new series of the

"SUT LOVINGOOD LETTERS,"

written expressly and exclusively for the ATLAS. Get your sides strongly hooped, or you will explode with laughter and expire in convulsions, for resistance will be ineffectual.

We are not authorized to give the author's Simon Pure name; but he writes us from the Great West, under date of June 11:

"I will forward you a 'Sut' in a few days, and hope thereafter to be a regular contributor to the ATLAS, with which paper I am much pleased."

Thus, with this announcement, we advise our readers to keep a "sharp look-out ahead" for the great

"SUT LOVINGOOD LETTERS,"

which are bound to take the people of New York, and the country at large, by storm. Smaller fry can step out of the way, for when

SUT LOVINGOOD

comes around, with his traps, and guns, and dog, there is bound to be no game left for anybody else.

Despite this outlandish announcement, Harris is known to have contributed to the *Atlas* only this story, its conclusion "Sut Lovingood's Adventures in New York" and "Sut Lovingood at Bull's Gap."

skeers es quick es they dus cheap drinks, an then they dus thar dirty best; but durn *thar* best! Their laigs aint wuf a cuss. I got arter wun misef, an' he *wus* skeered, fur he swet at the slack ove his britches, an' throw'd his revoltin' pepper-box, an' his stick and bott-il away—I saved the bott-il, in course I did, an' then run plumb over him. When I got stopped, I seed him trottin' down a cross-road onto three laigs, with his tail curled tite *onderhanded.* I follered a little piece, sorter slow, an' I found rite thar a special tribe ove es nateral born d – – d fools es I is, 'septin' this, Ise full-blooded fool about everything only what my laigs (d'ye see 'em?) an' a sutin quantity ove whisky kin do when called on. They's fools about paper-mills only, for here they goes on a trot, like piss-ants afore a rain, with a han'ful ove little papers, like onto a Tennessee note ove han', writ lengthwise on one side an' crosswise on t'uther; when two ove 'em bumps together, they teches noses, jist like onto the ants, an' then they swops two ur three ove the papers, an' each pot-bellied, trottin', bacon-faced son ove a gun ove 'em is redy tu swar that he's made money by the swap. There's no natral sence, ur corn, ur meat, ur honesty in the whole fixin'. I tell you another thing, George, thar's a streak ove onmitigated durn'd raskil about es big es a hoe-handil runnin' plumb through the last durn'd one ove them ar bulls an' bars. They aint neither; they's jist a new tribe ove nateral born durn'd fools, (mixed in with thief,) on one subjec'—an' that is that the paper-mills am starvin', an' they's morally bound tu help 'em out. Ise alers been feared ove paper ever since I seed the fust warrant sarved onto me, well I hes. Now, while Ise speakin' ove that ar narrer road, (I swar hit orter be the broad one,) one aind ove hit am stopped up with an infun'el big pile ove rocks ur dirtily cooked gingerbread.[1] When I fust looked up

1. Sut is viewing Trinity Church located on Broadway at Wall Street. The structure was completed in 1846, designed by Richard Upjohn, a noted contemporary architect and sponsor of the Gothic revival mode. It is constructed of dark brownstone in a free rendering of perpendicular English Gothic, and Sut reflects here and in the following lines the strong criticism and ire which was often elicited by the elaborateness of design in the Gothic revival churches. Federal Writers' Project of the Work Projects Administration, *New York City Guide,* pp. 310–313. A view of Wall Street sketched at approximately the time Harris saw it, looking west from William Street with the lofty spires of Trinity in view at the end, is reproduced in John A. Kouwenhoven, *The Columbia Historical Portrait of New York,* p. 202.

at the thing, I tho't hit wur a orful gir-aff-ey. (I'm kin tu *them* things; I knows by the neck an' laigs, an' I'm gwine tu see ef they hes the same famerly dispersition.) A part ove the pile runs way up inter the air, an' is adzactly like a big alligator's tail when he's skeerd an' making for water. I'm gwine in among hits guts some day, tu see what it dus for a livin'; hit su'tenly must eat a heap ove sumthin', an' I mean tu take good keer hit *don't-eat-me* —(d'ye see these here laigs?) I'll jist be durn'd ef I can't out travil hit on eny track, sidewise or *up; hit* mout beat me *down-'ards.* Can't say till I larn more ove hits nater; but we'll talk ove all these yere perplexin' things ag'in; my head is all runnin' round, mixed up sorter yet; an' now I'll try to tell you of one ove my fust scrapes. I'll jist tell 'em es I thinks ove 'em, or feels like; the mindin' ove 'em hurts me powerful, an' if hit warn't you I'd never speak ove the first durn'd one ove 'em.

The fust day I got thar, I crept inter a big room sorter onder ground,[2] with my bag ove rags onder my arm, an' I drapt inter a corner ontu a sheet iron fixin' full ove stone coal; 'twer sorter like an 'oman's bonnet in shape, an' I doubled my laigs—these yere laigs—three or four times, tu make myse'f sorter look human like, an' I tuck the best sight I could ove what an' who wus thar. I had on a *general* all-overish sort ove dull skeer et everything I seed; hit felt like I wur sowed up in a raw hide, an' hit a dryin' an' a drawin' tighter every minit, with a layer ove red pepper atween me an' hit. I wur oneasy, an' minded my pasted shirt— durn Betts Carr![3] Hit wur a room whar fellers cum tu eat, an' wur full ove little tables, what looked like they'd be mons'ous good fur a holesom game ove short kerds; sum sow-bellied fellers wur a wukin' with thar knives an' forks, like they hed bet sumthin' both on the bushell an' the minit. I wor hungry; hadn't tasted enything but a mo'sel or two ove whisky since bre'kfus' yesterday, an' wur sorter lookin at 'em eat my sheer an' thars too, when I spied two ole studs a whisperin' an' a p'intin' at me. One

2. As the headnote indicates, Sut is in the restaurant of Lovejoy's Hotel at 34 Park Row. Lovejoy's was considered by this date as among the numerous second-class houses of which Junius Henri Browne wrote, "They are said to be comfortable; though the class of persons you meet there are not apt to be as cultivated and agreeable as at the Broadway houses." Junius Henri Browne, *The Great Metropolis: A Mirror of New York,* p. 397.

3. A reference to the landlady who prepared the starched shirt for Sut with disastrous results in "Sut's New-Fangled Shirt," *Sut Lovingood, Yarns,* pp. 29–36.

ove 'em was the man [4] what shows the dead snakes en frogs, an'
the live wimmen an' gir-raff-eys, and sumtimes, a elephant ur
two, ontu the corner; the 'tuther wun was a kiln-dried, saffron-
fed, rat-eyed ole cuss, with specks what shined like ontu a bull's
eyes in bellerin' time. Sez the showman—"Du you think you
could presarve his perporshun in stuffin' him, an gin them ar
feeturs an' them eyes a far chance so es tu du him jestis, as a
speciment of the 'Ramus Scrambleusimus,' the only wun ever
kotch. Ef he only could keep his looks fur a durn'd fool, an' his
perporshuns es a beaste, es well arter he's stuffed es he dus now
alive, the Marmaid an' Jenny Lind jist be durn'd! [5] I'd make a
million out'en him sure, fur ole Agassis hisse'f c'u'dn't decide
whether he was man, beast, ur the devil." I be d – – d, that's jist
what he sed, George. "Who's tu *kill him* fur me," ses rat-eyes, an'
his specks turned sorter green. "Oh, never mine," sez the snake-
an'-'oman man; "I'll fix that. Ef wimmen an' whisky don't fix
him in a week, I know by his looks that I can skeer him tu death
in two trials, an' ef that fails, why—why, strikenine, my boy—
had you forgot *that*?" and he felt ove the fat on ole "fossil's" ribs,
an' they both grinned, an' lef'. Now a *pussonel* skeer begin tu
cum over me, sorter fillin' up my heart tite, an' a squirtin' outen
the wu'm-holes, and I begin tu fix tu run ef I seed eny bad signs,
but I wur so hungry I sot still in hopes sum man might offer a
poor strange varminty devil a bit. I wur holler plumb tu my heels,
an' the vitils smelt almost like tastin' ove 'em. In a minit a purty
little gal—she'd weigh jist about one hundred an' five pounds—
es clean an' trim es a hen-robbin, fannin' herse'f with a shaller
dish made outen iron, an' all painted with flowers, cum up
sorter skeery tu me. Thinks I, thar cums the *fust* trial to kill me
fur my skin. Sez she—"Mr. Libby [6] says set down at that table

4. P. T. Barnum (1810–1891), American showman.
5. References to two of Barnum's most noted attractions. The story of
the "Fejee Mermaid," Barnum's first highly successful exhibit at his famed
American Museum in New York, is related by Irving Wallace in his
biography *The Fabulous Showman, The Life and Times of P. T. Barnum*,
pp. 78–84, where it is described as "one of the most deliberate and
carefully plotted hoaxes in the annals of show business." Barnum's first
"cultural" success was as impresario for Jenny Lind (1820–1887), the
Swedish soprano who took America by storm in 1850.
6. James S. Libby managed Lovejoy's Hotel, which was owned and
operated by the firm Libby, Whitney and Company. Information furnished
in letters dated November 17, 1965, by James J. Heslin, Director of the
New York Historical Society, and January 18, 1966, by the American
History and Genealogy Division of the New York Public Library.

an' eat your dinner; he *knows* you are hungry, and—and s-says, to pay him some other time. Now do come, poor stranger; he took me when I had no one to feed me, and he means what he says; *somebody* loves you *somewhere,* and you sha'n't starve here. *Do come,* I'll wait on you." That *"do* come" foch me. I found great big durn'd-fool tears wus splatterin' her slipper outen my eyes—the fust what's washed 'em since poor little Kate Wills hed tu die. I haint got no soul; hit's onpossible; an' I wouldn't hev one ef I could, only in hopes ove seein' her ag'in, an' hevin' her p'int out tu me the sunshine an' the green ove that purty place she used tu talk so much about, whar nobody's arter you—whar thar's no skeer, nur no runnin', fur I railey wants tu rest.

"Stop Sut!" I've no more tu say on that p'int; I wur a dreamin' ove sumthin' I hev lost, an' it sorter seems tu me ef poor Kate wer alive I mout stan' a chance tu becum a human, git tu quit my runnin', an' see sum peace. Don't mine me, George; you knows I'm a poor durn'd fool, an' haint got no chance. Well I sot down, an' the little softenin' thing in plain clothes gin me oh, sich a satisfyin' feed. I looked at her es she kerried away the scraps, ontil hit seemed like she put on Kate's clothes an' wore her pacifyen' smile, an' I tho't I hearn my darlin', tho' she now sleeps onder the pea-vine an' the long grass ove the Big Frog Mount'in' away—away in Tennessee, whar the south birds chirp and the bar growls, whar the wild harycane dus es hit pleases, an' whar thar's plenty of a'r tu breathe an' plenty ove room tu run, say, "Poor Sut, I *still* watch over you."

"Oh, Sut, this is childish." Well, hit is I reckon; but what's childish is sometimes manly, an' ef hit aint manly, hit's perhaps sumthin' better. I haint got ara soul, an' can't see eternity, but she hes at least two, an' how quick w'u'd she gin me one, tu hev me thar in a partnership what couldn't be counted by years ur measured by happiness. "Why do you think so, Sut?" 'Caze she never told me a lie, never helped to skeer me, an' alers stud up that I wur a human, spite ove my looks an' behavior, an'—an' (Sut pointed upward with a trembling finger,) she believed in—HIM, an' often, on her knees, with her little hands clasped, hes she axed Him tu do sum favor fur me.[7] "Well, well, Sut, what

---

7. The identity of Kate Wills remains a mystery. Is she a fictional creation or someone Harris knew and respected in his lifetime? Seldom does Harris permit such an emotional, sentimental outburst on Sut's part. Milton Rickels records the fact that Harris and his first wife lost two children in *George Washington Harris,* p. 22, so perhaps Kate Wills was

next?" Arter I got my baggage-room full, I sot down ag'in on the iron bonnet, an' the fust thing what sot me tu straight lookin' wur a bullfrog-lookin' feller dressed in mournin', I reckon fur what he wur about tu do, what hed a short brass gun; hits bore wur ni ontu es big es a quart jug on the bulge, an' all boxed up squar' in some sort ove black wood, tu keep it from bustin', an' he hed hit mounted ontu three laigs sorter like mine, only they didn't trimble a bit; hit wur planted in 'tuther corner, about twenty-five yards off, an' he hed got my range, an' with a black han'ketcher over his head—I 'speck he felt sorter shamed tu see me die—he wur takin' sight at me, an' a feelin' along his durn'd stove-up gun fur the trigger, jist ready tu pull hit. I seed from the size ove the bore that he hed metal enough in hit tu tar off my head down tu the armpits, an' that he wur in yernest. I tho't ove the snake-an'-'oman showman, an concluded they didn't mean tu risk losin' my skin by waitin fur wimmen an' whiskey tu kill me, an' es I hed no room tu run, nur time either, I jist grabbed fur a chunk ove stone coal about es big es a mule's huff, tuck a quick aim, an' fired; hit went straight an' strong right inter the muzzle ove his durn'd bunty Connecticut gun,[8] busted out the breech-pin, an' then lodged ontu the bull-curl in his forrid. Hit wur more nur he could stan, so he wilted down in his tracks, like a pile ove wet rags, stuck up one laig an' quivered hit a little, an' then laid still, an' his cussed ole stage-lantern-lookin' shootin' mersheen fell atop ove him, hits three laigs all draw'd inter one, jist like an ole onbaited wore out rat-trap, the amernishion wur scattered all over the floor, an' now what do you think?—the

---

one of these children who died early. But a search of the available Knox county cemetery records and Knoxville genealogical material fails to reveal the existence of either a Kate Wills or Kate Wills Harris.

8. Perhaps a reference to the revolvers then being manufactured almost exclusively in Connecticut, according to information brought to the editor's attention by Robert P. Emmitt. "Sam Colt, having gone broke with his plant in Paterson, N.J., had, with Eli Whitney, set up a plant in his native Connecticut to manufacture the Whitneyville-Walker dragoon revolver for Captain Walker's use in the Mexican war. The huge bore of this gun, pointed directly at a person, might well be compared with the opening of a camera. Other companies were also manufacturing handguns of advanced design in Connecticut. Although the barrels of many of those handguns were quite long by modern standards, they would have been 'bunty' [short and stout] to a Tennessean, noted for favoring firearms with long barrels. They must have seemed outrageously advanced and complex to a rural Tennessean."

infu'nel cruel hard-hearted blood-thirsty hell-fired cuss hed loaded hit with broken glass, so es not only tu kill me, but spile my feeters es a corpse. The next time I sees you I'll tell you how I got outen that scrape, an' got inter a durn'd site wus wun. Ise in a hurry now. Ole man Wheeler makes a doublin' ove whiskey, an' I mean tu be thar. Ain't I the durn'dest fool you ever seed in all your born days?

SUT LOVINGOOD'S ADVENTURES IN NEW YORK

Sut's Adventures in New York—He gets a "Skeer—Pitches a Dandy into a Steamboat on Wheels—Runs away with the Dandy—Knocks over a Jew—Upsets the apple-stands—Frightens a horse—Cuts a streak for the Battery—Throws a Dandy into the River—Breaks for somewhere, and gets into a school-room—Frightens the "schoolmarm" —"Git eout"—Row with a policeman—Licks him—Rolls down stairs into the street—Encounters Horace Greeley—His description of him, &c., &c.

W HAT became of your brass-gun man, Sut, after you shot him with the lump of coal?"

"Durned ef I know, George; I hearn them say 'tote him to the Horsespital.' I 'speck he's j'ined the church, ur the perlice. Shootin' ove strange varminty critters ain't his gift; he ain't sly enuff, an' he'll git kingdum cum sum day soon ef he don't quit that trade. 'Spose he wer tu ondertake tu shoot Ole Beacher,[1] in open day, afore witnessis like he did me, why durn my melt[2] ef the

New York *Atlas*, XXI (August 8, 1858), 1.

Nashville *Union and American*, XXIX (August 15, 1858), 2. The following comment appeared in the editorial column:

"We have not received the first of this brilliant series of sketches which our friend Mr. HARRIS is writing for the New York *Atlas*. We copy from that paper today the second of the series, which the *Atlas* has embellished with a first rate wood cut representing "the follower of Moses and old close" rolling into the gutter under the persuasive influence of his "umereller pole." The artist does full justice to SUT'S beautiful features and elegant proportions as they exhibit themselves in his foot race with a dandy rider. We are truly glad our old correspondent is receiving a just appreciation from the public and a proper remuneration from the publishers in the metropolis of the Union. Mr. HARRIS already ranks foremost among the humorous writers of the country, and the publication of his volume of sketches will give him a still more extensive reputation. We hope in a few days to receive the first part of his 'Adventures in New York.'"

1. Henry Ward Beecher (1813–1887), independent Presbyterian clergyman, liberal orator, and antislavery leader.

2. Perhaps a dialect variant of *milt*, used in nineteenth-century low slang to mean semen, and hence possibly with reference to virility and related male qualities.

passon's sister [3] didn't have his haslet outen him, an' a dryin' atop ove thar church-steepil in a minit; ef thar's enything in looks, she'd be wus on him nor I wer. But I *kin* tell you what becum ove me; I jist relyed on these yere laigs, (d'ye see 'em?) and tuck up the steps an' started in a monsous fast wile-tuckey pace down the road, an' run inter sum man-an'-'oman's fool explite at making new-fangled invenshuns, an' hit flew all tangled up, inter the middil ove the road; while hit wer a sortin' an' a strai'tnin' ove hits laigs an' arms, I axed a little larfin boy with a heap ove noosepapers onder his arm, what he call'd the cussed grasshopper-lookin' thing. 'Hay!' says he, 'don't yer know? Why, hit's nuthin' but a dandy outen Fifth avener; hit can't bite, an' is tu weak an' wuthless to run; so, pitch in an' knock Jerusalem outen it. I'll holler fur you.' Now, afore I tells what happened thar, I wants tu talk sum of my noticin' ove things.

"No'th Ca'lina am noted fur pole cats, Georgia fur groun'-hogs, an' Tennessee fur coons; I knows this frum 'sperience; an' now I kin say that New York am noted in the same line fur dandys, (do you know the varmint?) an' I'd a durn'd site rather mix with the stink ove the pole-cat, the rascality ove the coon, an' the dirty ways ove the groun'-hog, then jist tu see one ove these cussed infunel spider-laig'd wuthless fixin's. They haint neither man nur 'oman, 'caze they can't talk good nor fight like wun, or kiss ur scratch feelin'ly like t'uther. They seems sorter like a strange wether [4] what had seed a heap ove tribulashun among an ekal number ove rams an' yews—they's butted about permiskusly by the one, an' is snufft at by t'uther; and as they can't fill or feel the instink ove a man, nur do the juty ove an 'oman, they jest settles on a cross-fence atween the two, an' turns inter the wust kind ove fool-monkeys—despised by wun, an' larft at by t'uther, and the most human view you gits ove 'em, is when they is above you a climbin' up. They haint half es smart as thar chatterin' kin-folks, fur they can't begin tu du what the monkey kin. I knows monkey nater pow'ful well. I seed one once, an' I studied hits nater and gifts, when I weren't skeared; he were pow'ful peart tu be a ugly littil beast; I seed him a killin' ove insex, an' then I observed what he did with 'em. Now, a dandy

3. Harriet Beecher Stowe (1811–1896), who by now had achieved national fame and southern notoriety as authoress of *Uncle Tom's Cabin* (1852).

4. The male sheep, usually castrated, which leads the flock wearing a bell.

haint smart enuf fur that; he jist lets his insex run. S'pose a expectashun towards him wer a cummin' frum a tarin wild school-gal what hed seed snow say about sixteen times, an' flowers an' leaves es often, wou'dn't she meet a disapintment? An' then she'd jist kill him with contem't, an' feed the ca'kus tu her daddy's work-steer what is yoked with his bull, in the view ove hit bein' suitable feed fur one in his condishun. They skims an' flutters roun' fool-wimmin, jist like li'tnin'-bugs roun' a tuft ove hollyhocks, only the bugs am six tu thar two, an' hes the deal at that on the amount ove fire they kerries, an' whar they kerries hit. I never sees one but what I wants him atween these yere thumb nails—the human way ove killin' all sich insex. Well, arter his laigs were ontangled, hit sed I had insulted hit, and wanted satisfaction. Now, the idear ove me, a natral-born durn'd fool, insultin' ove enything what c'u'd talk, sounds sorter like a hog insultin' ove a settin' hen, by tearin' up her nest an' eatin' the aigs; 'twer mons'ous like fool talk. But I tho't I'd gin hit satisfaction, enyhow, so I drapp'd ontu my all-fours, sorter behind hit, fotch a rale fightin'-hoss squeal, an' landed both my hine feet onder the fork ove hits coteail.

"Now, George, whenever I strai'tens out bof ove these yere laigs tugether, (d'ye see 'em?) kickin' fashion, whatever they hits am bound tu *go jist then,* so he riz in the ar an flew hed fust inter a door in the hine aind ove a steamboat-cabin on wheels,[5] among a passel ove men readin' noospapers, an' wimmen with babys ur big baskits ove garden truck, dead chickins, an chunks ove meat. You cou'dn't a onmixed all these things, takin' in a few par ove specks, a bird cage or two, an a crock ove flowers, in a week arter he lit among 'em. Oh! sich a mess, an' sich a cussin an' squawkin' in Dutch, an' French, Cherokee, an' other outlandish tongues, you never hearn since the Devil an' the Dutch, an' Tom Dawson fit;[6] the driver—a bald-faced, roach-maned,[7] wall-eyed Irishman—cum down ofen the harycane deck an' cotch mister dandy by the collar an' the slack, an' sent him up a flyin' outen the door ag'in, a loanin' him a holesum kick es he went. While he wer in the ar, I moved so es to let him lite astradil ove my neck; he turned heels up an' hed down ahine me; I tuck a

5. A horse-drawn streetcar.
6. Presumably, a reference to some folk tale which seems not to have been recorded elsewhere.
7. Hair closely trimmed.

bill holt with my teeth on the inside ove his thigh, an' paw holts ontu his breeches laigs, fotch a bray, an' put towards the ruver, about es fast es a big dog kin go with a tin bucket a chasin' ove him. He opened in a voice weak, sorter like a sick 'oman; fust he call'd 'perlice,' then he sed 'mu'daw,' then he sed sumthin' about 'dwedful vulgaw pussons,' then sum words about doin' ove things he hadn't orter done, an' a leavin' ondone things he had orter done.[8] I speck that wer sorter prayin' in his durn'd one horse way. He strung out his words over a heap ove ground, fur I wer a travelin' like a fox-houn' with a wolf arter him; he kicked out in every course with them pipestem laigs ove hisn, owin' to his skare an' the hurtin' I wer supplyin' him with, fur I hes an orful bill holt when I wants to keep hit. Him and me looked jist like a travelin windmill in full blast, with a cord ove fence-rails tied tu the arms by thar middils, a swingin' about every way, ur a big crawfish totin' off a bunch ove grasshoppers an' long-laiged spiders ag'in thar will—laigs, arms, heads, coatails, an' watch-chains wer so mixed an' tangled that hit wer bewilderin' tu the eyes tu foller us. He thought ove the grabin' game, an' snatched at everything we passed. I run, unbenowenst, onto an ole feller, whose years hung down like a houn's, an' his cheeks hung down like a ground-squirril's jaws when he's a totin' in corn fur winter, an' he kerried his belly in a sling, an' hed on a white throat-latch, an' wer fat enuff tu kill; he jist squatted, an' I straddled him in my stride. Dandy fastened in his har, and I jist wish I may be descriminately durn'd ef he didn't tar off his whole skulp—didn't leave a single har—his head shined like a tin ball atop ove a church. He flung the skin ove ole lard stand's hed away, an' went tu grabin ag'in. The nex' thing he fastened ontu wer a black minner-net an 'oman hed roun her shoulders; she turned wrong aind up; but he got most of the net; his watch-chain cotch on the hook ove her littil umereller, an' hit went along too. A wide-coupeled, duck laiged Jew, what had a nose jist the shape an' size ove a goose-wing broad-axe, hed a string ove about ten histed umerellers tied one below t'uther, an' hung outen a high winder in his loft ontu a pole; well, Mister Squt snatched the handil ove the bottom one, an' fotch pole an' all. The follower ove Moses an' ole close cum out a tarin' an' a chatterin jist in time fur the hine

8. Cf. "The Order for Daily Morning Prayer," *The Book of Common Prayer . . . According to the Use of the Protestant Episcopal Church in the United States of America* (New York, 1850).

aind ove the pole tu lite on his slick hat—face, nose, black-whiskers an' all disappeared inter the hat, an' then the hat struck the groun' an' rolled, with the Hebrew intu the gutter. Now, you had orter seed that pole an them open umerellers clar the road; sumtimes the pole wer on one side of the road, a barkin' ove shins an a smashin' hoops, then hit wer on t'uther, a bustin' out winders an' a sweepin' ove appils an' gouber-peas ofen the tables, an' a crackin the ole wimmin the side ove the head; every wun hit totch about the head laid down; an' then the umerellers was a scoopin up babys an' go-carts, an' littil dogs at wun place and drapin' them at another, jist to scoop up more. Thar warn't a pusson on that road that know'd what we wer; an' sum tuck intu the houses, sum down the cross roads, an' sum tried tu outrun me the way I was agwine; but the last durn'd one what played that game got run over. I was a gwine like a crazy locomotive skeared at a yeathquake—in fac, I *was* skeared by this time, fur I'd got more nor I'd paid fur; I hed suckseedid in raisin' h––l generally, an' all that road wer either mad ur skeared at me, an I know'd they'd want my pusson mons'ous bad, so I jist hilt my bill holt on Mister Squt's thigh an' kept on. We met a feller in a slick roun' cap, a sittin' on a par ove wheels,[9] (they all believes in wheels) with his feet ontu the shaftez each side ove a fast-trottin' hosse's hips, jist a leanin' back an' a gwine it; the hoss jist tuck one look, turn'd tail, an' Jehosefat! how he mizzled [10] t'uther way; the next thing I saw, was slick cap, doubled at his hip-j'ints, with his toes, hands an' years within an inch ove each other, a flyin', sturn fust, through a big glass winder, among a passel ove doll-babys, bonnets, caps, fans, gloves, an' purty wimmen; he j'ined Orful Gardner's church [11] the nex' day; his hoss left his

9. The rig used in harness racing.

10. Departed in haste.

11. New York city was the scene of a fervent religious revival during the early months of 1858. George Templeton Strong reported in his diary, "The great object of the meeting seems to be to drug men up to certain points of nervous excitement and keep them there. Was told today on good authority of an incredible hymn said to be popular among 'revived' Methodists, of which this is one verse:

> Ye Saints rejoice, give cheerful thanks,
> For Awful Gardner's joined your ranks.
> And, while the lamp holds out to burn,
> There still is hope for *Patrick Hearne*."

Allan Nevins and Milton Halsey Thomas, eds., *The Diary of George Templeton Strong, The Turbulent Fifties 1850–1859*, p. 391. Thus, "Awful

wheels fast ontu a forked cart-tail, an' betuck hisse'f to the country, with nothin' on but the collar, an' the wust kind of a big skeer fur a hoss. I run through atween the leaders an' the wheel-hosses ove one ove them steamboat-cabins on wheels, (they loves wheels,) what wer a cummin' outen a cross-road, an' thar we turn'd our string ove umerellers wrong side out, an' left 'em, pole an' all mixed up with hosses. The perlice, what oughter been arter me, gathered round tu save the umerellers an' arrest the driver, an' one ove 'em toted a little newspaper boy off tu jail onder his arm fur larfin', while another stole his papers, an' a third went along to help guard that orful boy, an' they didn't seem a bit more fear'd tu du hit than I'd be tu take a horn ove tanglelaigs whisky. Now, all this time Mister Squt kept up his prayin' in his way, mixed in with hollerin', cussin', and cryin' an' when we run inter that team ove hosses, he sweat orful, fur my shoulders wer plum wet. Well, I went a tarin' ag'in' a fence, what's built between the road an' the ruver, (they calls hit the Battery,) intendin' to bust through hit, drownd Squt, and swim for t'uther side. I cum ag'n hit ni' ontu as hard as an ole bull c'u'd a done, but hit wer thar, an' I like tu a busted myse'f open. All my holts tore loose, an' Mister Squt's eatin aind cum round over handed, makin' a big cirkil in the ar, an' he lit hed fust, kachug, sixty foot out in the ruver. Arter his boot heels went outen site, I seed a greasy skim on the warter, sorter green an' yaller, an' purple, a spreadin' over about a half acre. He didn't cum up; but lots of dead fish did. I know'd he wer p'isen. Wonder ef thar's eny law in this yere place fur drowndin' sich reptiles. I wer fear'd thar mout be, they're so durn'd curious, eny how. So I tried tu make myse'f mons'ous sca'se.

"You never will know, George, what a discumfort hit is tu be a natral-born durn'd fool; hit makes ag'in a feller so, an' allers keeps him onder cow. Why, when I meets a 'nowin'-lookin beast I'se feard ove hit, an' watches tu see that hit don't git me inter sum cussed skeary scrape. Arter that feller fell in the ruver, I jist biled, tuck down the lane, an' seein' ove a pair ove stairs gwine strai't up inside a door, I tuck up 'em, aimin' fur the loft, tu hide in the hay; I busted inter the room an' lit about the middle, an' thar wer about forty gals a cypherin', an' a mons'ous strong-

Gardner" must have served as an example of the notoriously wicked man whose conversion marks a triumph of the godly.

minded 'oman a walkin' about a teachin' ove 'em. She squar'd herse'f an' tuck a look at me, an' then it wer I seed she wer strong-minded tu kill; her foot wer the biggest, saftest piece of meat I ever seed not to hev guts in hit, an' her ankils wer like ontu the eye ove a mattick,[12] sorter diamunt shape, an' she wer coupled es wide es a bedste'd; her laigs looked like they j'ined her cackus like a wheel-barrer's handils j'ines hit; she stamped that ar carpet-bag foot ove hern, an' squawked, 'Yeou get eout!' *She* took me fur a beast, an' talked dog talk tu me. I seed her eyes a turnin green, an' she sot in tu sharp'nin ove her nails ontu the back ove a bench, like she wer hungry for har. I knows the nater ove cats mons'ous well; Ise studied 'em. Thar I stood a fixin' of my laigs tu run. She went tu the winder and made a moshun, an' the fust thing I seed thar wer a perlice, in the room atween me an' the stairs. I jist swung round one ove my fistes an' sent hit at him; I split hit onter his nose, an' two ove my 'nucks went inter each ove his red eyes; I seed the fire fly myself, an' he turn'd a back summer set over a bench, an' while he wer a tryin' tu git up ontu his all fours, I seed run in every laig he hed—they wer a makin' the moshuns a ready, so I jist grabbed him ontu the back ove his bar neck with my teeth, an' gin him a good coon-dog shake, a sorter growlin'; he made the *no nothin' sign*,[13] mixed in with a heap ove 'O don'ts,' that made me wus nur ever; I shook him ag'in, an' mended my holt. Sez he, 'Hurrar fur Buckcannon,'[14] sorter enquirin' like. I let him go when he sed that, an' swung one ove these yere laigs (d'ye see 'em?) arter him; hit landed rite whar he forked, and he lit belly fust an' head down atop ove the fence built down aside ove the stairs; an' don't you think the durn'd fool warn't a snappin' his fingers an' a chirpin' with his mouf every chance he got; the 'hole time he tuck me fur a dog, too—durn his ugly perlice cackus! Well, he slid tu the foot ove the stairs like a lizzard a gwine down a fence-stake, and made fust rate time down the road, a feelin' the nap ove his neck with wun hand, while he wer a pullin' his breeches loose

12. Mattock.

13. In its early days, the Know-Nothing or American political party was composed of secret lodges active in nearly every state, complete with fraternal passwords and secret signs. W. Darrell Overdyke, *The Know-Nothing Party in the South*, p. 36.

14. James Buchanan (1791–1868), a Democrat then unpopular with Southern secessionists, was serving as fifteenth President of the United States.

behind with t'uther. I turn'd roun', an thar *she* was a standin',
with all her laigs so clost together that a buckit-hoop w'u'd a
went roun' all ove 'em—above them ar feet o' hern, ove
course,—an' her back wer like an ox-bow, an' reached up a'most
tu the ruff ove the house, an' her tale wer made inter the shape
ove a goard-neck, an' es big es a kaig, an' es long es a fence
rail—all the har on aind like a bottil brush; in fac', she wer all
eyes an' claws an' tail. Oh, she wer dre'dful tu behold! an' all the
t'uther shes in that ar rume wer in the same persishun an' fix,
only not over half es big, an' their tails warn't bigger nor a
stove-pipe. All heads turn'd towards me, an' thar wer groanin' an
spittin' enuff tu skeared a team ove bull dogs. I never seed so
many green eyes afore, or since, an' thar were little devils a
dancin' in all ove 'em, like yaller jackets in a em'ty green
whisky-bottil. I tuck a skeer—jist made myse'f inter a ball, an'
rolled down stars, across the pavement, an' inter the road—a
rollin' in among a windin' blades-lookin' feller's [15] laigs, what wer
a blunderin along in a ole white hat, with a mud-dauber's nest
built in the crown, a throat-latch made outen a piece ove ole
sweaty saddilgirth, an' a ole dirty white coat, with a small soap-
factory in full blast in one pocket, an' a patent nigger trap in
t'uther; [16] he uses his shut to clean stove-pipes with, an' he gits
his boots by stealin' a par ove leather fire-buckets—hes 'em
footed, an' then pulls 'em on by the bales, over a par ove britches
what he hes hed patented es a flea-hatchin mershean.[17]

"I tuck fust a look fur runnin room, an' then a look at him,

15. According to the editorial headnotes, this is a caricature of Horace
Greeley (1811–1872), radical editor, politician, and reformer. Winding
blades are long spindles upon which yarn is wound.

16. The contents of his pockets symbolically represent two of Greeley's
most notable activities: his reform attempts to clean up licentious New
York, and his opposition to slavery which led him to devote time and
money to helping escaped fugitive slaves. These activities are treated in
full in Glyndon G. Van Deusen, *Horace Greeley, Nineteenth-Century Crusader,* and Henry Luther Stoddard, *Horace Greeley, Printer, Editor, Crusader.*

17. The accuracy of Harris's description of Greeley's clothing is sub-
stantiated by historical accounts. "The oddity of his appearance, with his
pink face of babylike mildness fringed by throatwhiskers, his broad-
brimmed hat, white overcoat, crooked cravat, shapeless trousers, and white
socks, his shambling gait and absent-minded manner, was exaggerated by
every caricaturist." *Dictionary of American Biography,* VII, 531. See also
Stoddard, pp. 96, 100, 127.

an' I seed he didn't onderstand my nater, an' wer feared ove me; he kep' a tryin' tu look ahine me, like he thought I toted a string. Sez I, 'Mister, ar you agent fur a paper mill? ur dus you make soap fur a livin'?' He commenced a backin'. I picked up a little rock, an' whetted my teeth an' finger-nails with hit, an' now sez I, 'Hev you eny word tu send to your marm, yer gall, or the Mare?—ef you hev anything a weighin' on yer mind, jist onbuzzom yerse'f tu that bladder-lip'ed nigger, an' gin him all yer loos change tu carry the word, fur, *dam me, ef yer time haint cum!*' He jist never sed a word, but rounded too and put in a lumberin sort of cow-gallop. I never seed so many different moshuns gone through, an' so many tracks made in a minit, to get no furder off than he did; he distributed 'em all over the road, a pi'ntin' every way; frum the work an' the number ove tracks, I'd a dun been outen the city while he wer still in reach ove a pound-rock. 'Tis a pity runnin' aint one of his gifts, fur he's a mons'ous skeery man tu be es dirty es he is. He printed sumthin', nex' day, in his paper about 'Free Love an' Human Progress'; [18] sed he believed that crosses yet would be made atween animals an' varmints, an' sutin mersheans, what would perjuce sumthin' tu answer in place of humans—(Dad tried that explite once, durn his pot-headed soul! an' Ise a kerrien the consekenses)—that he hed seed, the day afore, the projuce ove a cross atween a broken-laiged kangaroo and a fust class mowin'-mershean; that it tuck mostly arter the mershean; that hit hed a sting the size an' shape ove a reap-hook, (what a h––l ove a lie!) but in the laigs hit wer all kangaroo; he hed never obsarved jist sich laigs; (what did I alers tell you, George?—thar haint sich anuther par on yearth, d'ye see 'em?) that I'd be wuf a great deal, tu tote expresses an' steal niggers, ef I only wer tamed; ('speck I would, but *who's in New York tu tame me?*) sed he wer onable to get a satisfying inspeckshun ove me, owin' to my vicious natur; that he'd tu withdraw cautiously, for the wild beast perdominated tu much in my cross, but take me all tugether, I wer a livin' sample ove human progress an' free love atween a kangaroo an' a mowin'-mershean, an' he thought much mout be done in that way;

18. Greeley had a firm faith in progressive movements and scientific advances, although he was not quite the radical Harris makes him out to be in this paragraph. He never supported free love and in fact wrote pieces against those liberals who did (see Van Deusen, p. 199, for example).

calls on Misses Branch [19] tu try a few small 'speriments with a steam rock drill, while he practizes a while on a thirty-ton locomotive, an' 'specks the konsekenses will 'stonish the world. I speck hit will; he'll keep on till thunder strikes him yet, see ef hit don't. He's the only man in New York what kin hold a candil fur me tu act durn'd fool by, an' he wurks onder a disadvantige, fur I'm told he won't tetch a drap ove sperits. Oh! he's a mons'ous promisin' ole durn'd fool, ef he don't get sot back, ur thunder-struck!"

19. The identity of this person is not known.

SUT LOVINGOOD AT BULL'S GAP

I HAINT never gin you the account ove my travels in the regin ove Bull's Gap,[1] last winter. I hev kep hit back, caze I wer feard while I wer mad I mout do the cussed branch of hell enjestis. But now I'se got over hit, an am perpared, bad as hit is, to gin hit far play. Ef ever a yearthquake cums round en dus the same, you'd never see Bull's Gap agin, that's all.

I means to tell jist what I seed, hearn and felt, and don't speck enybody what haint been thar'll believe a word ove hit; but I don't keer a durn, for I aint spected tu act ur talk like a human, no how.

Well, Bull's Gap am a bottomless mud hole, twenty odd miles long, mixed with rocks, logs, brush, creeks, broken stages, dead hosses, mean whiskey, cold vittils, an cross dogs. Me an about forty other travilers wer a makin the trip amongst all this mixtry, while hit would fust rain the best six outen eleving; then hit would snow awhile tu rest hitself, then sleet a littil jist to show what hit could do, freeze awhile an begin anuther rainin match, an a doin wun ur tuther all the time es hard es a shoemaker workin by the job ur the devil a splittin fat pine tu lite up a new comer, and him a Congrisman ur a suckit rider.

When we got in sight ove whar we wer tu eat supper, I loped ofen the stage waggin an put out at a peart lick towards the supper bell; an I hearn a feller say, "I'd gin a hundred dollars fur them laigs (speakin ove mine), they'se the only par what'll git thru this piece of saft country, tu tuther railroad, caze they kin touch bottom sometimes; an, darnation! how they reaches forard towards better things—jist watch him measure the yeath with

This story appeared in New York *Atlas*, XXI (November 28, 1858), 6.

Nashville *Union and American*, XXIX (December 5, 1858), 1. Reprinted without editorial revision.

1. A small town located in Hawkins county, Tennessee, between Bristol and Knoxville. It became the scene of a battle during the Civil War. A local blacksmith named Buhl is thought to have given the town its name, and a number of families named Bull still inhabit the area.

em. Why, he looks like a cussed ole winder mop with two handils, dam ef he don't. He's split from the yeath to his haslet, an is still a splitin. Jist watch him wade thru that pile ove rocks an cross ties," an a heap more sich talk about me what I'se forgot. Wonder what he'd said if he'd seed me a workin em onder a orful tarin big skeer? Durned ef I don't speck he'd a tuck one hissef, an turned tuther way. George, I never wer es proud ove these yere laigs afore (d'ye see em?), only when I outrun ole Burns' houns.[2] I'se tuck tu ilin ove em every day with frog ile; hit helps em powful, an they'se my only pendence on this yeath; an I thinks I onderstands how to use em. I'm gwine to be more keerful ove em, an not run fur nuthin, but jist tu save to use em onder big skeers.

Well, the wimmin travelers went intu one room an the ballance ove us intu anuther, whar thar stood a littil meetin house looking stove what had been tryin tu git hot; an as hit couldn't, hit tuck the studs [3] an wer a smokin like ontu a Noth Calina tar kiln, and smelt like burnt har. The warter an slush stood in the room more nor half way up hits laigs (that's what comes ove havin common laigs), but we all waded in an stood round that littil cussed cold sulky nigger-lookin cast-iron smoke-box, sum a cussin hit, sum a cussin tharsefs, sum a cussin Bull's Gap, sum a cussin wun another, sum a cussin the lake they stood in, sum a cussin that are shanty tavrin, sum a cussin fur supper, sum a cussin the strike nine snake whisky, an all a cussin thar levil best. One monsous clever little feller frum Nashville endorsed all the cussin, an then sot in an cussed the world; sed hit wer all vanity an vexashun ove spirit—a dam onmitigated humbug frum the center all round tu the sea—an then run the neck ove the bottil up tu the bulge down atween his shoulders and hilt hit thar es long es he had breth ur hit hed mixture; flung hit agin the stove, an then cussed the bottle fur bein the strongest ever he wanted tu smash.

I axed the tavrinkeeper how he liked that cussin es a specimint ove the gift in perfecshun. Oh, he sed, hit were ornary, not third rate in quality, an wantin powful in quantity; hardly listened tu hit; in fac, hit did'nt even warm him up; wouldn't do as a sampil ove the art at all; an axed me ef I hadn't been fotched up by monsous pius pussons ni untu a church, fur hit wer clar I

2. The text of this story is not extant. It is also mentioned in the fourth installment of "Sut Lovingood's Love Feast Ove Varmints," paragraph one.

3. Became obstinate; originally applied to a stubborn horse.

wer a poor judge ove cussin. Sed he hed a crowd the nite afore
what onderstood the business—sixty-seven ove em; an they wer
so well trained that hit sounded like one man, only sixty-seven
times louder. Sed they cussed him pussonely, till his jackit buttons flew off an the ainds ove his har cotched fire; then they
turned in ontu a stage agent an cussed him into a three week's
spell ove fits an diarrear, but he hadn't much ove a constitushun,
no how; an then finished off by cussin wun ove the stage waggins
ontil hit run off inter the woods without eny hosses tu hit. "In
fac, mister laigs," sez he, "I got the best nites sleep arter they got
throu, what I've had in six months; never felt the fust durned
bug, an would gin a duller ef your crowd could jist cuss half es
purfectly. Hits a monsous holesum quietin thing fur a man tu
get a tip-top cussin jist afore he goes tu bed, perticulerly if the
wimmin ove the crowd jines in with that ar 'nasty hog,' and 'aint
you shamed ove yersef, you stinkin brute you!' chorus ove theirn.
I tell you, mister, hits all I keeps tavrin fur." An I believed him;
fur, bein a natral-born durned fool, I never onct thought ove the
half dullers he got arter the cussin wer over. They mout a kep
him from feelin his bugs, moutent they?

Well, when that bottil smashed agin the stove hit skared out
from onder hit the all-firedest, biggest, spottedest, long laigedest
bull frog I ever seed. He hed a iron teaspoon crosswise in his
mouf, an he struck out an swum to a injun rubber over shoe
what wer floatin about boat-fashion loose. He climbed aboard, an
sot in tu paddlin hissef with his spoon, injun way, fust one side
ove the keel and then tuther, across that ar pond. The cussin hed
stopped by this time, an I never seed as meny big eyes afore; they
were es round an big es ef their leds hed been stretched over
martingil rings [4] an durn the word wer spoke. He steered fur the
bluff bank ove an old har trunk,[5] an clomb tu the top of hit with
his spoon in his mouf agin, an then tuck hits bowl in his paws,
stood up on his hine laigs, an scratched his back over-handed
with the handil. Arter he satisfied hissef at that devarshun, he
tuck aim at me (he'd been a watchin me afore), an fired his
durned ole rusty spoon at my hed. I hearn hit whiz apast my

4. Martingale rings: the rings through which the martingale (the
strap on a horse's harness for holding its head down) passes from the
headgear, between the forelegs, to the girth.

5. Hair trunks: trunks, one very common, covered with leather from
which the hair has not been removed.

year. Then he squatted ontu the har trunk, spread his fore laigs wide like ontu a bench laiged fice,[6] a facin the crowd, an in the most human-like way yu ever hearn in all yer born days, begun in a orful hoarse voice a croakin, "Bull's Gap"—"Bull's Gap"—"Bull's Gap," an as the tail aind ove the word gap lef his mouf he'd snap his lips tugether like shettin ove a par ove woffil irons in a hurry, and his countinance looked like he wer powfully discumforted about sumthin. The thought got throu my har that hit were the ghostez ove some Frenchman what had got pizened with sumthin he'd et thar, ur got hisself drownded in the mud. The whole performance wer too human like tu suit me; so a fust rate big skeer begun in the middil ove my heart an wer a spreadin fast; an when hit got intu my laigs, I jist loped outen the door inter the slush in the middil ove the road. The ballance ove the crowd seemed to be waitin for a hint ove that sort, fur durn my gizzard ef they didn't pour outen that ar door in a solid sluice into the dark and mud, an every now an then sum feller more skeered an active wud cum out a flyin over the heads ove the ballance; an thar warnt a mossel ove cussin done, nor a single pusson lef in that ar warter tight room. The frog had hit all tu hisself, durn his spotted soul; I reckon he wer satisfied now.

Well, don't you think, George, nex mornin every cussed infunel lyin raskil ov em didn't deny the whole thing, and swore thar warn't ara frog seed at all, an hit were nuthin but the strike nine whisky I hed drunk, what hed hatched a frog in my hed. But I'm durned ef hit warnt just es I tell hit; fur, es I cum back, a week arterwards, I seed his skin stretched up agin the house, an hit wer es big es a old he coon's, an the tavrinkeeper wer a rubbin in ole butter intu the fleshy side. I axed him what he were agwine tu du with hit. He sed he ment tu make a night cap outen hit fur the President ove the Railroad, es a compliment. I wish he wud. Now won't he dream skary dreams when he socks his hed inter that frogskin cap? A durned fust rate idear, warn't hit? an hit will look so becomin on him, spotted side out. How I'd like tu bounce a brick bat ofen hit yearly sum frosty mornin, jist tu see ef hit wud do to risk in a big fight.

Well, arter a while the secon bell rattilled, an we all sneaked roun the house an went in at the back door, fur that orful frog sot monsous heavy ontu our minds. Thar wer a big-thunderin

6. Bench legged feist: a small mongrel dog with widely separated legs.

Duchman along, the wust Duchman I ever seed fur fat an unon-derstandable lingo; he looked like he'd been moulded in a ele-fant's paunch, an his laigs in a big crooked holler log, an stuck on arterwards. His britches wer es big es a bedtick,[7] with two meal-bags sowed tu hit fur laigs, an his hed wer es round es a ball; an his har—well, hit mout a been a sandy boar's [8] skin tuck ofen the beastez when he wer mad an had all bristils sot an then fitted without eny combin ur cleanin tu his skull. His face looked like sum stout pusson hed busted a ripe tomato ontu hit, an seeds an innards an skin hed all stuck an dried thar. He talked like he hed a jewsharp in his throat; an when he sot in tu cussin, he did hit in Dutch mostly, an hit sounded like sawin a loose sheet ove iron with a dull hansaw. I tell you, he wer fearful tu look at, an dredful to hear, an overpowerin tu smell. Well, he planted hissef at the tabil forninst [9] a two year old chicken cock biled whole, an a big tin pan ove sourcrout what smelt sorter like a pile ove raw hides in August, an a bullit ladil wer socked inter hit. He jist fotch a snort an socked his fork up tu the hilt in the rump bone ove that misfortinate ole cock an started him down his throat head fust, and then begun tu hump hissef an grunt. Every yerk he gin the chicken went an inch, an he'd crook his neck sorter sidewise like a hen does with a lump ove dough stuck in her throat. When he'd swallered hit apast the rump, the laigs stuck out at each corner ove his mouf es wide apart es the prongs ove a pitchfork, an then he sot intu ladlin in the crout atween em. At last the toes ove the rooster went outen site, an he sent the ballance ove the crout arter him, now an then pitchin in, lef handed, a chunk ove bull-steak es sorter mile stones tu separate the ladles ove crout. He rubbed his belly an pernounced hit "tam goot," an axed ef they had eny more "lettle schickins." The tavrin keeper jist shuck his head; he wer too full tu speak. I were feared that his feelins would overcum him entirely. Dutchy then axed fur lager bier, an Noel fotch him a yeathen crock ove dish warter with a teacupful ove red pepper an a pint ove tanglelaig whisky mixed in. He tasted hit, smacked his lips, an said hit wer "tam goot too;" then he jist dried the bottom ove the crock afore he sot hit down, an then rubbed his belly agin.

Right forninst whar I sot thar wer a sumthin onto hits but-

7. The fabric case, usually made of ticking, for a mattress or pillow.
8. A boar of the color of sand.
9. Forenent: opposite, directly in front of.

aind in a plate, ni onto the bigness an shape ove a beef's heart, an carved like ontu a pine burr, an mout (mine I dont say hit wer,) been made outer flour mush with a scrimpshun ove indigo in hit, an hit cudent keep still—jist sot thar an trimbled an quivered every time every body totcht the tabil, like hit wer skared durnd ni ontu death, an knowin hit hed no laigs tu run with, jist tuck hit out in shakin.[10] I begin tu skeer myself at hits human like kerriens on, for I made hit out tu be a infunel mershean, the invenshun ove sum cussed infunel murderin know nothing, calculatin frum my nater that I'd swaller hit whole when he ment hit tu go off an scatter my meat over a squar acre ove that black jack mountain, an make a breakfus for the tucky buzzards what waited roun thar fur stage hosses an misfortinat passengers. Them ar buzzards got so sassy at last, that ef a hoss or man stumbled an fell, they'd kiver him all over afore he cud get up. Why, they hilt a lection every month, an hed meetin every Sunday, same es humans. They'se monsous nowin critters, them ar Bull's Gap buzzards is, as they wer the best fed fowels I ever seed. Rite here, George, I'll tell you why I thought that ar tremblin thing wer invented an sot thar to turn me inside out. When I wer a boy, an my laigs not longer nor John Wentworth's, dad fotch home a durnd wuthless, mangy, flea-bitten, grey old fox houn, good fur nuthin but tu swaller up what orter lined the bowels ove us brats. Well, I natrally tuck a distaste to him, an hed a sorter hankerin arter hurtin his feelins an discumfortin ove him every time dad's back wer turnd. This sorter kep a big skeer allers afore his eyes, an a orful yell ready in his throat tu pour out the fust moshun he seed me make. So he larnt tu swaller things es he run an alers kep his laigs well onder hisself, fur he never knowd how soon he mout want tu use em in totin his infunal cacus beyant the reach ove a flyin rock. He knowd the whiz ove a rock in moshun jist as well, an he never stopped tu see who flung hit, but jist let his head fly open tu gin a howl room tu cum, an sot his laigs a gwine the way his nose happened tu be a pintin. He'd shy roun every pound rock he seed in the road, fur he looked on hit as a calamity tu cum after him sum day. Ef he lef home, sum neibor's dog tanned his hide, an ef he staid at home, I was allers arter hit tu tan hit, so he dident see much more peace ove mind nur a suckit rider dus in a baptis neiborhood at sacramint time when the ruver am up in good

10. What Sut sees, of course, is a plate of gelatin.

dippin order. And in all my born days I never seed him a gwine the same way I wer; he made that an onbreakabil rule. I think I got my fust noledge ove gittin away frum imijut trubbil an cummin tribulashun frum him; an with the vantage ove a holsum par ove laigs an the power ove usein em quick, I allers found his plan tu werk well. I tell you, Georgy, that running am the greatest invenshun on yearth when used keerfully.

Whar'd I a been by this time, ef I hadn't relyed ontu these yere laigs? (D'ye see em?) Don't they mind you ove a par ove cumpusses made tu devide a mile inter quarters? They'l do, I'l be circumstanshuly durned ef they don't. Well, one day I tuck a pig's bladder ni ontu the size ove a duck aig an filled hit with powder an corked hit up with a piece ove spunk, rolled hit up in a thin skulp [11] ove meat, sot the spunk afire, an flung hit out; he swallered it at one yerk, an then sot in tu gittin away fur doin hit. I hearn a noise like bustin sumthin, an his tail lit atop ove my hat. His head wer way down the hill an hed tuck a death holt onter a root. His fore laigs wer fifty feet up the road, a makin runnin moshuns, an his hine ones a straddil ove the fence. His innerds wer hangin in links onter the cabin chimley, sept about a yard in mam's bussum, an his paunch cum down permiscusly like rain. Es tu the dog hisself, *es a dog,* I never seed him agin. Well, dad, durn his onsanctified soul! flung five or six hundred onder my shut [12] with the dried skin ofen a bull's tail, an gin me the remainder nex day with a waggin whip what he borrered frum a feller while he wer a waterin his hosses; the waggoner got sorry fur me, an hollered tu me tu turn my beggin an squallin inter d——d fust-rate runnin, which I imejutly did, an the last lick missed me about ten feet.[13] Well, now, ye see I minded all

11. Scalp; here, apparently, the skin of an animal.

12. That is, his Dad gave him five or six hundred licks.

13. The above digression about Sut's dog (beginning with the phrase, "When I wer a boy, an my laigs not longer nor John Wentworth's . . .") despite its use of gory and cruel detail, was frequently excerpted and reprinted widely during Harris's lifetime. Five examples have been noted by this editor:

"How 'Sut' Dosed His Dog," Sioux City (Iowa) *Register,* June 2, 1859. Reprinted with editorial revision: the dialect is regularized, some of the dialect words translated into standard usage, the name "Wentworth" spelled "Weatworth," the mention of the circuit rider in a baptist neighborhood omitted, and all curse words deleted along with the description of the dog's entrails hanging "in links" on the cabin chimney and in Mam's

this, an I thot that shakin new-fangled fixin wer the dog's ritribu-
shun (I believes in ritribushuns, I dus), an the biggest kind ove a
one at that, an hit were morally intended fur me tu swaller, an ef
I had, I'd a been jist about as easy tu bury as the dog wer. But I
didn't happen tu swaller hit, not that time. I gin Dutchy a punch
an pinted tu hit, jist arter the chicken-cock's toes went outen site,
in the hopes that if he seed hit he'd send hit arter the fowel.
Suppose—he—had? I wanted orfully tu see the roof cum ofen
the house, and tu larn whether tucky buzzards will eat dutch
meat tore up fine an mixed with chicken cock, bull-beef, crout an
linsey breeches.[14] But he jist gin hit one spisious look an shuck
his head—too durned smart for the no nuthins ef he wer a
thunderin Dutchman. So thar hit sot and trembled, and they lost
all thar trubbil and powder, fur thar haint a pusson bornd durnd
fool enuf tu ondertake tu eat enything while hit trimbled as hit
did, an run the risk ove kingdom come fur doin hit. Durn thar
souls, they's been tryin to kill me ever since I dreamd about old
Buck a beatin Fillmore and Freemount at a game ove old sledge
fur the Presidency.[15]

---

bosom. The source of the sketch is indicated as *"Sut Luvengood's Revela-
tions."*

"How Sut Lovegood Dosed His Dog," *Yankee Notions*, VIII (August
1859), 234. Reprinted with essentially the same revisions and deletions as
in the above version, except that a larger number of dialect words are
translated into standard usage and "Gregory" is substituted for "Georgy."
Both this and the Sioux City *Register* version seem to have been reworked
from a common source but not the original printing, perhaps an interven-
ing version now lost.

"Sut Lovengood's Dog" in *Hill's Tennessee, Alabama and Mississippi
Almanac and State Register* (Fayetteville, Tennessee: E. Hill, 1860). This
editor has been unable to inspect a copy of this rare paper-covered pam-
phlet.

"Story Number Five," in *Beadle's Dime Book of Fun*, No. 3 (New York:
Beadle and Company, 1866), pp. 21–22. An abbreviated version and
apparently another editor's reworking of the same text used by the Sioux
City *Register* and *Yankee Notions* editors. It is introduced by the following
comment: "You've all heard of Sut Lovegood. Well, Joe met the real Sut
and had from his lips the following *Dorg Story*—or, as he called it, 'the
dorgondest tail I ever didn't hold on to.' I'll give it in his own words: . . ."

"How Sut Lovingood Killed His Dog," Atlanta *Constitution*, II (July 18,
1869), 1. Another reworking of the same basic text used by the above
editors, with strong emphasis on translating and modernizing the dialect
for readability.

14. Pants made of linsey-woolsey, a coarse fabric.

15. See "Playing Old Sledge for the Presidency."

I wer monsus hungry miself, so I levied ontu a chunk ove beef fried in cake taller,[16] about the size an shape ove an iron wedge that had been cut outen the back ove sum misfortunate ole bull's neck, jist ahine his hons. I socked my fork thru one aind an ondertuck tu bite off tuther; but I dident. I hilt on with fork an teeth, an tried tu saw off a bite with a case knife. Couldn't do that. Tried tuther aidge, an hit wur es dull es the fust. So I made up my mind tu cum slutch over hit an swaller hit whole. I hed like tu let the fork go arter hit, twer so hard tu pull out. Hit hed rusted intu the meat. Now, jist like a durned onthin-kin, onmitigated, cussed, natral born fool es I is, I hed swallered hit with the grain the wrong way; an like crawling grass a gwine up yer britches laigs, hit started up agin an felt like ontu a terbacker wum a crawlin up my breakfus pipe. But I hilt hit down by sendin anuther hunk arter hit with the grain the right way. Then I drunk a bowl ove coffee made outen an ole chopped wool hat, and a stage driver's ole boot laig. The grease, sweat, glue, leather, blackin, an wool in ole hats an boots, makes a fust rate biled drink, when hit am sweetened with a mixtry ove Orleans sugar, pissants an cockroaches; hit jist dus that, hoss; durned ef it don't—that's so.

Well, arter we hed et up most everything but the cook and skillet, they went off in bunches tu bed. I dasent [17] ax fur a bed, least they mout take me fur a beastes an send me tu the stabil; so I sneaked inter the room whar Dutchy wer, made a piller outen my bag ove duds, an lay down ontu the floor, an sot intu the darndest, hardest sleepin now in fashion, an dreamin the durn-dest, skariest dreams now in use—dreamed that two hundred head ove horned cattil wer arter me, with thar tails up an thar heads down, follered by a ole sick bull with a chunk ove meat es big es a boot jack, cut outen the back ove his neck; an they looked like they thought I had hit inside ove me. Ole hats with wings like ontu bat's wings flew round, not makin a bit ove noise, an ole boots ontu wheels trundled over the floor. I don't know what would hev becum ove me, (for in dreams yer laigs wont go off—yer can't use em a bit,) ef I hadn't been wakened with the durndest doleful soun I ever heard. En thar wer that infernal bag ove soap-fat, the Dutchman, in his shuttail, mounted up ontu the

16. Tallow allowed to harden into a cake.
17. Dare not, partly a contraction of *darst not* (Middle English) and partly of *dares not*.

foot board ove his bedstead, a flappin his wings and a crowin like ontu a durned ole shanghi cock with a June bug in its craw.

Hit sounded like a mule colt a brayin in a emty barrel, and hit farly shuck the tavrin, wakin up everybody, an a settin the cussin agwine agin; then he loped down ontu his all-fours on the floor, an his shuttail looked shorter nur ever, an sot in tu rakin up dirt with his huffs, an a honin ove the bedstead with his hed, an a bellerin orful. Bo-wo-wo woof—bo-wo-a woah a woah, a woah—woof. I sot up on aind, an, thinks I, well, I be durnd, you never hearn bull acted es perfectly in yer life. His voice suited the job he'd ondertuck adzactly, only ef eny thing, hit wer too loud fur a common mountain bull. The passengers were fool'd with hit, an got all thar wimmin huddled inter one room, an they drug a bedstead agin the door, an all ove em got ontu hit, fur they wer morraly durnd sertin that thar war a rusty ole bull up stairs, en mad at that. I seed that the infernel ole crout barrel wer fast asleep, an I fell on a plan to wake him up. So I tuck a crockery war vessil from onder his hed an socked hit onto his hed, a snappin hit over his years an snout, nite-cap fashun. He seem'd tu take hit es a challenge tu mortal combat, fur he fotch a loud whoof outen his snout, gin a short beller, an tuck a runnin butt at me by guess on his all-fours. I tell you he cum a tarin. I jist histed one of these yere laigs, so, gin a crow hop with tuther, and let him charge atween em; an es he went throu I cum down ontu his but aind with a fire shovil, an hit cracked like ontu a pistil, an, I think, added sumthin tu the force of his rush. He cum agin the board wall so hard that his shuttail flew over his head, and he smashed the crockery night-cap intu a thousand bits; hit flew all over the room, and sounded like sum feller hed flung in a shovelful ove gravil. He hisself bounced back from the lick inter the middil ove the floor, an lit on his sturn with his laigs doubled onder him, an looked monsous like the snake an picter tent what goes with a suckus. Some ove the sharp scraps ove the delf war [18] wer stuck in the wall, an some in his head. Thar he sot, plumb wide awake. His greasy-lookin eyes wer wide open, an sorter like the butt ainds ove two green bottils. He sot em on me, an then he shot em up rite slow, an opened em with a jirk an anuther whoof outen his snout; an es he did hit, he sed "Cott am." The cussin by this time wer a gwine on all over the house at an orful rate, an like thar hearts were in their work, the

18. Delft ware.

wimmen were a chatterin es bad es a campmeetin ove crazy monkeys with a bulldog amung em. Sez I, what the hell mistopher dus you mean by actin the bull in a bed-room, at midnite, an makin yer self a durnd fool generally for, kin ye tell me? He jist went throu his moshuns with his eyes an sed "Cott am," agin. Is that all ye kin say? has ye busted all yer Dutch talk outen you but that fool "cotam?" The idear now seemed tu strike him fur the fust time that he could talk Dutch, fur he jist sot intu a long job ove cussin in good Dutch. Hit run outen him in a solid sluice es thick es a hoe-handil. I listened ontil hit guv me the toothake, an I had a sour taste in my mouf. When he stopped tu take breff, I axed him how does that chicken cock rest on yer bowels what yer cum the boarconstructor over. The thought on hit seemed tu tickle him, fur he spread out his mouf into a greasey grin an sed, "Tam goot, all put de does an de spurs, dey schraches shum mine pelly;" an he rubbed hit onder his shut with his paw an made a face orful tu behold. "Put shune I trinks von bitcher ove viskey vot vill eat de boints of de sphurs an does an ten all coshe goot—tam goot;" an he put his paw onder his shut tu rub his belly agin, but fotch hit out with a jerk an anuther cotam. An now, George, I jist wish I may be infunely durned tu scrimshuns ef he warnt busted open for more nur a foot. Hit hed happened when he smashed the delf agin the wall. I tell you, hoss, that wer a orful jolt he got—that's so. I jist laid him ontu his back, tuck a nife fur a needil, an a ole bridil rein fur a thread, an sowed him up adzactly like ye sows up the mouf ove a par ove saddil bags with the strap, an then tied a knot on bof ainds ove the rein. While I wer makin the holes in the aidges ove the tare, he axed me to look inside fur the spurs of "tat tam schicken cock an gut tem off," but all I could see were his paunch, an hit looked adzactly like the flesh side ove a raw hide. Arter I got done, I axed him how he prospered, an he sed "tam goot," and that he wouldn't keer a cuss fur the whole scrape, only he knowd that ontil he growd up he wer bound to *leak his lager bier*—knowd that with my long stitches he would loose "te las tam trop." Jist at this minit a big Shanghi bellered out a big crow ni ontu the house. Dutchy widened his mouf ontil hit opened onder his years, an his eyes shined, an he sed: "Gut off hish sphurs an pring him to me." I wer feard tu do hit, least the old bridil rein mout break, ur the knots pull out. The last I hearn ove Bull

Dutchy, he had got well an war at Bristol,[19] whar he hed bet a feller his trunk agin a barrel ove sourcrout that he could drink lager bier faster and longer nur a big muley cow could salted meal slop, an durnd ef he didn't win on bof pints. The bridil rein had hilt hits holt. That's so!

19. A city in Sullivan County, northeastern Tennessee, on the Tennessee-Virginia line, contiguous with Bristol, Virginia.

SUT LOVINGOOD AND THE LOCOMOTIVE

THE first locomotive Sut ever saw, was standing with steam up, and nearly ready to go, making no noise save a suppressed humming from the safety valve. Sut had, in his skeery, cautious way, clambered up to the top of the tender to find out "what sort ove a beastes," it was, when the engineer slyly gave the whistle lever a long pull—shay y-y-y! Sut lit twenty feet distant on a pile of cord-wood, and after running until he got straightened up, he turned around all eyes, and said,

"What in the deuce *did* you do tu it, mister?"

Just at this moment a negro came trundling a trunk, with a cooking stove, a joint of pipe on the flue hole, and pots and pans hanging all round. Sut took a look first at the stove and then at the locomotive: a light broke out over his perplexity, and he shouted to the engineer:

"Oh, yes, I understands it all now; *the darned old brute was jist a nickerin' for her colt!*"

This sketch appeared in *Nick Nax,* IV (April, 1859), 356.

New York *Picayune,* XI (April 16, 1859), 123. Reprinted with slight editorial revision.

Since Harris never composed brief anecdotes of this type, this may be an excerpt from the text of a longer story, now lost.

SUT LOVINGOOD'S HOG RIDE

HEARING an unusual noise on the road one morning, I looked for the cause. Ducktown[1] was all alive, shouting, cheering, laughing.

Here came an "Israelite, in whom there was *much* guile,"[2] hatless, breathless, coatless, as fast as his abridged legs would allow, protesting most vociferously that he "vash *not* Levi Shacobs." Sut was in hot pursuit, with a table knife in his mouth and a clothes line in his hands. He would throw the coils over the Jew's head, lariat fashion, with great precision of aim, and he, with equal dexterity, would shed them off again, increasing his speed and his protestations against the "Shacobs" charge.

Sut would shout furiously in reply, "Yes you am Jacobs. Whar's my breetches, yu durned close clipt, Ch--st killin, hog hatin, bainch laiged son of a clothes hoss? I means tu fust circumsize yer snout, and then hang yer arterwards. *Yeres* the tools," brandishing the knife and rope.

The vender of raiment made his shoulder-blades and elbows fairly flutter with his terrible efforts to "get on more steam." When Sut failed in his efforts to lasso his victim, he would bring the coil with whistling force across the Israelitish hips, fairly raising him from the ground, accompanying it with *"Thar*, that's wus nor yer bed bugs, an fleas, haint hit? *Whar's* them breetches?" The individual who "vash not name Shacobs" darted into the mouth of a mining tunnel, and I detained Sut.

"What's the matter, Sut?"

"Nuff's the matter, by golly. If old Job himself wer inside this yere shut, he'd shed hit an wade into that dumpy cuss afore you

This story appeared in Nashville *Daily Press and Times*, III (September 14, 1865), 1.

1. A village in Polk County in the southeastern corner of Tennessee in the Copper Basin area.

2. A play upon the words of Jesus who commented upon seeing Nathaniel, "Behold, an Israelite indeed, in whom is no guile!" (John 1:47).

cud say drink. That ar cussed one story varmint in the tunnel thar, stole my breetches, my cross bar'd breetches; he stole em from a ole sow in Nashville, he did, an I'se arter em."

"But he says he is not Jacobs."

"Yes he am Jacobs. Haint he got a white face, a goose wing snout, rat eyes, black har, bainch legs, slick hat, an a breaspin, and dont he sell shuts, and jackits, an coats, an fishin lines? Oh you cant fool me. I know a chesnut hoss from a hoss chesnut."

"Yes, but your description is general; it is adapted to most of his race."

"Well, it mayn't be him, but ef you'd a let me alone, I'd soon skeer'd im outen a par ov breeches in the dark ove that tunnel thar. His skeer was commin to a head pow'ful fas. Jacobs, Jerusalem or Jehosaphat, hits all the same tu me. I'se arter britches hot: sum britches mus' cum now."

"Tell us about your breeches, Sut, and let that poor frightened fellow alone."

Sut thrust his head into the tunnel and shouted, "Say, old tabernickil, Ise got you now whar Alexander had the pole cat,[3] an I'm gwine to watch the hole. A par ove breeches or a jackit for intrus', ur rite thar you'l lay yer bones.

"Well, I speck I mout es well tell hit my self, fur hits boun to leak out anyhow: Everybody in Nashville knows hit, and my karacter's made thar fur life, es bein the durndest plum fool ever in Davidson,[4] not sceptin my own Dad.

"I hed foller'd a whisky waggin wifout a halter, plum inter town, and were slungin along a narrer lane name Union street.[5] My eyes swelled es big es aigs at the bran new sights and sounds, and me just plum ready to ketch the runninist kine of a skeer. In wun of my sudden jerks a dodgin somethin, I felt boff ove my hine gallus buttons loose holt, an my cross bar'd britches war beginnin to wrinkil round my ankils bad, and a gittin lower every move. Tu make hit wus, thar wer a pint flask of swell hed whisky in wun pockit, and a pone of corn braid in tuther.

"The infunel street wer sock full of rale fine sunflower

3. Presumably, a reference to a folk tale which seems not to have been recorded elsewhere.

4. Nashville is located in Davidson county.

5. At that time, Union street ran east and west parallel to and between Spring and Deaderick streets. John P. Campbell, *Nashville Business Directory*, p. 9; 1854 map of Nashville in Jesse C. Burt, *Nashville, Its Life and Times*, facing p. 32.

wimin, smelin ove bargamint,[6] and a smilin kingdum cum all roun em. The men folks ove that ar town mus be a ornary set ove cusses, not to gin the wimin sumthin else tu du besides huddlin tugether in that street, jis like a drove ove red comb'd hens. Hits a durnd shame.

"I cudn't strip tu fix things thar, es I orter dun. I wus so monsous shame faced it hes made agin me in gittin along mos es bad es my unyealthy looks and my durnd fool nater; but sumthin hed tu be dun, and that durnd soon. Spose them trousis hed fell jis thar, why I'd a follered em tu the pavement in a twinklin ded es a stone hammer. I begun tu sarch fur a hole, and seed a narrer path, they calls hit a alley, gwine out from the corner ov a gingercake and gouber pea factory. I took a 'zaminin look up hit, and seed nobody, so I gits me a savin holt with bof hans ontu the waisbun, and I shot in thar tu fix things. I felt sorter like a rabbit dus jis arter he's got inter a holler tree, and hears the dorg tar a mouful ov bark off clost ahine his tail. I tuk me a double ho'n the fust thing on the strainth ov findin a safe spot.

"I hed on a notail coat, sum calls it a rounabout, an a bobtail shut. In a jineral way I likes bobtail shuts; they dusent ketch dust es bad es long fan tails, an ef yu hes deep wadin tu du, they dusent git wet. A dry shutail is a comfortin thing tu go tu sleep wif, arter a holesome ho'n. Did you ever try hit?

"Well, arter I'd traveled up a piece, I turnd my face toards the street, an I cud see ef eny ove the wimin follerd me tu watch me. Theys powful curious things enyhow bout men folks' doins. I let my britches drap tu the groun, so es tu see what had cum ove the hine buttons. They wer thar; hed jis got tharsefs onbuttind. I cotch my trousis by the front tu hist them agin, and had got my han holt es high es my knees, the starn part yet lyin on the yeath, and I war stoopin *low* forrid, when a cussed, medlesum New Founlan dorg, es big es a yearlin, an es black es the devil, cum a tarin outen sumbody's gate way up the alley ahine me, clost arter a thundin big spotted sow. He wer jis a movin her from haste, head down, bristils all sot, an a sayin booh, woof, goosh, every jump. I wer a lookin at em cum from atwixt my laigs, an a wonderin ef he'd ketch her. Thars a nuther 'vantage in bobtail shuts—I cud see good wifout risin up or turnin roun. The sow's eyes wer wallid [7] back at the dorg, fust wun side and then tuther,

6. Bergamot: perfume made from the oil of the bergamot fruit.
7. Walled: with eyes rolled in an expression of emotion.

an she never seed me, but dam ef the dorg didnt. Instuntly he hung out signs all over im ove big skeer. He wer the wust surprised, wust 'stonished, and the wust trimblin dorg I ever seed. He sot all his laigs and his tail ahead tu stop hissef, and he slid fifteen feet, whinin pitiful, and lookin monsous wishful back up the alley, the way his hart wer gwin. He hadn't the melt tu venter a secon' look—the fust wun hed run him crazy, an ef he ever sees the likes agin, which I doubts much, I'l bet high he jis gins up the ghost, not wantin tu live anuther minit in a world whar dorgs' souls am tu be harrowed wif sich orful, onnatr'l, onuseful, an tarifine sights. He's right, dam ef he aint. When he got his headway sorter stopt, he whirld roun, sez he, 'meew ra a ap,' an ove all the durnd wholesale runnin—the pint ove that ar bushy tail ove hisn war glued clost tu his belly atwixt his fore laigs, an wer drippin wet wif sweat. He flung his hine laigs onder him like he wer tryin tu send em home fust atwixt his fore ones, and his backbone seemed es limber es a string. Oh Jerusalim, what a site he mus a seed, to a throwd im intu sich spasms. I'll bet a hoss you cant hawl im down that ar alley agin wif a pair of mules an a log chain. Ef dorgs hes churches he's jined wun sure. Well, he orter be surcumspeck in his ways arter sich a warnin. I wish frum my heart the sow hed seed me tu, an preshiated me half es well es the dorg did; hit wud a saved my feelins, my cross bard breeches, an prevented an undue exhitement amung the sunflower wimin. But yere she cum jis a tarin, big black dorg weighin pow'ful heavy ontu her mine, run her snout atwixt my laigs *over* the hine waisbun, and sock *intu* the fork on the inside ove my trousis, jerked my heels frum onder me, an sot me squar and bar sturn'd ontu her rump, my laigs nakid frum my shutail mos tu my nees, up my britches in tu hundred short wrinkils frum thar to my feet, an she blindfolded in the seat ove em, rather discumfortin to a sow ove delicate feelin's, warn't hit? I rid her outer the mouth ove that ar alley intu the street es fas es a bird kin fly. I hear'n the hem ove my bobtail shut snapin in the wind way up level wif my year's; jis then misfortunately, very misfortunately, a big red faced 'oman 'bout the size ove a stack of oats, dressed in black silk, wif a fan in wun han, and a haf grown umbrella in tuther, wer crossin the mouf ove the alley ontu the stepin stones. I know'd what were cummin now, so I duck'd down my head low ontu the sow's withers, and shot up my eyes fas' fur manners sake. She run her durn'd old britches kiverd snout ahine the 'omans formos' gaiter, and afore the hinemos' gaiter, and underminded her; hit were dark es midnight in the devil's tater cellar in a moment, an staid so jis long enuf fur the sow to say "booh, woof, goosh," and we busted intu daylight agin, way up the midil ove the street.—I looked back at a big black pile of sumthing in the gutter, wif a white stockin stickin out as big es a chun. I hed the young umbreller ontu my hed, an half ove a red flannel petticoat acros afore me, like a suckis rider toats his overcoat on his saddil ove hot days. The 'oman mus a bin sorter flustrated, fur she tole her husban' the steam fire ingine wif four hosses in full blast hed run over her, an he, like a durn fool, believed her, an tuck a shot at the ingine wif a hoss pistil nex day.

"We tuck down towards Collige street,[8] makin things happen every jump; you orter seed the slick niggers in gole hat ban's atop ove shiney carriages, a tryin tu rein thar fool hosses outer store doors; every durned hoss wanted to hide hissef, an were a dancin the 'Devil's dream'[9] in quick time. Down Collige we flu. 'Booh, woof, goosh,' everybody dartin hither, and yan, an ove all the durned laughin you ever hearn, cum frum the folks what were outer our way.

"Wun big fat feller, plenty fat tu kill, standin in a taverin porch, sez he, 'Ha-ha-ha, say, shutail, he's arter yu, what'l yu take fur yer spotted mar?'

"Lord geminy, how bad I wanted a bridil jis then. 'Gallus up them britches, ur yu'l sun burn yer starn,' sed one. He were a pusson ove clost observashun, he wer.

" 'Lainthen yer stirrups,' squeeked a smutty faced boy. 'Hole hard, gingercakes, yer gwine down hill,' shouted a feller outer a packin box. 'Hole h-a-r-d.'

"Jis then we upsot a feller, wif a big pocket book under his arm; he wer a bank president. Sez he: 'Shoot that durnd fool, afore he kills sumbody,' like I cud help hit. I wernt thar apurpus by a durnd long site.

" 'Say, hog express, what's happened in Cincinnaty?' sed sum one.

" 'The loonatic asslum's burnt down,' sed sum one else—that feller mus a knowd me pussonally.

"I her'n the words 'dam fool' cum frum sum whar; thinks I,

8. College street (Third Avenue North in modern Nashville) ran north and south parallel to and between Market and Cherry streets.

9. A traditional American fiddling tune for square dancing. The music and verses are printed in Ira W. Ford, *Traditional Music of America*, p. 62.

mister, yuse hit hit tu a dot, whether yu mean me ur this yer infernel sow. Wer eny body else roun yer?

" 'Hits nuffin gentlemen, but a lard oil advertisement got drunk an runnin outer time,' surjested a red nosed youf wif a patch over his eye. I wanted sum body tu say 'dam fool' jis then agin, but they didn't an I hadn't the time.

" 'The devil's in that swine, and she's makin for the river; better roll off yer yaller laigs,' sed a pale man wif a han saw under his arm. I ventured tu surjest tu him tu go tu hell, but hadn't time tu see if he minded me.

"Thar wer a big shiney bed stid a standin acrost the pavemint, whar they sells sich plunder, an a feller in a paper cap and bedtick apron, wer a whitewashin hit wif varnish; we went atwix him an the yeath frum ahine; his brush lay in the store door, his pot tother side ove the street, an him flat ove his back, wif his arms spread like he wer crusified dead fur the time es Nebucadnesar's off-ox.[10]

"I rekon, he thot hit mus' abeen lightnin.

"The sow shot onder the bed stid, a skinnin me plum outer my britches, still totin em ontu her snout, wrong side out, an lef me sittin on the very pint ove my tail bone ontu the pavemint; by golly, the stones felt powrful hard an cold.

" 'Ha, ha, ha,' sed a nigger, 'sumbody ketch dat crazy man's hoss.'

"Thar I war, wif my long har, yaller laigs, socked into a par ove short hoss hide boots, not fillin em up much more nur the dasher dus the chun. I swar they lookt tu me jis then tu be es long es a par ove stack poles;[11] a bob tail shut, a rounabout, and a little flimsey umereller, made up the picter, an ef it warn't purty, I'm durnd, an sooted tu a nicity, a street full ove wimmin folks. I jis wanted sumthin wif a big mouf an strong stumack tu swaller me. I thot if I jis hed my britches, I cud stan it, so I riz an tuck arter the cussed sow. The old rase hoss fool. She'd tuck down Broad street,[12] and when I got thar, she wer outer site, tuck the

10. An off-ox is a stubborn, clumsy person. The biblical allusion is obscure, but in the fourth chapter of Daniel, when King Nebuchadnezzar grew too proud, he was abused by the Lord, driven from men, and forced to "eat grass as oxen."

11. Poles about which hay or forage is stacked.

12. Broad street (now Broadway) ran east and west parallel to and between Spring and Demonbreum streets in Nashville.

rever,[13] sure enuf I recon, but I seed that feller in the tunnil thar, ur his twin bruther, a brushin my cross bard britches, an agin [14] I got tu him, he'd hung em up tu a nail at his door, wif 'Fur Sale' in chock on the stern; sez he, 'O mien frent, yu vants shum pants vera mosh, zey feets yu goat, so vera long in ze laig.'

" 'Yas,' says I, 'gin em up, theyse mine, you durn raskil, you stole em,' an I made a grab fur em. But he dodged atwix us sayin 'yu steal my goots, I puts yu in shail.' Jis then two perlease grabbed me, flung a blankit roun me and hauld me tu the work'us, ontu a forkid tail coat, charged wif an ondecint showin ove my pussin, 'soltin an 'oman, killin a painter, bustin a bank, an raisin hell ginerly an never sed the fust durn word agin the sow, ur the Jew; that's jistis haint hit? Now Ise yere, an arter my britches; they mus cum. Say yu in thar, Moses, Levi, Solomon, Samuel, Jacob or Pontshus Pilit, cum out yer an 'goshiate like a human, ur I mus cum in thar arter yu, wif my rope."

Sut got a pair of breeches, and the "follower of Moses" went his way.

13. The Cumberland River which ran alongside what was then the eastern edge of the city.

14. Again, used in dialect to mean "by the time that."

SUT LOVINGOOD'S BIG DINNER STORY

I'L agree to be doddrabited, if my bristils ain't sot this morning. I has a right sharp appetite to fight sumfin, I has. Don't you believe, that bald faced, check apron'd, calicker cap'd, ole she pot ove purgatif intment, Misses JARROLD, on Willow Creek, haint sot in to writin' about *me*, in IVINSZES' noospaper,[1] a-belitilin, an' a-bemeanin me, wus nor if I wer a suck aig dorg—yes, wus nor if I wer even a radical,[2] an' all for nuffin. Now, by golly, no body can't tramp on *me*, wifout gittin thar foot bit.[3] I means to let a cat outen the bag, an' if she quiles[4] up her snout about hit, I'l print the cat, all along a noospaper. She'l find hit heavier to bare, than the tiltin' hoop disease, what she says she has a ragin' so bad in her famerly, or that cross she has to tote, weighin' a ton, or bofe ove em together.

You know, GEORGE, that thar is some folks powerful feard ove low things, low ways, an' low pepil, an' everlastinly a-tryin'

This story appeared in Nashville *Union and American*, XXXIII (August 10, 1866), 4.

1. The Democratic Athens (Tennessee) *Post* published by Samuel P. Ivins in Polk county between 1848 and 1887. According to J. M. Sharp, in *Recollections & Hearsays of Athens, Fifty Years and Beyond*, p. 20, Ivins originally came from New Jersey in 1848 to help encourage the building of the Hiwassee Railroad and finally settled there. The surviving file of the Athens *Post* is fragmentary, and a search of the available issues has not turned up anything by a Mrs. Jarrold criticizing Sut or his creator. If Mrs. Jarrold, her husband Simon, and her daughter Susannah Jane actually existed in or near Athens, there are no records to verify it. The same is true of all the other persons mentioned in the story. Although the 1850 and 1860 unpublished United States census schedules for Polk county do contain a listing of several Watson families, no Violet Watson appears among them.

2. A member of the political group in the North who favored drastic reforms and extreme measures against the South during and after the Civil War.

3. An allusion to the inscription "Don't Tread on Me," beneath a coiled rattlesnake on a field of yellow, the design of the early Colonial flag of the Virginia colony.

4. Coils.

their durndest, to show that they ain't low. Always on a fiddil string strain, a-lookin' up for a higher limb to roost on, an' wringin' in every chance far or onfar, what a h—l ove a feller thar granmamey was, never seed a louse—smelt a bed bug, or hearn tell ove the eatch, in thar lives, no sir, never. They ginerily has a pedigree wif one aind tied to thar sturn, an' tother one a-soakin' in NOAH'S flood, an' they'l trace hit back for you, round the jails, onder the galluses, apast the soap works, an' over the kitchens, ove four thousin years, an' if you'l notice clost, hit makes some ove the shortest kind ove dodges, to miss 'em all, but by golly, hit does miss 'em, an' hits every durnd castil, an' throne, on the whole road.

I likes that pattern ove pepil most wonderfully I does, an I think, GEORGE, if ever I could jist git to sleep wif one a night or so—a *he* one I means, durn you, what are you grinnin at, I sees nuffin to laff at myself—hit mout fix *me* for mixin in decent society, roostin high—eatin peas wif a fork, an play h—l wif my insex forevermore; but durn em, I never hev yet got nigh enuff to one, even to larn his smell,—thars a gulf atwixt them an me, an I speck hits well for me that thar is. Well! Old Misses JARROLD is one ove that brand ove cattil, her big pints ove gentility is kiverin the looking glass wif bobinett, quilin up her snout at "low trash," scourin the door sill, havin a red cushion stuffed wif hen feathers on her banch at church, makin old JARROLD tote a hot rock arter her when she goes thar. Scoldin neighbor wimmen for sucklin thar brats afore folks, hangin paper nets up to the ceilin to ketch flies, larnin her gals to play the "Flowers of Edinburgh," [5] on an accordeon with the rattles, growin a row of hollyhawks from the door to the gate, an back agin, marryin her gals to a pedigree, whitewashin the— springhouse, keepin the Pilgrim's Progress on the candle-stand, an' a par ove plarster ove paris pigeons on the mantle-shelf,—an' thinks callin dung—dung, bad grammer. *Her* granmamy wer a h—l ove a feller, I reckon. Now, a hongry lookin' young lawyer, wif black freckils an' mink eyes, one ove the kind ove varmints that wud hide onder a bed to listen—peep through the key-hole

---

5. A popular nineteenth-century musical piece. A copy of the music, without words, published sometime during the eighteen-fifties as a single sheet (along with the music for "The Girl I Left Behind Me") by G. W. Brainard & Co., of Louisville, Kentucky, is on deposit in the Kenneth Rose music collection at the Tennessee State Library and Archives.

ove a gal's bed-room, or break open other folks' letters, had settled on the crick, offerin' to practize law, an' while he wer breedin' a few suits amung the old neighbors, Misses JARROLD was a breedin' a weddin' atwix him and her darter SUSANNAH JANE, (her "bud ove promice," as she calls her.) Very well! her fust move wer to make a big dinner, an' invite all the ugliest gals round thar what cum up to her idears ove decent standin', so as to set off the "bud ove promice" in the eye ove this legal fickshun, named GRIPES. Amung them was VIOLET WATSON, not a purty gal, I know, but smart, neat an' as full ove mischief as a turtil is ove aigs in May. She had no sort ove fancy for Misses JARROLD'S fool ways, an' valued Mister GRIPES about as she would any other peckerwood[6] or pole cat; so you see she woudent stand back a minit to devil 'em any time. I warn't invited, in course I warn't; Misses JARROLD would as soon tho't ove invitin' old BARKLEY'S big bull.[7]

The arternoon afore the big GRIPES' dinner, VIOLET WATSON an' me hilt a convention, sorter barin on the subjec. I wer to follow her to JARROLD'S, an' then she wer to tell the old quilt, that I had toted her across the crick dry-shod, an' for her to please let me slunge[8] round the kitchin, an' give me some dinner in a tin pan, or skillet, provided I kep outen sight ov her cumpany, an' behaved mysef. I kep my contrack; I never behaved myself better in my life, an' VIOLET WATSON will say so, any day. As soon as she got farly in the house, she pinned up her frock, an' tucked up her sleeves, an' sot in to helpin the old jade get dinner ready. What wif her neat ankils, plump, white arms, an' the comeing mischief a sparklin in her brown eyes, she looked rale holsum—sorter eatable like, I swar she did. Hit warnt long afore she coaxed old climb-a-pole outen the kitchen, an' got her to go to the big room whar the cumpany was, when she imejuntly sot in to lecterin on pedigrees, an' spreadin herself generally. Now this give VIOLET full swing in the kitchen, an' me helpin in my rough, fool way, we sorter *did* fix things. If anybody had been a noticin right clost that mornin, they mout a seed me a hidin three or four little pokes full ove sumfin in the

6. Inversion of woodpecker.
7. This is the only mention by Harris of Barkley's bull, which is not one of the two bulls involved in "Sicily Burns's Wedding" and "Old Burns's Bull-Ride," *Sut Lovingood, Yarns*, pp. 86–107.
8. Slounge, an alteration of slouch under the influence of lounge.

jimson weeds ahine the smok'ous—them are pokes, GEORGE, contained venemous rep-tiles, too numerus an' horrid to men-shun. Well! VIOLET, she cut two holes in a sheet, socked my arms through them, pinned hit clost roun' my naik, tucked hit in an' pinned hit roun' my wais', and hit reached to my heels—the all-firedest, long, graveyard lookin apron you ever seed. I tell you, hoss, I looked like the ghost ove a dead rope-walk.[9] I were bof sickly, an' skeery to look at, I swar I wer. Then she sot me to totein in the kivered dishes ov vittils an' things, an' a settin em on the table in the dinin room. I had filled some ove them for her, she bein feared to handle the vittils, if hit could be called vittils at all, what wer in em.

Ole Misses JARROLD had gin up the dinner bisness to VI-OLET, out an' out. She know'd she couldent be beat—her mind was easy, an' so she jist lumbered [10] on the needsecity ove pedi-grees to her company, to her heart's content. Oh geminey![11] What a misplaced confidence that wer. I tell you, hoss, I would-ent trus' myself outer my own sight a minit to save my life. Well! while I wer a totin in the last dish, VIOLET sent word to Misses JARROLD that dinner wer ready, tuck her bonnet, slipped out the back way, an' cut for home, by-golly—onbenowenst to me or any body, leaven me thar among inemys, shrouded up in a durned old sheet, onable to make the first bulge towards a run, an' a h–ll ove a big storm about to bust. But thinkin I had good backin in the kitchen, I wer carlm enuff to watch things as they happened, plum through the whole rumpus. Down they all sot, Misses JARROLD at the head, an' her ole corn-stalk ove a man at the foot ove the table, GRIPES on her right, the "bud ove prom-ice" on her left, an' the ugliest, cross-grained gall in the house next to the "bud." Passun BUSSUM sed grace: sed "make us thankful for what we are about to receive," an' so forth, an so on, an' so along. Thinks I, old hoss, if these folks *am* thankful you may consider yourself *a whale*. She had her boys an' galls, an' five or six young free niggers standin in rows behind the chairs, drill'd, and waitin for the word to lift the kivers. That wer another climb-a-pole idea she'd picked up some whar. She

9. Perhaps Harris means a ropewalker, an acrobat who walks on a high, suspended rope.

10. Figuratively cut wood, or talked a great deal.

11. A mild oath or expletive, an alteration of *gemini*, third sign of the zodiac.

'spected hit to hev a perfoun' effect—an I'm dam if it dident. She looked as solemn as a Tuesday night arter a funeral, or a snow-storm, an' ses she, a tappin the table wif her finger, "one—two—three, *onkiver*." All at onst they did hit, and all at onst, an' durnd quick, too, they drapt the kivers smashin onto the floor, an' jist went sluicein out ove the doors, a climbin one another, an' a screamin—boys, galls an' young niggers—they hustled, by golly. You see they wer a standin, an' got the first good peep into the dishes. Now, doleful things begin to happen all along the table, an' all at onst; but as I cant tell hit all at onst, not bein a 'oman, I'l take a dish at a time, an go slow.

A big, brindil tom cat, in a state ov hot agravation, with his tail swell'd as big as a rollin-pin, ris outen a dish; as he flew he gin a surjestif hiss, an' lit on Passun BUSSUM'S head, whar he jist staid long enuff to gether nail holts, when he went agin for the lookin-glass; stickin, spread-eagle fashion, to the bobinett, an' wavin that orful tail, he looked green-eyed over his shoulder down at us, an' issoed a long, fightin groan. Sez I, "skat," an' he skated instuntly. This time he made a bee-line for Misses JAR-ROLD'S cap crown, but havin' in a leetle too much powder, his belly jist brushed her top bow of red ribbon, an' he lit a tip top ove the "bud ove promise," scratchin up a shower ove rose leaves from among her har. He jist staid long enough for me to "skat," him to hiss, an' her to screech, when outen the door he flew breast high, his swell'd tail flyin round an' round, like the crank ove a grindstone, an' him lookin as big as a fox, closely chased by a 'vengeful dish kiver, what I tried my durndest to kill him wif, for not stayin amung us longer. I sorter liked his company, an' his performance—he wer jist four secon's in the house arter the kivers wer lifted. Outen another dish cum a half peck or so ove striped garden frogs, an' one big bull feller—every cussed one had a idear ove his own as to the course home. The bull, about as big as a smoothin' iron, made a lubberly lunge at random, an' lit, flat ove his belly, spat on top ove a big mound ove butter, an' thar he stuck, with his laigs mixed up in it to his body. He contented hissef by sorter grittin his teeth, an' sayin somfin like "jugsrum." One long laiged, acktif little cuss made a vig'rous lope at old JARROLD'S snout, an' shot into his mouth up to his hamstrings. The old feller gin a vomitin sort ove a jerk, an' blowed him half the length ove the table. He lit on his back, but flirted over like a flash, lookin knowingly roun' for another hole to jump at. He seed Passun BUSSUM'S havy breast through the crack in his shut bussum, jist sed "chouk," an' in he went a flyin. The old fat rip ris from there, a holdin out his shut wif bofhands, like hit wer red hot, an' sot into dancin Killacrankey,[12] in double sole hoss-hide boots, powerful thankful fur what *he'd* received, I speck. Another uv the interprizin little devils mistakin hit for a hole in a stump, went head fust into a fat, sweaty, sour lookin gall's bussum, an' set in to scramblin down the valley. She did the durndest, slickest, slight ove hand trick I ever seed any 'oman do. She jist jump'd with her feet up in the chair, an' cotch hold ove her shut back ove her naik wif bof han's, an' commenced a haulin hit up overhanded, from onder her dress, until she got hit all out from behine, an' over her head, then she jerked the front tail out ove her bussum, as slick as you could draw a hand-kercher. I seed the frog jist then, fall between her feet on the chair, and lope into the fire place; he looked powerfully out ove countenance, an' stonished. Seein a baby-faced feller a sittin opposite wif his pop eyes sot, a starein impudently at her, she flung the ruffle tail thing over his head, an' then busted a full soup tureen on hit. I speck he thought the infunel shif' had exploded. Then she broke for home, a durnin old Misses JAR-ROLD an' all her crowd, orfuly. I thot she were a little· hostile like, from the way she behaved herself. As she walked off, I 'zamined her general 'ppearance, an' you couldent tell to save yer life that she had no ruffle tail thing on. She shook her hips tho', powerful as she walked—mad, by golly, mad as a hornet.

GEORGE, you never did see a matter of half a peck or so ove frogs show as much anxiety to distribute tharsefs abroad, as they did, an now comes the reason for thar hurry. When the kiver come off the dish next Misses JARROLD, (she wer a lookin for roast venison,) GRIPES, he peeped in, an says he, "dear me, madam, what a remarkable sassenger." "Law, MAMEY," sez the bud ove promise, "if it haint got eyes." Jist then, the purtiest, slickest, shiniest four and a half foot black snake, what were quiled in the dish, begin to pour out over the aidge ove hit, onto the white table cloth, like a stream ove ink, as big as a broom handle, runnin slowly towards madam JARROLD; he wer a whippin out his blue steel spring lookin tongue, first towards a pile ove sassers on one side, an then towards a milk pitcher on tother. Now, hoss, I reckon you know what hit wer that skeered

12. Presumably, a traditional folk dance.

the frogs so. Misses JARROLD aimed to scream, but dident draw
the puckerin string in her throat tight enuff, an hit cum out a
pitiful blate, like onto a calf, when you is a crowdin him. She
tried to shove her chair back wif a jerk, but hits hind laigs cotch
agin the aidge ove a puncheon, and over hit tilted. She flung a
summerset backwards, showin her shoe soles to every body at
the table. She had on gray garters, bein the selvidge tore off a
piece ove white flanin.[13] Now, she had tuck about two yards, ove
black ribbon, an' had pin'd one aind to her back, then fotch hit
round her, to mark the huggin line, and made tuther end into a
big bow behine, fastenin hit wif a pin. The jerk of her tumble
backwords, lost out this last pin, an' the ribbon trailed arter her,
as she run, sorter ratlin over the chips in the yard, she look'd
over her shoulder, an' coch a glimpse ove hit a cumin. "*Snake
arter me,*" shot through her head like a hot knittin needle. She
jist tuck up her coats, mos' to her knees in bof han's—its a habit
she's got any how. Old JARROLD is a mitey slow, rumatick,
keerless, forgetful sort ove body—she hates draggild skirts—an'
has a rale purty laig, so for these three reasons she shows hit. By
the ghost ove old FLYIN CHILDERS,[14] she jist tore through the
orchard, like an old doe, her white stockins flashed apast each
other so fas', you couldent begin to count. Old JARROLD, in
runnin outen the door, saw what he tuck to be the black snake, a
climbing his wife's back; this made him as hot as a ho'net, so he
grabb'd up a hoe, an' tuck arter her, to kill hit. Ketch the
comit—kill the devil,[15] the durnd old rumatick fool, why she tuck
four steps to his one. Old Squire BALL, wer jist ridin up, sorter
belated to the dinner, an' seein old SIMON JARROLD, hot arter
his wife, wif a drawn corn hoe, he thought theyd been a scrima-
gin, so he jist reign'd round his mule—went home, an' issooed a
warran' for im, chargin salt, an' batter, wif intent to kill, an' hit
tuck the durndest, hardest swarin, you ever hearn, to keep the
old cuss outen jail.

Now the rale snake hisself jist glided clost roun the bottom

13. Dialect for flannel.

14. E. W. B. Childers, a minor character in Charles Dickens's novel
Hard Times (1854). Childers is one of the riders in Sleary's Circus Troup
and is noted for his daring vaulting and reckless riding.

15. Presumably, a proverbial saying. Harris is implying that Simon
Jarrold was as likely to catch his wife as he was to catch a comet or kill
the devil.

ove the milk pitcher, an' started to pour hisself over the aidge ove the table, but he couldn't get good scale holt on the hangin' cloth, so he fell and lit in GRIPES' hat, what he had sot by his chair, an' forted hisself onder some law papers in the crown. GRIPES seed 'im fall, but couldent see what become ove him, an' tharfore took the skeery fool idear into his head that the snake wer in *both* ove his boots. You jist orter a seed him shell them boots; they jist shot ofen his feet. He socked on his hat an' broke to run in his stockin' feet, an' the fust thing I seed were the snake a comin' out from onder the hat behine, an' a gwine in atwix GRIPES' shut collar an' his yaller naik, strait down his nakid back. Sez I, "GRIPES, he's a cold one, ain't he?—powerful pizen, too." He fotch a snort an' a shiver, an' knocked off his hat wif a back-handed lick, jist in time to fasten bof han's on blackey's tail. Now, hoss, believe me, hit wer pull DICK, pull devil;[16] he could-ent haul the snake up, and the snake wouldent come up, but mind you, GEORGE, that reptile wer four foot an' a half long, an' he wer obleged to strenthen his purchase against the pullin at his tail some how, so he straightened out some ove his kinks, down the dark, greasey, pimply holler, along that legul back-bone, ontil he cum to the forks ove the road; then he would roun' the turn, a leavin' a laig on his right an' a laig on his left, an' started up hill agin, along the legul belly, aimin' for a little sink-hole, jist onder the waisbun buttons ove the crazy, frighten'd cuss, but afore he got thar he seed a streak ove day light, an poked out ni onto a foot ove hissef to 'zamine the open country a little; this wer as fur as he could git, for the holt onto his tail, so he made the most ove hissef, an commenced a reachin' roun, an about, in all directions, now an then makin letter S's, an whippin out his tongue, the madest, sassiest kind. He looked sorter curious, durned if he dident. GRIPES had gin his hole sole up to the lively bisnis ove bouncin, from the moment he found hissef to be astradle ove a snake—stradlin bounces, two foot high bounces, nervous bounces, and a heap ove em, by golly, keepin his socks fur enuff apart to have rolled a whiskey barrel atwixt em, wifout barkin his laigs. I tell you, hoss, a bull cockroach, in a hot skillet, would a been thought sorter lazy. Snakes, you know, GEORGE, *do* feel dreadful cold—then thar scales, a scrapin the dander off

16. A common proverbial saying. See Archer Taylor and Bartlett Jere Whiting, *A Dictionary of American Proverbs and Proverbial Phrases 1820–1880*, p. 101.

yer skin—then the sarchin idear hitself, *snake* atwixt you an yer trowsis behine, an before, wif no yeathly hope left, that it mout only be a wet rope arter all; for thar a starin you in the face, you sees a libral seckshun ove the bitein aind ove the shiney, vengeful lookin reptile, jist a cavortin, an a sloshin, and you have nuffin atwixt you an imejut death an durnation, but a few slick inches ove onsartin, live, taperin tail holt—bounce! Hu the h——l *wouldent* bounce? GEORGE, jist look at my forrid. See how I am a sweatin, let me res a minit.

Well, I'll try hit agin. GRIPES had been a doin his bouncin purty much at random, until he seed the snake, then he reversed the engine, an' sot in to bouncin backwards. I tell you he retrograded over every thing, hands still fast at the back of his naik, ontu that life or death tail, an' his eyes jist *hanging down,* by golly, sot an' glassy, onto tother aind ov the snake. I'd bout as leaf been well rubbed wif gunpowder an' in the devil's buzzum, on a hot arternoon, as to had his thoughts an' feelins for a minit.

Says I, "risk one han', and yamp [17] him by the naik, you durned fool."

(Advice, you know, GEORGE, feels *so* good when you is skeered out ov all idears ov yer own.)

Says he, still a bouncin, "Han' me some san' to mend tail hold wif."

"San' be d————d," sez I, "risk one han' dry so."

He ventered hit, and made a wipeing grab at the snake's naik; hit dodged like a weazel, an' come back wif an open jawed lick at his han'.

Sez I, "Oh, by gravy, he'll fight, hoss, but snakes don't know anything about left hands; try hit."

He changed han's, and made a *long* wipe, sorter like you would at a fly on yer hoss. The snake struck this time afore he dodged, an' the wipe turned into a dodge. GRIPES fell back on double-handed tail holt an' bouncin agin. I could think of nothin else to tell the poor devil, an' hit grieved me. When I comes to be hung, I don't think I'll hev any hard feelins at the lawyer what pleads agin me, unless I forget GRIPES.

The mos' ove the boys an' galls wer in the yard, or on the fence, an' the sight ove GRIPES, ridin' an onbroke, cavortin', four year old snake, made them forgit all about thar own skeer, so

17. Steal or swipe, usually, although Harris seems to be using it as a substitute for grab or jerk.

when his terrible hoss druv him crazy, an' he tho't he wer in open Sarkit Court, an' holler'd, beggin' like, givin' a backward bounce atwix every word, "May hit please yer honor, he's a sawin' me in two, I feels the hot links ove my intrals down bof laigs ove my britches—a injunction, Jedge,—a injunction—quick, lord, Jedge,"—I tho't in my heart, they'd all die, sich yellin', screamin, an' laffin', was never hearn before. One stutterin', onthinkin', durn'd fool, blind ove one eye, arter two or three hurtin' lookin' trials, to git his mouf on a full cock, said "W-W-WO, ALBORAX!" [18] The words warn't cold, afore Passun BUSSUM sprawl'd him on the wood pile, wif an old ax helve. Passuns, you know, are always a-watchin' for some chance to repruve pepil, an' I think old BUSSUM took the slimest chance, that time, I ever seed; what yeathly harm was there in, "WO, ALBORAX?" I had been tryin' my durndest, to think up some more advice for GRIPES, an' at las, the ginuine idear come, an' I belched hit out. Sez I, "Tail holt be durn'd, hit'l break some time anyhow, let hit go, an *run*, by golly, run plum outen yer close, that's yer ticket, hit never fails." The infernel fool had wasted bouncin' enuff already, to hev put him three miles beyant the last snake in the world.

He tuck me at my word, an' bulged; [19] he run jist adzackly like you'd take steps wif an open par ove compuses, a side at a time, but faster nor a flutter-mill,[20] the snake's head swayin fust apast one hip an' then apast tother, so quick I thot thar must be two ove em. Thinks I, solemnly: "Hoss, the 'bud ove promice' wudent have you now to save yer durn'd life." He tuck through a co'nfield, whar hit was higher than his head, makin hit roar. I watch'd his course by the fluttern ove the co'n tassils. Torreckly I seed his coat an' jackit fly way up in the air; still furder away I seed a shut sail up an' fall, lodgin on the tassils; stil furder, an' up went his breeches, galluses an'—a snake. Follered my council to a dot, dident he. I haint met up wif that snake, as I knows on, an' durn'd ef I dont fear I never will. *He* knows a few sumfins. As

18. "Al Borak (the lightning). The animal brought by Gabriel to carry Mahomet to the seventh heaven, and itself received into Paradise. It had the face of a man, but the cheeks of a horse; its eyes were like jacinth, but brilliant as the stars; it had the wings of an eagle, and glittered all over with radiant light." William Rose Benét, *The Reader's Encyclopedia*, p. 129.

19. Dashed or rushed away.

20. A small water wheel placed in a stream as a toy.

to GRIPES, I haint seed him; hes you? I *has* hearn that he's in Texas, tending sheep for GEORGE KENDALL,[21] an' day an' night totes a snake-pole.[22]

When "ONE-EYE" cum too, he sot up on aind on the wood-pile, and sez he, sorter weak like, "L-l-lets go—d-d-dinners o-o-over."

You haint axed me how I got out ove the grave-yard aprun; you forgot hit, GEORGE, dident you?

21. George Wilkins Kendall (1809–1867), noted nineteenth-century journalist and adventurer, was born in New Hampshire, came to the South in 1832, and in 1837 founded the famed New Orleans *Picayune*. He became interested in the desire of the people of New Mexico for independence from Mexican rule and in 1841 joined the disastrous Santa Fé expedition sponsored by the president of the independent state of Texas. After suffering extreme hardships and imprisonment, Kendall was rescued by influential friends, and he returned home to write his widely read *Narrative of the Texan Santa Fé Expedition* (2 volumes, 1844). A few years later he returned to Texas and reported for the *Picayune* as one of America's first war correspondents on the major campaigns in the war with Mexico; out of this experience came his account of *The War Between the U.S. and Mexico* (1851). After his marriage in 1849, Kendall bought a ranch in Texas and settled down to raising sheep. The definitive biographical account of his life and adventures is Fayette Copeland, *Kendall of the Picayune*.

22. A goad for driving oxen.

SAUL SPRADLIN'S GHOST

INSTID ove layin hit as we aim'd tu do, we misfortinatly made a mistake in the cungerin an' raised the devil."

—(Am you listenin', you durn'd littil cuss?)—

"You mines, George, tother night I tole you 'bout promisin' the widder Hunter that I'd tell Passun Small tu cum over thar an' lay Saul Spradlin's sperrit. Well! I stud up to my word like a man—hunted 'im up apupos, an' tole 'im all the doleful facks."

"Do you mean, Sut, that you acknowledged yourself to be the cause of the fright and stampede at Mrs. Hunter's?" [1]

"I wishes I may be dad shaved if I minds sayin' any thing 'bout *that*. I warn't sent to tell what *I* know'd, I wer sent to tell what *the ole widder know'd,* an' as hit wer his bissness, not mine, she orter, by nater, to a know'd more nor me. An' tell me, hoss, how the devil you cud 'spect a passun to lay a ghost, if you tole him aforehan' that hit wer only a fat gourd? That wud a been durn'd nousince, an' sides all that, by golly, I wanted powerful bad to see im lay a ghost; I'd never seed sich a thing done. I onderstood hit to mean spirituly knockin' out the durn'd things brains an as Saul Spradlin warn't no kin to me, I'd jis as lief as not seed his'n spatter.

"I met the passun in a bline road, an' jis as soon as he sot his eyes on me he pull'd a sour skin over his face an' tuck a steady sight at the road ahead atwix his hosses years; didn't mean to condecend to even *see me,* by gravy. That's the way, every durn'd one ove em sarves me, ever since Passun Bullen fail'd to convart me at the Ratil-snake Springs big meetin', an' cotch the lizzard by hisef. [2]

"Sez I, 'Passun, they're in a power ove trubil over to Misses Hunter's—danger too frum the way they tells hit, an' they wants

This story appeared in Chattanooga *Daily American Union* (October 31, 1867), 1.

1. Presumably, a reference to events in a Sut yarn not extant.

2. A reference to the events related in "Parson John Bullen's Lizards," in *Sut Lovingood, Yarns*, pp. 48–59.

175

you imeguntly and sent me arter you, hoss, saddil bags an' congerin' book.'

"His stirrups wer well sot forrid an' had a power ove his heft on em; the corners ove his mouf hung down jis in the right shape to a fitted the withers ove his hoss, if hit had happened to drap loose frum under his snout, all the puckerin strings ove his face wer drawd ontil hit wer like a wet sheep skin, hilt too clost to the fire, an' he flogg'd the dus' outen his laiggins wif a sourwood switch as he ax'd, 'Cudent she fine no body better nur *you* to sen' arter *me?*'

"That questin caused me to sour on Passun Small right thar, an I made up my mine *to help him lay Saul Spradlin's ghost.* So I slipped on a powerful sorry face over my fool one an' sez I 'Passon, hit wer the bes they cud do; all the men folks am run plum off but me, an' I speck I'd a dusted too but fur bein', you know, a natral born'd durn'd fool.'

"Sez he, grittin his teeth an' makin' a moshun like he meant to light to me, 'don't you cuss afore *me* you *skound-r-i-l,*' his head quiverd, as he sed that las' word an' sounded like hit weigh'd seven or eight poun's.

"Sez I, 'Passun, hole on to yer wrath till you hear whats happin'd; thars terrible times on the ruver—*terrible* times, an wifout givin 'im time to light to me or even say a word, I tole the hole thing as hard as I cud tar, an' lookin' all roun' like I wer feard ove seein' sumfin mysef, when I cum to tell 'im 'bout the brilein chickins an' coffee an' the oodils ove flour, I seed him swing roun' his year squar to me, ontill I seed the black hold in hit. Thinks I, now's the time to put in the sugar for he's 'bout ready to drink, so sez I, 'Passun, you orter go over thar fur the widder dus think a power ove you.'

" 'Which widder?' sez he, right quick.

"I look'd at 'im to see his appetite, an cudent for the life ove me read which he liked the bes', mutton or lam', so sez I, '*bof*' on em; they mos' quarils which likes you bes'.'

"Sez he, hittin' his hoss a vigrus cut.

To be Continued.[3]

3. The subsequent issue of the *Daily American Union* containing the remainder of this story is not extant. The only available file of the newspaper, at the Chattanooga Public Library, is fragmentary.

SUT LOVINGOOD REPORTS
WHAT BOB DAWSON SAID,
AFTER MARRYING A SUBSTITUTE

I ASKED Sut one day, why he had never married."

Becaze I ain't fon' ove them kine ove inves'mints. If you hes obsarved me clost, you never cotch me foolin' with ile stock, patunt rights, lottery tickets, cheap jewelry, ur marriage licunses. Sum how, my turn runs more intu the substanshuls ove life. Whisky an' sich. In fac' I won't trade fur eny thing that I can't 'zamine, at leas' es clost es I ken a hoss.

I'l tell you another thing George, I wish I may be substanshualy durn'd if I don't b'leve the breed ove wimmen am run out enyhow.

Hits true the hen tailors,[1] an' sich cattil, hev invented a substitute, but hits sorter like rye for coffee—hit may look like coffee, an' smell like coffee, but durn my swaller if hit tastes like coffee, I don't keer how hot you make hit nor how much sugar you put in.

Bob Dawson, the sharpest trader I ever saw—jist outsmarted 'em all at tradin'. He bit at a substitute wonst, an' hit like tu a put him in the asylum. If you will listen tu me, I will norate in his own words as nigh as I kin the case; hit may be a warnin' tu you by golly. I know hit hes been tu me. I sleeps in a one hoss bed the ballunce ove my nights, aymen!

Sed Bob tu me, "Sut, I never mind ove gittin foold in a trade in my life but wonst. I wer over in Tennessee buying up stock, an' met up with es, I thought, the nicest material tu make Missis Dawson out of, I had seed. I cudent git tu 'zamine her pints much tho' for she wer as skittish as a colt, but I ballunced that by thinkin that she warn't spiled in breakin, an' bein' onbroke I cud break her in tu suit mysef; thar wer sumfin tho' in her gait, an'

This story appeared in Chattanooga *Daily American Union* (November 27, 1867), 1; (November 28, 1867), 1. Published in two installments.

1. That is, tailors or fashion designers for women.

177

was that made me think she had been broke to the saddle, if not in harness, an' I spisioned her too for bein' older than she claim'd, so I tried mitey hard to git to look in her mouth, but not a bit ove hit wud she hev—didn't kick nor bite, nor show vishusness, only shyness—jis' adzactly the shyness ove a three year old, what had never looked through a bridil.

"Well, she nibbled grass daintily, an' trotted roun' me circumspeckly ontil at las' I bid on her an' I be cussed if ever I closed a trade quicker in my life. Me, a fool, thinkin' I had her dog cheap.

"The weddin' cum off soon, rather onusualy soon, but you see I was expectunt, an' anxious, she wer feard of a back down, or a rue bargine,[2] an' what the devil was to hinder hit coming off soon.

"Arter we wer hitched in, an' an hour or so spent in passin round vittils—dancin—playin a peaner with dropsy in its laigs, an' a wheezin ailment in its chest—pomgranatin'[3] up an' down the porch, giglin, amung the galls, an' winkin amung the men, she whispered to me to slip off to bed, that she would foller in my footsteps in a half hour. I plead to have it a quarter. But no, she must have it a half 'jist for delicacy's sake you know dear.' We compromised at last on twenty-five minutes, arter whisperin about it ten. An' Sut, if it was to do over again I should sujes' twenty-five years, an' never fall a single dam snake.[4] 'Jist for delicacy's sake'—the allfired ole umbreller frame ove durnashun.

"I, Robert B. Dawson, the fresh married stock trader, went up them stair steps four at a bounce, an' heard old 'Squire Mankham remark, as I did so, 'That's faster than Bob will ever go up again.' Miss Squills, an old maid of the steel trap persuashun, replied, 'I wouldn't be astonished tho' to see him come down faster.' If it hadn't been for prolongin' that dismal gulf of half an hour atwixt me an' paradise, I'd a cum back an kill'd both of them. I did cuss the old 'Squire to myself, for his want ove confidence in me, an' Miss Squills for her want ove it in my wife.

"But when I went in atwix sheets that smelt ove dried rose leaves, an' found myself bouncin' on a steel spring mattras, I freely forgive him and all the ballance of the world. I could see floatin' in the air wreaths of honeysuckles, an' sich, with humminbirds flashin' among 'em, until I thought I was a hummin-

2. Rue bargain: a bargain that one regrets.
3. Promenading.
4. Presumably, a proverbial phrase of obscure meaning.

bird, or would be one, as soon as that doleful half hour, devoted to delicacys, should drag its slow sled away.

"'Delicacy,' Sut Lovingood, there never was a durnder humbug on earth than it is, except the delicates themselves, an' their appurtinances. Oh! its jist so.

"Well of course the half hour ainded, you know, sometime, and with it went all my confidence in old Hymen, and the left hand half of his worshippers—a whole skinfull ove hopes and expectashuns, an' leavin' me about as doubtin' a Thomas as ever you heard ove. *But* one of the durndest knowin' men you ever seed out ove Utah. When I hearn her turn the door knob, my heart was poundin' so hard that I hearn the echo again the head board. I felt like I wer floatin' atwix the mattrass and the ceilin' like Mahomet's coffin,[5] an' the mountin' a mile off.[6] I'd a give fifty dollars to have had a bar of railroad iron in my hands, to hold me down to the bed.

"She glode into the room like the embodiment of a Haleluigah, or a vision of unspeakable joy. She had a candle in her hand; its flame looked (to me, that is) like a boquet ove a thousand shades, an' as big as a half bushel. It was the effort ove my life to keep from snortin', but I *didn't* snort, nor hev I yet, perhaps never will, at a substitute for a woman, I'm sure I wont.

"She set down the light, smiled towards the wooden run on the middle ove the head board, and commenced drawin' her pins, an' slingin' them right an' left as cool as if I, Robert B. Dawson, had been only anuther gall, or a bolster or sich. I was astonished to the frontiers ove elysiun,[7] an' could almost see the rough crags of the common world.

"Says I, 'Julianner, my dear, hadent you better blow out the light? Jist for delicacy's sake, you know.'

"She replied in a firm voice, 'Robert, my true love, delicacy is one ove the fanciful atributes ove unmarried wimmen, an' jist as useless avterward, as their peaner or paint. You an' I are one

5. "Legend used to have it that Mahomet's coffin is suspended in mid-air at Medina without any support." William Rose Benét, ed., *The Reader's Encyclopedia*, p. 675.

6. "When Mahomet introduced his system to the Arabs, they asked for miraculous proofs. He then ordered Mount Safa to come to him, and as it did not move, he said, 'God is merciful. Had it obeyed my words, it would have fallen on us to our destruction. I will therefore go to the mountain, and thank God that he had mercy on a stiffnecked generation.'" *Ibid.*

7. Elysium: the classical paradise or abode of the dead.

now, so there must be no secrets or flummey [8] atwix us; you will see me strip, sooner or later, and I might as well begin tonight. I hes my fate to meet, and I wont do eny useless dodgin'; I'll meet my crosses like a man.'

" 'But, my—my dear,' ventured I, 'hadent you better administer the comin' effulgince to me in broken doses. I—I think I can't stand—that is, I mean it will last the longer.'

" 'Never mind,' said she, 'if you are afraid ove effulgences, shut your eyes,' and she stepped out ove a huge pile ove hoops, an' countles square yards ove starched muslin, standin' revealed a darn bean pole, in one layer of linnen, more like the ghost ove Jezable's mother,[9] than Misses Robert B. Dawson, the stock trader's bride.

"Mister Lovingood, a cold horror swept over me like a huge wet wing.

"That self-poised, deliberate swindler, now Misses Robert B. Dawson, ontied a garter, an' drew from between her stockin', an' her laig, the counterpart of a big dried codfish, made of muslin stuff't with something—bran suggested itself to me at the moment—and as she did so, her stockin fell limp, in a pile around her shoe mouth, and her laig looked like the pint aind ove a buggy shaft, with nearly the same crook to it, an' bed––d.

"I swallered a time or two, an I sed 'Julianner, dear, I never knew before that you had a wooden laig.'

" 'Neither hev I,' she replied, rather tart-like. 'But I is ove a delicate organisation. That adjunk,' pointin' to the imitation, 'now goes with delicacy.'

"She looked at me, feelin' in her bussom the while, an' said, 'Robert, my love, when I come to look at you clost, your eyes seem larger, an' rounder than I thought for, an' more bulgin— they bulge as much as these palpitators,' [10] drawin' forth a pair ove somethings like sugar bowl leds, knobs an' all. When she flung 'em on the table, they bounced a time or two. Mister Lovin-

8. Presumably, based on the archaic verb "flummer": to get around a person by flattery, to beguile.

9. Jezebel, who married and dominated Ahab, king of Israel, and became the personification of bold, vicious womanhood, was the daughter of Ethbaal, king of the Zidonians (I Kings 16:31). Information about her mother was not recorded. This may be a proverbial phrase or common expression of obscure meaning.

10. Rubber devices for creating the effect of a bosom; also known during the nineteenth century as "patent heavers."

good, I was speechless, but I thought to myself, 'I jist wish I may be d – – d,' with all my power ove thought, and will twice or three times, at least.

"Deliberate-cool-slow, she stuck a thumb in each corner of her mouth, an' brought forth a full set ove both upper an' lower teeth, fastened together behine with a spring, an' laid *them* on the table, gapin' open an' facin' me. They looked like a saw tooth'd rat trap, ready set to ketch another dam fool.

"Said she, lookin' at me again, 'Robert, my love, I do declare, you are real pop eyed. I hope you are not habitually so, it would be *so* disapointin' to me.' I jist had brains enough to think one word emphaticaly, an' that word was 'He – –.' She with her fore finger, bounced out one of her eyes, and put it in her mouth, while she lifted her whole head of hair, leavin' her skull white, an' glossy as a billiard ball. When she laid these down, she looked one eyed at me, an' then at the candle, a time or two as if un-determined. I busy all the while recapitulatin'. 'False calves, false breasts, false teeth, false eye, false hair,' what next? The most horrible idear that ever burnt an' blazed in the brain of man, was now fast resolving itself into its dreadful shape in mine, an' her remark, 'Don't be impatient, Robert love, I is most through,' flashed it into its fiendish maturity. Without darin' even a glance at her, I was up *out-gone;* I went down them stair steps six at a bounce in my shirt tail through that festive throng in my shirt tail out of that house, out of that lot, out of that town, in my shirt tail. States separate us now, an' I wish they were oceans."

Now George, arter hearin' that 'sperience ove poor Bob Dawson's, I puts hit to you, as a man ove gumshun, if I orter add another word only to forewarn you not tu menshun marryin' tu me agin, onless you wants that durn'd shriveled little snout ove your'n scabb'd. Ketch me rockin' cradles, or totin meal home for a palpititytator toter, or buyin' stockins for a par ove bran bags, or givin' an 'oman a legal right tu bite me, with teeth made out ove delf. *No sir,* I'd marry the figger head ove a steamboat first. I jis' can't sit still, an' think 'bout thar menyfold shams an' traps an' gewollytockery,[11] speshuly the palpititytators. Why dont you believe, that even Ratsnes', hes got her a par, a homemade par.

"Who the dickens is Ratsnest, Sut?"

Why sister Sall, an' be durnd to you; she saw'd a round dry

11. Presumably, a word coinage as a synonym for sham and deceit.

gourd in two, a gourd as big as my head, an' then made a hole in the middil ove each half, an' stuff'd in white oak acorns, but first, an' dad shave me if she dident hist the whole contrapshun intu her buzzum. I wish I may be dam if you cudent see the bulge ove the acorns across a field. Then she went on a rale turky gobbler strut to church, a leanin' back from 'em like a littil boy totin a big drum. She looked like a dairy, by geminy. I sware I jist wanted tu kill the dam-fool, that's what ail'd me.

My stars, George, 'spose an' 'oman *wer* tu stock a par ove palpititytators ontu me, what has no more stimilus in em than the buffers [12] ove a freight car, on a cold frosty night, wudent I be in a devil ove a fix, say? Why dam if I hadent rather swim the Tennessee with a powerful interprizin fourteen foot alligator arter me when the mush ice is runnin. I jist woudent be half as feard tu face an' 'oman with a peck measure ove sanke [13] in her buzzum, as a palpititytator toter. Now jis' answer me one questin, what in the thunder an durnashun do you recon the comein generashun ove babies am to do for milk? That's what's a pesterin' me. Oh, the devil! I wont think about it any more—le's go to sleep—George—George, say, George, am you awake?

"Yes, partly."

Well then lisson tu my las' words. If ever I interjuces, insinuates, or socks ary one ove these paws in atwix the silk callicker or gingham an' the bustez ove one ove the tother sort ove cats, onless I hes had a pufeckly fur sight afore han', I jis' wish hit may get bit off at the wrist.

No, by giminy hoss, *that* appertite's dead, an' the ballance of 'em scept for sperrits ara sinkin fas', thanks to the hen-tailors, an' dam fools.

> "The galls am all a made up show,
>   For fools delusion given,
> With pads above, an' hoops below,
> An' gizzards cold as mountain snow
>   Thars not one soun' in seven." [14]

12. The apparatus on the end of a railway car designed to absorb shocks incident to coupling and movement.

13. Sank: usually British dialect for blood.

14. Possibly verses from a contemporary popular song, but the source has not been located. Cf. the comic song "Because She Ain't Built That Way," one stanza of which goes:

Dident I sing that vearse in a way tu bring tears intu the eyes ove a brick kiln? Say.

Don't rave of her figure so perfect and neat,
Because she ain't built that way.
With bustles and padding, and heels that are high,
With blending of colors to capture the eye,
And the real from the sham you can't tell if you try
Oh, there's lots of them built that way.

Ira W. Ford, *Traditional Music of America*, p. 377.

SUT LOVINGOOD'S BIG
MUSIC BOX STORY

MUSIC hath charms to soothe the savage breast.[1]
George, stop readin' a minit, an' look at that ar substantial lookin' dorg, a sittin' on his sturin over yander; see his crap years, an' watery eyes, an' that countinance; would you trus' *him* in a meat hous'?

I tell you, he minds me a power ove dad's ole Boze, a half bull, half raskil ove a dorg, what dad had stole from a Noth Caliney movin' famerly. He soon proved his se'f to be the bes' match for that h––l fired ole cuss, what had the misfortin to call me "Son, Sut," when he dident call me "Pot head," that I ever seed or hearn tell ove.

He wer jis' as ugly in pusonel bild, an' feeters—Jis' as cross, an' mean in temper—Jis' as lazy, an' jis' as durnd a fool. The only 'vantages Boze had over dad wer, he coudent drink whisky, an' woudent whip the dorgs. But then agin, dad woudent eat mutton with the wool on, nor suck aigs. At leas' I never cotch him at hit. He mout tho', for I never yet seed eny thing walkin' on aind, as hard to 'count for, as my onregenerit dad. Why he jis' cud beat a pinchback watch,[2] a hen, or the devil at bein' onsartin.

Well, one day I wer sittin on the fence in the sunshine, with my trousis rolled up mos' to my pockits, a saftenin' the holts of the dorgticks on my laigs with spittil, so I cud pull 'em off without leavin' thar heads in the hide.

Did you ever pull a dorgtick, an' leave his head in yer meat, George?

"No Sut, I do not think I ever did."

This story appeared in Chattanooga *Daily American Union* (December 11, 1867), 1; (December 12, 1867), 1. Published in two installments.

1. William Congreve, *The Mourning Bride* (1697), Act I, Scene i.

2. A cheap, undependable watch with a casing of pinchbeck, an alloy of copper, zinc, and tin, forming an imitation of gold, named after the eighteenth-century English inventor Christopher Pinchbeck.

Oh! You be dadrabbited, you is tryin' tu be finneky. Well, any how, tick bites am curious; they makes the sweetest scratchin' spots, for about a day, I ever had the scratchin' ove, an' arter that the sorest bump, an' the blackest scab outside ove the small pox.

While I wer at this delicate job, an' jis' beginin' tu make hit inturestin' tu the littil blood suckin' cusses, what shou'd I see a coming along the road but a hongry lookin' varmint, in a slouch hat with a twine band, an' linsey briches with a big casinett [3] patch on the sturin. He had strapp'd ontu his back a squar passel, kivered in ile cloth, about the size ove a faro dealer's chist ove tools, or a rezin box. I happined to cast my eye up towards our cabin, an' seed Boze a cummin' in a squatin sneak strait for slouch hat. Thinks I, yere is a chance for a race, an' by golly I'll be the jedge.

Sez I—"Hello thar mistopher, if you hes eny superfine runnin' amung yer mussils, now is the bes' time in the worild tu be a usein' some ove hit durnd profitably strait up this road. That is, if you sits much valuer on that ar sampil ove blue casinett what you sits on. For thar cums a regular onintermittunt calamity, wropped in dorghide arter you. Don't you see him sightin' at the patch on yer latter aind? He means sumfin, old hoss." The cussed fool cuss looked roun', an' instid ove follerin this holsum savin' advice, he aim'd for a sour apple tree; as he made his bulge, Boze changed his sneak intu a rush, sot his bristils, an' sed "wouff! wouff!" Thinks I, blue patch, or appil tree, which will hit be, an' I hilt my breff, anxiously.

Slouch hat, as soon (or perhaps a scrimpshun sooner) as he reached the tree, started up the body by yerks, like a cat goes up a saplin, when sumfin exhitin' am a crowden her; *jis* as he got han' holt on the fust lim', Boze reached the casinett, an' secured hise'f thar to, an' thar he dangled.

Sez I, "*Thar*, you durn'd fool, what did I tell you? That's what comes ove bein' jis' a littil too slow." (Thar's pepil you know, George, allers jis' a mossel too slow all thar days, never ketch eny thing, an' never git away frum eny thing.) An' thinks I, which will break fust, han' holt, or sturin holt? I ruther doubted the sturin holt, for I hadent 'zamined the sowin, an' plum forgot that the gallus buttons had a han' in the game.

Sez he, "g-i-t o-u-t" loud enough for dad to hear hit in the

3. Cassinet: a light mixed cloth of cotton and wool.

cabin, whar he wer half solin his shoes. As Boze dident git out, I put up the game at about six an' six, an' Boze's deal, an' sorter hoped that he mout turn Jack.

Sez I, "Stranger listin tu me. You now hes a hangin' tu your sturin, about as parsevarin', vengeful, an' interprizin' a dorg, as ever froze tu a casinett patch, or 'et up a man." I sed this yearnestly.

Sez he, "Call him off, you dam san' hill crane, why don't you?"

"Jis' becaze, I dident sick 'im on," sez I. "I never interferes in fights amung kin, an' hit seems about a even thing enyhow, stranger, only you can't eat the dorg, an' he can eat you. Don't you hope that ar patch sowin' may be rotten?"

Sez he, "go tu —— then, I ken hold on as long as yer dorg."

I now tho't ove the gallus buttons, for the fust time, an' so I tho't I'd help the poor devil tu a idear, that mout *sorter* set Boze, back a littil.

So I sez.

"Onbutton yer galluses, thars no wimmen about."

"You mus' be a dam fool," sez he; "how ken I? Don't you see I'm usein' my han's."

"Oh! I had forgot that," sez I, an' I wonder'd who'd told him my nater. Jist then, yere cum dad a runnin, with a poplar fence rail in bof han's, an' I, knowin' his onsartinty, wer studyin' which ove us three wer tu ketch the rail, when I hearn crack-pop. Hit wer the gallus buttons by golly. An' the britches cum off inside out, afore you cud bat your eye, Boze a shakin the fleas out ove 'em rather vigrusly, an' vishusly as I thought.

Dad wer now amung us, smokin' an' snortin', an' when I seed him draw back for his lick, I foun' hit wer intended for the back ove my naik, an' if I'd a been jis' a mossel too slow, he'd a onjinted hit as sure as shootin'. But I warn't, I duck'd my head, like drakes a courtin', an' slouch hat cotch hit all along his jowl. I swar hit sounded like smashin' a fat gourd, an' han' holts broke imejuntly, lettin' him drop, bar laiged atop ove Boze. Dad flung down the rail, an' kivered *him*. Thinks I, by golly, yere is a fust rate chance for me too tu be the upper dorg in the fite, one time in my life, so by the jumpin jinney, I lit astradil ove dad. Jis' think ove *that*, a minit, George, while I takes a ho'n.

Well, the instunt I lit across the small ove his back, he

grunted, an' so did barlaigs, an' Boze he did too, whilest I sot intu maulin' dad, on fust one side ove the head, an' then on tother— left, an' right, a sayin', "Oh! you cussed, barlaiged raskil, dad, an' Boze, an' me'l give you h– – l, *we'l* show you how to climb our sour appil tree, without axin' my dad's leave."

Sez dad, aidgin in a word, atwix' every one ove my licks.

"Barlaiged—bedam—you—durn'd—fool,—hits—*me*—youre —givin—h– –l."

You see, George, dad wer pufickly awar that I allways had been the biggest fool in the worild, an' that's why he call'd my attention tu the fac' that hit wer him I wer a poundin', an' not bar laigs.

Well, while this wer agwine on, poor Boze, wer fightin' tu a powerful disadvantage, he bein' the ondermos' dorg ove all, but he wer a doin' the best he cud in the dark, bitin' roun' an' about whar the casinett orter been, yes by golly, whar a dry hoss hide orter been. Dad, wer counter bitin' above, so atwix' 'em, bar laigs mus' a had a very happy time, at leas' I jedged so; from the way he kicked, an' hollered, durn if I don't expect he tho't the mer-leanyum had cum.

But misfortinatly every rashnel enjoymint hes tu cum tu an aind. Jis' about now, I hearn sumfin below me somwhar begin tu play, "Billy in the low groun's," [4] jis es plain. Thinks I my soul, which ove 'im is hit? Dad, bar laigs, or Boze, that is a havin' the music mauled out ove 'im in that style; I don't keer a durn which hit is, he'l be a dead dorg in five minits, hits beyant natur, tu stan' hurtin' long, that fetches music instid ove gruntin' ur squawkin'.

Then I calkilated how, if hit were Boze, an' he *did* live, that I'd git plum rich, by holdin' him by the tail, an' cowhidin' him ove court, an' muster days, at a dime a tchune. I tho't the same about dad, but then who the devil wer tu hole *him* by the tail while he wer bein' cowhided. I hearn "click-whizz" an' the music changed to, "Oh! she wouldent, an' she couldent, an' she dident cum at all," [5] louder, an' faster than ever. By golly, this fotch forth Boze; he cum from onder, tarin', an' whinin' as pitiful as a purp.

Now George, when Boze begun that rumpus, he wer as com-

4. "Billy in the Low Land," a traditional fiddle tune. The music appears in Ira W. Ford, *Traditional Music of America*, p. 65.

5. A line from an unidentified popular song of the day. Harris also quoted this line in "The Knob Dance—A Tennessee Frolic," paragraph six.

pack, an' chunky a bilt dorg, as you ever seed. Hit's true, I had but a moment tu 'zamine him that mornin' atwix that appil tree, an' the back fence, eighty yards off, but, he looked more tu me, like the wooden axle-tree ove a two hoss waggin flyin' aind foremos' than eny dorg; he jist *sailed* over that fence, without tetchin', his tail clost atwix his laigs, an' givin' only one short bark, while he wer in the air above the rails. He disapeared in the woods, purhaps the worst skeer'd dorg that ever wagg'd a tail.

Talk tu me, 'bout "music soothin' savidge beastes"—durnashun!

A skeer about the music had been workin' powerful on bof dad, an' me, but hit broke out tho' on him furst, when jis' arter Boze lightened across the lot, the music changed to, "Hark from the tombs a doleful soun'," with the deepest bass you ever hearn rumblin' seeminly *in* bar laigs. Dad he jis' made a mustang lunge, on his all fours, an flung me, as slick as if he'd been a mule. Then, Lord you ought tu hearn him whizz, an' seed his bald head glimmer down the road. *Ho'nets!*—why all the ho'nets in Georgy, cudent a made him hum, like that tchune did. He never looked over his shoulder but wonst, an' then he seed *me*, instid ove *hit* arter him, for the durn'd supernatral cuss wer then playin' "The devils dream," [6] an' I jis' know'd that meant me.

Well, Boze never cum up ontil nex' arternoon, draggiled, gaunt, an' sneakin'; the sight ove the dorg, sot me to hummin' sorter onthoughtedly, "Oh! She woudent." He jis' looked at me wild, half a moment—whined, an' axle-treed hisse'f intu the woods agin, like a injun arrer arter a groun' squirrill. A few days arterwards, about a mile frum our cabin, I finds Boze, layin' straiched out flat on his belly, tail still clost under him, an' *his years shut up with his paws,* dead, dead, by golly, as a stone hammer.

"Well, Sut, did you ever ascertain how the music was made?"

No, an' dod rabbit me, if ever I try.

"Might it not have been a large music box, under that oil cloth?"

Dam if *I* know.

"Well what caused your dad to run when he heard 'Hark from the tombs'?"

6. A traditional fiddle tune. The words and music appear in Ford, p. 62.

Feard ove his herearter bein' clost about, by geminey.

Sceptin' ove Sumner, Wade, Ashley, an' Stevens,[7] four sich d– – d fools wer never together before as Boze, Barlaigs, dad, an' me. Mam allowed the last durn'd one ove us orter be hung.

7. Charles Sumner (1811–1874), Senator from Massachusetts, Benjamin F. Wade (1800–1878), Senator from Ohio, James Mitchell Ashley (1824–1896), Representative from Ohio, and Thaddeus Stevens (1792–1868), Representative from Pennsylvania, were all Radical Republicans who advocated harsh measures against the South during reconstruction. All except Ashley are directly satirized by Harris in "Sut Lovingood's Dream: Tartarus and What He Saw There."

SUT LOVINGOOD, A CHAPTER
FROM HIS AUTOBIOGRAPHY

Efforts made to find his special gift—The disastrous gingerbread speculation, with the "hickory oil," finale

Mam's great fight with Sall Simmons—Prudent non-intervention by dad.—"Wet or Dry"—A brilliant strategic movement by mam, with a twisting stick—Down fall of Simmons

Trapping for varmints—Catches the wrong one—Wonderful smartness of steel traps—Corn stealing suggested, and trapping abandoned

Tries mauling rails—Finds a steel trap in a chestnut "buttcut"—Wonderful tanning operation

Trimming up shade trees, a failure—Trimming up shade trees, a success

The stuck up man name Poulter, calls Sut a nuisance, and meets a lively moonlight retribution therefore. Wife partakes of the excitement—lively active people those Poulters, so are black ants

H IT takes a feller a long time, George, to fine out what his gif' am, his bes' pint, what game he's stronges' on. I knows hit tuck me a mortul while, but at las' I got hit narrer'd down to two things. Gittin' intu trubbil wer one, an' then runnin' out ove hit wer tuther. I wavered a good while which ove 'em I'd bes' foller fur a livin', an I studied, an' studied, an' sum how I cud see no way ove siperatin' 'em, so at las' I made up my mine to run the dubbil ingine, that is, take 'em together, an' I finds 'em to suit together jis ad-zackly, an' better nor all that, they bof suits me. "Man am born'd to *see* trubbil," you know, an' natral born'd durnd fools to *feel* hit. Well, to go back a littil, so as to show you how yearnisly I hunted fur my gif', mam sot me up as a merchint (I wer about thuteen year ole I recon) wif a willer basket ove red ginger cakes an' sour apples; that wer the fust thing I

This story appeared in Chattanooga *Daily American Union* (March 31, 1868), 1; (April 2, 1868), 1. Published in two installments.

Knoxville *Press and Messenger*, III (April 16, 1868), 1. Reprinted without editorial revision.

tried, an' hit wer a splendid failur. I et up the las' durn'd one, apples an' all, an' los' the baskit a playin' mumble the peg afore dinner. Mam jis' got hostile, an' soaked hickory ile intu my back, ontil hit greazed my shut buzzum. The effeck ove this kine ove linamint wer to take all ove the merchint, an' mos' ove the ginger cakes outen me right then an' thar. Mam orter felt powerful sham'd ove herself, but she dident. She druv me into the crick, roll'd a big rock on my shuttail to keep me frum floatin' off, an' scour'd me wif a scrub broom an' san' ontil I shin'd, an' what wer mos' 'stonishin' to me, arter she'd finish'd the job, she then purnounc'd me to be "a nasty stinkin' littil devil." I still thinks I wer *sorter* clean at leas'. In 'bout a half hour, yere cum ole Missis Simmons, what lived a mile below, a axin mam what had mudied the crick so, "that she'd spiled a washin' ove clothes, an' she b'leved thar wer a ded hoss in hit." Thar wer an ole grudge atwix 'em enyhow, sumfin 'bout dad, I think, so mam, sez she "the warter's good enuff fur the clothes madim," an' she bow'd her naik. Missis Simmons sot her han's on her hips, an' stood so strait that she lean'd back, an' sez she "the clothes *you* war, you means I recon, you dirty, drabbil-tail,[1] slop eatin', ole louse pasture." "I dusent suckil cum by chance childer, an' hev no latch to my door, nur *greaze the hinges* either," sez mam. Missis Simmons jis' squeal'd like a hoss, an' mixed wif my mam afore you cud bat yer eye. Thar wer a purty levil san' bank on the crick, whar they cum tugether; I look'd at hit, an' thinks I, a proverdenshuly perpard fitein groun', no loose rocks to take an onfar lick wif, good foot holts, an' *no body to show foul play.* What more cud a body ax for. So I clomb a dogwood wif a chip in my mouth, an' sot astradil in the fork, to watch the fust fight I ever seed, whar I had no choise ove sides, so I meant to holler for bof ove 'em. To be purfeckly far atwix 'em, I flung up "wet or dry," to see who I should holler fur fust. I spit on the chip fur mam, lef' the dry side fur Sall Simmons, an' toss'd hit up in the air. I watch'd hit lite in the san', dry side up, an' sez I as loud as I cud "Hurray *Sall*." Mam wall'd up one monstus blazin' eye at me, (Sall wer a gougin tuther one,) an' sez she, "Dad like, fur the yeath." Sez I "Hurray mam," "Hurray Sall," "Hurray mam," strait along. Well, they fit, an' they fout, they scratch'd, an' they claw'd, they grab'd, an' they snatch'd, they knock'd, an' they hit, they

1. A combination of "drabble," which means a wet mess, and the second half of "draggle-tail," slang for a prostitute or slut.

grunted, an' they groaned all over every durn'd foot ove that san' bank, ontil hit wer tore up wus nor hogs sarves a tater patch, then intu the crick knee deep, an' thar they tried the drownin' dodge. If they flung one another once, they did twenty far falls, time about by golly, an' jis' as I wer hollerin' fur 'em. If they'd a quit right then, they'd abeen the cleanis' wimmen in the county. I never did see warter slosh'd about so, an' the eddy below 'em wer kiver'd wif bubbils as big as tea cups; thar har wer down thar backs, an' over thar faces in five hundred littil dripping strings, an' sum ove 'em tangl'd the wus' kine. Thar pins, an' strings in thar onder geer wer failin', fur every now an' then a petticoat wud pop up an' float down the crick. They fit thar plumb acrost an' out on tother bank. I tho't they had the whites' laigs I ever seed onder wimmen. Jis' then I hearn dad cummin' bellerin', "you Betts, you Sall, *stop that, stop that.*" He kick'd off his shoes, an' commenc'd rollin' up his britches laigs to wade over to 'em. Sez he, "What's the cussed fools a fightin' about?" Sez I, "Better not go over thar Dad, fur I thinks they'se fightin' 'bout *you.*" "Oh! no, I recon not," sez he; pickin' up his shoes, he jis' stuck his feet in 'em slipshod, an' started up the crick to the stillers, mumblin' as he went, "I think, durn 'em, they 'mout live in peace, thar aint so many ove 'em." They still fightin' away, at las' mam broke about a foot off ove a dead knotty lim', as big as yer finger, an' run hit in amung Sall's har, an' commenc'd a twistin' roun', an' roun'. As soon as she foun' hit had good holt, she jump'd behine Sall, an' kep on a twistin'. Thinks I, oh shaw! that's a gwine to spile the fight, thar's no use in my hollerin' for you Sall, eny more, so I jis' hollered for mam, hopin' to make far weather fur my ownsef. Well, when the stick begin to tighten to her head, she begin to lean back to hit, mam still a twistin' away. "Let me go, Betts Lovingood, durn you," sez Sall. *Thar,* by golly, thinks I she's caved. Mam stood 'way back frum her, wif her laigs sot wide, holdin' on still to the stick, an' sez she, "If you hes eny reques' to make ove me, you merlatter lookin' strumpit, you mus' put hit in perlite words," an' she gin the stick a littil more twis'. "Oh! outch, please Missis Lovingood, let me go, that's a lady." Sez mam, "them words sound sorter decent, now *aint* I a natral born'd lady, every inch ove me, say?" An' she jis' threaten'd more twis' wif her wris'. "Oh! yes you am, *indeed* you am," whimper'd Sall. "An' aint *you* a dirty, drabbil-tail, slop eatin', ole louse pasture?" Sall farly busted out a crying, an' sez she, "ye-yes, I rec-recon I *is.*" Sez I, thar mam, let her go, dont be gluttunus. Mam let go the stick, an' waded across, an' I swar I never seed a frock fit an oman as clost as hern did. I cud count her ribs thru hit. Arter they rested a spell, they bof went down the crick, one on one side, an' one on tuther, to hunt up thar petticoats, not sayin' a durn'd word. I clomb down outen the dogwood, thinkin' what a blessed thing hit wer that mam hadent et the apples an' ginger cakes, an' then went a huntin' huckelberrys.

The nex' trial I made to fine my gif', wer trappin' fur varminty things, musrats an' sich like, an' I thar larnt one thing, an' that is, that a steel trap am a powerful smart thing, not to be able to talk, fur durn me if the very fus' varmint I cotch warnt name Sut. I los' all confidence in steel traps right thar; they know too durn'd much. When I tuck hit to a feller to git him to onlock the durn'd bull dorg thing off ove my han', dont you believe he hinted as much, as that I had foun' hit in sum man's co'n crib. Trappin' warnt my gif', I wer plum sure ove that. Nex', I tried rail maulin', an' I hadent been at hit two hours, ontil I foun' the crack in a log shet up on my fingers; thar I staid ontil I durn'd ni starv'd, even arter I'd et all the bark off ove the log. While I wer fas' thar if I tho't once ove the baskit ove apples an red ginger cakes, I did five hundr'd times, an' the whippin' I got fur eatin' 'em never enter'd my head 'onst—strange that, warnt hit?

Tryin' tu maul them rails tho', hes saved my life I think at leas' fifteen thousin times since then. You see hit wer a chesnut oak, an' the bark I et tann'd my paunch into upper leather,[2] an' hits been pisen proof ever since. I'd like tu see a sampil ove the whisky what cud gnaw a hole in hit, ur even make hit yerk.[3] Ole Pike his sef never made a drap what cud singe the fuzz on hit, an' he made spirits mean enuff to set a passun tu stealin', an' pisen enuff tu kill a alligator, if he jis' sun'd his sef on a barril. Nex' a cute ole devil, coax'd me tu the idear, that trimmin' shade trees wer a trade tu git rich at, an' that seein' hit wer me, he'd let me larn on his'n fur nuffin. Thinks I, thar's a chance to git up in the world, so I clomb one ove his tall white oaks, wif a han' saw in my mouf, got astradil ove a big lim', an' saw'd hit off atwix my belly an' the tree. I never cotch the idear ontil I hearn the saw hit the ground clost by my year. I think I beat hit down ni onto three feet; that wer sum comfort. Dont you b'lieve the durn'd ole raskil

2. The leather used to form the upper of a shoe or boot.
3. Jerk.

dident threaten tu snatch me bald-headed, fur duin' hit apupus, tu break his han' saw. Sum men am durn'd fools, that's a fac'. Well, trimmin' shade trees warnt my gif'. I cudent afford tu take a fall fur every lim' I saw'd off. I never trim'd but two arter that, an' yeres how hit happen'd. Thar wer a feller what everlastinly kep a devilin me 'bout sawin' my sef out ove ole' Bell's white oak, ontil I got sorter tired ove hearin' hit. You know folks kin keep a tellin' you the same thing, ontil hit will smell sorter mouldy like. Well, he had a par ove the purtiest big oaks afore his door I ever seed, an' he tuck a notion to hev 'em trim'd. Sez he tu me, "Sut, do you think you kin trim these trees, wifout fallin' ara time?" I tole 'im I'd bet a hoss on hit. Well, he call'd up witnesses, an' pinted out the lim's he wanted tuck off, an' if I fell ara time, I warnt tu hev any pay, an' the money wer put in Holt McClellun's han's to hold stakes. He started off tu town, an' I wer tu hev the job dun by the time he got back. Now, he tho't he'd git my work fur nuffin, ur I'd kill mysef, which wer all the same tu him, so he went off sniggerin' at a good trade. Holt wer buisy plowin', so he sed he'd take my word 'bout fallin', an' when I got dun to cum by an' git my money. Well, I trim'd bof trees, tuck off adzackly the lim's he tole me to, an' piled the brush, went to Holt an' got my pay. As I wer a puttin' hit in my pockit, sez Holt, "How did you manage, Sut, so as not to fall?" Sez I, "I never clomb, by golly." "Why, how did you trim the trees then?" Thar wer a monstrus wide fool grin a straitchin' my mouf, (fur I felt hit thar) as I anser'd Holt, *"I cut 'em down, an' trim'd 'em a lyin, by golly!"* Now strange tu tell, this gin me more standin' as a durn'd fool than sawin' mysef outen old Bell's white-oak dun, an' I swar I dont see why, fur I got my pay, an' nara fall. Well, this bisniss rais'd the devil, as mos' everything I ondertakes dus. That ar feller what hired me wer named Poulter; he'd lived in sum town afore he bought the farm whar I trim'd the trees. He wer a high-headed, stuck up, whelp, an' tho't hissef better nur *eny* body. His wife wer ove the highfalutin perswashun too, an' I tell you how I knows—she toted a parasol, an' kep' her shoes black'd. Him an' her talk'd a power 'bout me, all over the settilment; I cud hear frum 'em mos' every day, bemeanin' me the wust kine; at las' I hearn ove 'em callin' me a *"nusance."* This made me hos-tile as be durn'd; hit wer the meanis' soundin' name eny body had ever gin me, an' I jis' know'd hit meant sumfin wus nur hoss thief, so I makes up my mine tu purswade 'em tu change the subjeck—"nusance," durn the nasty word, I hates hit tu this day. Doctors oughter call pukes "nusance," hit wud make 'em cum up a heap quicker.

I foun' a log in the woods, wif a nes' ove big black ants in hit, so one night when they wer all in thar den, I sets one aind ove the log afire, an' fix'd me a bag over the rotten heart hole in tother; hit warnt long afore the heat an' smoke druv 'em intu my bag, an' when I cum to tie hit, I foun' I had at leas' a quart. Hit wer a purty moonlight night in July, the Katydids wer jis' makin' the leaves trimbil wif thar fuss, an' hit wer powf'l warm. Poulter an' his wife wer gone tu bed, an' lyin' onder a sheet. I tuck off my shoes, an' clomb in at a winder in the passage. I crawl'd keerfully on my han's an' knees, wif my bag ove ants in my mouf, ontil I got tu the foot ove thar bed. I hearn him snorin', an' her a mumblin' in her sleep. Jis' as easy as ever you seed an' 'oman lift a blister plaster, I turn'd up that sheet, laid the ontied poke atwix' 'em 'bout knee high, an' put the kiver as I foun' hit, then I got outen that house soon, monstrus soon, an' squatted amung the mornin' glorys, onder the winder at thar head. He grunted, an' she ansered wif a moan, bof on 'em begin to scratch an' roll, an' that sot the ants to hurryin' roun', an' wharever they crowded one, he bit. By golly, sez he, "Evangeline my darlin', are you awake?" (He tuck a power ove pains wif his words, an' allers spoke 'em slow.) Sez she, sorter spiteful, "Tobesure I am, the fleas is eatin' me up. Oh! grashus me." Sez he, "That is what I wished to speak to you about, they are annoyin' me prodid——." "Dear bless me," sez she jumpin' up on her sturn, an' lookin' roun', "thars ten million ove 'em." By this time, he wer standin' on *his* sturn, in the bed. Now, mine you, all this time they wer bof busy, slappin', scratchin', an' rubbin' thar sefs, fust one place, an' then another. Sez she, "Good lord! I cant stand this," an' out ove bed she plouted,[4] over the foot board, a shakin' her shiftail, the savagest kine. Out he bounced; sez he, "Evangeline my darlin', what *shall* we do?" Sez she, "dont bother me with your nonsense, dont you see I am busy?" "Evangeline my darlin' I ——" "Dont talk to me, but get the broom an' sweep me, sweep me quick, dunce head." The full moon wer a pourin' lots o' light thru the winders tother side ove the house, makin' 'em look tu me like a par ove ghostes a dancin' an' sloshin', an' slappin' roun';

4. Dropped suddenly, or fell heavily.

they sorter skeer'd me by golly. The flutterin' shiff, an' the bouncin' shut, look'd too durnd white tu suit me adzackly. "Evangeline, my darlin', this is intol––––." "The broom, the broom, you idiot," she sed as she whipp'd her shif' over her head, an' hit cum whizzin' apas' my years, crumpl'd up in a ball an' stuck fas' amung the mornin' glorys. Poulter stagger'd back agin the wall, an' while he scratch'd savagely onder one armpit, sez he, "Why, Evangeline, my darlin', shame honey wrap the sheet roun' you, do dear.' Sez she, "No time this fur finickey feelin's; if you are *much* ashamed leave here." I swar she minded me ove the shadder ove a par ove scissors, a openin' an' shuttin' powful fas'. 'Bout now hit got a heap too hot fur him, modes' as he wer, an' his shut cum flyin' thru the winder, arter the shiff', an' sez he, "Evangeline, my darlin', pardon me, I am druv crazy." Down he drap'd on the floor, an' roll'd frum one side the room tu tuther, fas' as a barril gwine down hill; she wer dancin' in the middil ove the room, a rale Firginy break down, when he went onder her, trippin' her tu her all fours. Yere he cum back again an' she had tu loose a step or two ove the dance, tu jump over 'im as he cum. Sez she, as she lit, "Mister Poulter, dont be a fool." Sez he, as he cum agin, "Evangeline, my darlin', clear the road." As she danc'd roun' his head, she wer so mad she kick'd at 'im. He ainded hissef up in the corner, a rubbin' his shoulders agin the wall, an' sez he, "Evangeline, my darlin', it cannot be possible that these are fleas." Sez she, "How can I tell, they wont give me time to 'zamine 'em. "Oh! my grashus goodness, they'l kill me." Out he cum, on his all fours, frum the corner, sayin', "Evangeline, we must retreat." "Whar to?" sez she, "for my sake say whar to?" Says he, "Evangeline, my darlin', I have been thinkin' ove the crick." Sez she, slappin' fust a hip, an' then a shoulder, "Why dident you think ove that afore I got to sweatin', but go I mus', sweat, or no sweat." Intu the passige she darted, an' out at the back door, he arter her. I tho't she wer the longes', slimes', whites' 'oman I ever seed by moon shine. She went in a stretchin' lope an' every jump she slapp'd her sef sum whar, an' him, I think he hit hissef five hundred licks, atween the house an' the crick; a twix 'em they kep up a wus poppin' than a big skillet ove parchin' co'n. I listen'd, an' hearn 'em slung [5] in. Thinks I, that's the fus' smart thing you hes dun since the ants awaken'd you, an' as I dident

5. Plunge.

want tu bring trubbil on mysef, I tho't I'd slip intu the house, git holt ove my littil bag, an' git frum thar. I seed 'em sittin' at church nex Sunday, finely fix'd up, an' lookin' so quiet, an' inner-cent, an' pius that I cudent to save my life make mysef feel that they were the same par I had seed nakid, by moon light, jis the Wensday night afore, rarin' an' scutterin' roun', like two crazy kangaroos. Folks in public dont look much like folks in private, no how, dus they, George?

Now mine you hoss, he's the feller what call'd me a "nu-sance," the durn'd stuck up, ant killin', perpondrus raskil. If he thinks me a "nusance," I'd like powful well to hear what name he calls black ants, so I cud use hit on him, durn 'im. Folks do say, that him an' her dont agree very well, since they danced that Firginey reel [6] naked, by moon light. But then folks do lie so, you know, George.

6. "Virginia Reel": a popular country dance and fiddle tune. The music appears in Ira W. Ford, *Traditional Music of America,* p. 108.

BILL AINSWORTH'S QUARTER RACE.
A STORY OF THE OLD TIMES (1833)
IN EAST TENNESSEE

Sut's View of Hypocrites and Whisky.—Being Insisted on, starts to Tell the "Tick Story," but Adroitly Dodges it.—Kate, the Alabam' Race Mare.—Ariel, "the Little, One-Eyed Grey."—The Day of the Race, Who was There, What They Did.—The Sheriff Gives an Oracular Judgment.—The old Negro Woman "dat don't Want to Marry."—The Boy and his Pony.—An Untimely Interruption in the Narrative, by Hyram.—The "Fist Fight" with sticks.—The Horses out.—Talladega, the Horse Shoe, and Orleans.—"The Riders are up." The Start.—"I've Got you, Bill."—The Race.—The "Out-Come."—The Mountains Roar.—The "Dark Hoss" superstitution.—Sut Aint Ashamed, but Sleepy.—Will Tell the "Tick Story"—that is, Sometime.

A STORY of the long ago, when "William the fourth was King." [1]

Thar now, does that fire suit you, George? If this camp wer bilt facin the south, a little more, hit wud be better, on account ove smoke. The wind sets plumb from the no'th. Hoy! [2] yander comes Hyram, with the jug. Hush, say George, Hyram don't drink you know, now jis 'zamine that jug, when he comes, an' see if thar ain't a tear track, down over the bulge. I rubb'd hit all dry, with flour, on a rag, afore he started.

"Well! Sut, what if the poor fellow has taken a drink, he is welcome to it." Oh! Sing sam's to a dead mule, an' then watch if his years move,[3] will you! I warnt begrudgin hit to him. You pays for hit, an' hits only a mile to the still house.[4] But, I is studyin'

This story appeared in Knoxville *Press and Messenger*, III (June 4, 1868), 1.

1. William IV reigned in England from 1830 to 1837.

2. A colloquial exclamation of address at a distance, or summons to attention; a mean between the archaic *ho!* and *hullo!*

3. A proverbial saying; see Archer Taylor and Bartlett Jere Whiting, *A Dictionary of American Proverbs and Proverbial Phrases 1820–1880*, p. 297. Cf. "He mought just as well have sung psalms to a dead horse, for my mind was made up," from *Col. Crockett's Exploits and Adventures in Texas*, p. 81.

4. Distillery.

caracter. I wanted to see, if he aint a hypocrite, that's all.

"What if he is!"

Nuffin, only I'l pizen the jug.

"Why?" Becaze, whisky warnt made to be drunk on the sly. Hit warnt intended no how for wimmen, passuns, nor hypocrits.

"Sut."

What?

"I have heard several accounts, of your difficulty, at Bill Ainsworth's horse race, something about catching a flea, or a bug, off a young lady."

'Twarnt neither; hit wer a *tick*—that is, I *tho't* hit wer. But, wait till the jug comes. I ken allways talk better, when I see a jug with a wet corn cob in hits mouth, leanin' up amung the saddles, an' hoss geer, like hit wer a listenin' to me. A feller feels sorter like he has backin. Pour out a morsel for me, while yer han's in. Thar. Thar.

Well! You minds the time (hits "long ago," now) Bill Ainsworth, had Ariel, "the little one eyed grey." The fastes' quarter hoss with a ketch on 'im that ever mark'd the yeath, by golly!

Hit was the day that he run aginst "Kate" the fas' Alabam mar' for a thousin dollars. Thar was swarms ove people, from all parts, to see, an' share in the joys, an' sorrers, ove what every body expected to be the fastes' quarter race ever run. "Kate" wer a powerful mar', almos' sixteen han's high, an' every inch a race hoss, from her iron up, an' as yet, she had never foun' enything wearin' shoes that straighten'd her out. She walked with a limber, sassy step, that look'd like she cud step as fur agin, if she wanted to, and she actid as if that was jist what she was thinkin'. She look'd right at every body, an' thing roun' her as a human would. But Ariel, she never even seem'd to see him at all. I has seed wimmen in my time adzackly like Kate, both in looks an' manners, an' every one ove 'em wer oncommon people; either for good, or bad, jist as the toss up chip fell, when thar lot wer chalk'd out. 'Oman like too, she cud show her temper, an' heels, like gun flashin', an' had tharfoar, a rather wide circle ove aquaintances. I has spoke ove Kate afore Ariel, becaze she wer a shemail. That's manners, haint hit? I tho't so, by gravy!—I ken guess right now an' then, if I is let alone, an' not flustrated. Ariel wer from Kaintuck, onder fourteen han's high, but adzackly as long as a fence rail. His mussils moved onder his glossy grey hide, like cats crawlin' onder a carpet, an' the shape ove his short head minded you ove a fox squirril's. His eye, (he had but one you mind,) was a lazy, sullen one, an' his brows were jackass, to a dot; his years wer short, an' seem'd as stiff as boards, study the littil hoss as long as you wud, all you cud think was, *danger*, an' *he* notised nothin'. When they pass'd in exercisin', they actid like humans in a huff—never seed one another at all, that was the way.

Standin' side by side, they 'minded me ove a locomotive, with steam up, all brass, polish an' power. An' a lathe, for making sich things, squat-long-heavy-an' still. No more alike than a bullit an' a bird, yet you jist *know'd* that both could fly. Now, who the devil wer to judge atwix 'em, an' pick the right one; the one you look'd at las' was the one you tho't *mout* beat, an' you never tho't eny thing more positive than "mout." Kate wer a splendid, rich, bloody-brown, changeable-in-the-sun; while Ariel, as I sed before, wer a gray, almos' white. Kate wer the "dark hoss." So people, the evenin' before, was wonderin' what kind ove a day tomorrow wud be.[5] Out, tharfore, wer every body, by day-break, smokin' cob pipes, in bunches, in pars, an' alone, watchin' for the first streak. *It was a dark day.* Now the bettin' begun, an' Kate had the call. The race warn't expected tu run ontil late. So kerds, in the stable lof's by the sly ones, an' kerds under the trees by the "don't keer" ones, wer plenty—"three up," "seven up" an' "twenty deck poker," for from a dime to fifty dollars. Ox carts, (with the oxes tuck loose, an' hitch'd in the shade,) full ove har trunks an' kaigs, an' them full ove cider, an' ginger cakes. While fat ole wimmen sot on top, in brass speks, an' frilled cap borders, kep busy a drappin' fourpence ha'pennys into a black, press'd-paper [6] snuff box, with a red face an' cock'd hat, call'd the juke of Wellington, painted on the lid. While a favorit dater sot on the tail board, keepin' off the flies with a green bush, lookin' soft an' sweet. Little boys, with clean, homeade shirts, an' wool hats, with a rose under the band, look'd up, open mouth'd, into men's faces, an' listen'd, wonderin' if ever they could rise high enough to be a rale hoss-racer. Young men, in their shirt sleeves, with the collar unbutton'd,[7] an' a fresh cut hickory club in their han's,

5. "A popular belief, that on a dark day, the darkest colored animal would win." [Harris's note.]

6. Heavy paper or pasteboard usually used in binding books.

7. "In those good old days, of homespun, and honesty, the buttons on shirt collars were often as large as a dime, and sewed on with flax thread.

slung'd roun', winkin' at the red daters ove the cake wimmen, or listen'd to Claib Nance, sittin' in the porch, playin' "Billy in the low groun's," like no other man ever has, or ever will, play that tchune.

Settled men stood facin', in pairs, with thar hats down over thar eyes, whittlin sticks as they talk'd, thinkin' more than they sed, an' wonderin' if they'd bet on the right hoss. Or sot, or lay roun in the shades talkin' of other races, an' other days. Old men tottered aimless about on long smooth sticks, so stoop shoulder'd that they had to throw thar heads back to see levil, from onder thar faded, flopped hats, with a white string ban', an' a pipe twistin' in hit, mumblin [8] tobacco or bark on thar toothless gums—fast, like a sheep dus fodder. Trimblin', an' dartin' quick looks from face to face, like they wer huntin' some one, that they warnt sure they wud know, if they did meet 'em. These wer the men that fit Furguson, at King's Mountain,[9] or Rawdon, at the Eutaw Springs,[10] an' run quarter races, fifty years before Kate or Ariel fust staggered to their feet. Two actif, red cheek'd fellers, with thar galluses tied roun' 'em, jumpin' thirty-six feet at three jumps, here. Thar, a par ove slick, laughin' niggers, wrastlin "briches holts," with the hems above thar knees. Yonder, a mess ove boys stonein a sqirril, up a tree, an' everywhar fun in some shape. Roun' the low log stables, folks peepin' thru the cracks, at the hosses, an' boys rubbin 'em. Back ove the barn, two fellers, one in grey an' tother in brown jeans, swappin poneys, while a dozen more squatted on thar hunkers, agin the wall, listenin' to

---

It was precautionary therefore to unbutton the collar in joining social gatherings for in the event of a fight. A twisting grasp on the throat, secured by such buttons, and thread, was sure strangulation." [Harris's note.]

8. Chewing slowly and ineffectively.

9. On October 7, 1780, during the American Revolution "a Loyalist force of about 1,100 led by Major Patrick Ferguson, screening Cornwallis' left flank, was caught atop King's Mountain on the border between the Carolinas by a 900-man force of American frontiersmen under Col. Isaac Shelby (1750–1826) and Col. William Campbell (1745–1781). The marksmanship of the backwoodsmen prevailed over Ferguson's bayonet charges." Richard B. Morris, ed., *Encyclopedia of American History*, p. 103.

10. Appointed by Washington to command the Revolutionary forces in the southern theater, Nathanael Greene (1742–1786) defeated the British at the Battle of Eutaw Springs, South Carolina, on September 8, 1781, and compelled the enemy to fall back on Charleston. Morris, pp. 105, 718.

'em, an' chawin a dimes worth ove cold chicken laig an' biscuit. The Sheriff too with saddil-bags, hangin' over his arms, an' his arms cross'd afore im, while a loaded whip, mounted with big ivory rings, stuck out from onder the left one, stood well back an' wide on his laigs, with his hat cock'd before, tellin' an open mouth'd dozen, "to a dead moril sutenty," which hoss wud win. Jis' to look at him, you'd a bet yer shirt on his judgemint, an' then went home bar back'd.

Down at the spring another crowd. The grey hair'd tax collector, sittin' on roots ove the big sicamore, with a quill pen in his mouth, turnin' the leaves ove the tax book, for the name ove the straw hatted man, in ragged linnen coat, standin' stoopin' before 'im, with his han's on his knee caps, lookin' at the book upside down, like he cud read hit, or pay his taxes either, not knowin', that the red headed young devil, behine him, was hookin' the water gourd to his tail. A fat, clean, holsum lookin', old nigger 'oman, with her grey head, tied up in a white hankecher, comes with pitcher, an' plate, arter milk, an' butter for dinner, from the cold spring hous', an' has to anser half a dozen "dat she *don't* want tu marry,"—"dats what." Crowds, an single ones, begin from every direction, to move towards the field; the judges hev gone, an' got up the white,[11] startin', an' out cum stakes. The boys ar chasin out the hogs with dorgs, an' the hosses hitch'd near the paths, am now led furder away, out ove sight. Men ar walkin' along the tracks, kickin' out, or pickin' up, everything bigger than a grain ove corn. While sum boys foot racin down nigh the start, or climbin' into trees, near the outcum. Hunter, Kate's owner, axes Ainsworth, "if they moutent as well hev hit over, that his mar is frettin' a little, in the stable, at the crowd, an' the noise." Bill pulls out his watch, looks fust at hit, an' then up, whar the sun orter be, with his one eye, an' sed, "Well! I'm easey, I reckon the bettin's 'bout done, fetch out yer nag." "I'l bet my pony, on the little grey," said a quick, lispin, gall like voice. It wer Wash Morgan, a boy then, but es a man, the fastes' foot racer livin', 'sceptin' Beverly Brown Pryor. "My son," sed the game Hunter, layin' his han' on Wash's cap. "I won't win a boy's pony from him." "Oh! yes, ma sez, you may, *if you ken*." The pony was staked agin forty dollars.

11. Perhaps a white flag to signal that bettors should place their money.

"Stop, Sut. Say! Did Hunter win the pony?" asked Hyram, whom we all thought asleep.

George, don't that durn'd fool need stampin'? That question seems more like speakin' out in meetin', than any thing I has ever hearn. That ar cuss wud break an aig, to see how fas' the chicken wer hatchin', an' then be fool enuff to poke hit onder the hen agin. Go to sleep, you cussed goat with no beard.

"They're fetchin out the nags," flew from mouth to mouth, every whar in a moment, an' that great mass ove people settled in two black acres, one at the start, an' one at the outcum, lookin' like bee swarms, an', like the bees, hummin' an buzzin'.

> "If you'd a been thar, to a seen them run roun',
> You'd a tho't in yer soul they'd ne'er touch the
> groun'." [12]

This, an' t'other song,

> "Bet your money on the bob tail-hoss,
> I bets mine on the grey," [13]

floated up, here an' thar, from the swarms, with, now an' then, a laff, or some one hollerin for some one else to "come thar." Watch the centre ove that black acre, at the outcum, how hit's a swayin' about, like high rye in a wind. See hats an' coats fly up in the air. Look at them sticks, circlin' roun' above thar heads— crack, crack, "Hurray, Blount!" [14] "Hurray, Monroe!" [15] "Far play!" "Stan' back!" "That's hit, Jo!" "Close in, Tom," an' in a moment or so you sees two fellers led out from each side ove the crowd, with bloody heads, an' no shirts. Jis a fis' fight, with sticks; that's all.

"Look, look, yander she comes," "Why don't they take her blanket off," "Geminey! watch her, how she jerks that big nigger at her bits," "Look at her plates a shinin'," "Oh! but she's a beauty," "Ten dollars on Kate, ove Alabam'." This, an' more too,

12. From an unidentified contemporary song.

13. From Stephen C. Foster's popular song "Camptown Races," originally called "Gwine to Run All Night," published in 1850 and adapted from earlier folk music. See Sigmund Spaeth, *A History of Popular Music in America*, pp. 106–107.

14. Willie Blount (1768–1835) served as the third governor of Tennessee from 1809 to 1815, being elected to the office for three terms without opposition.

15. James Monroe (1758–1831) served in the Continental Army and later became fifth President of the United States (1817–1825).

you cud hear twenty times at once. A bald-headed man, in his shirt sleeves, cut the pidgeon wing, an' hollerd "Hurray for Alabam'. I was with Jackson, at Talladega, an' the Hoss Shoe."[16] This wer answer'd by "Hurray for Kaintuck an' the one-eyed grey. I wer at Orleans, whar we whipp'd British, an' not Injuns."[17] "See, see, yander comes the little grey." Sure enuff, about eighty yards behine the mar, here comes Ariel. Ainsworth, barheaded an' in his shirt sleeves, with a red hankecher, tied like a sling, hung roun' his neck, leadin' by the bits, with little Bob Maddy, a purty, blue eyed child, weighin' seventy-two pounds, switchin' the weeds with his whip, whistlin' an' follerin close behind the hoss. In the toss up, Hunter had won both the word an' choise ove track; so he put Kate *on Ariel's blind side.*

"Clar the track; the riders is up," was shouted along the line. I look'd, an' seed a white spot, circlin' roun' over the crowd; at the start it was the shirt ove the little nigger on Kate; in a moment more I seed another, but hit wer rather still. "Maddy's up, that's Maddy," somebody said low. "Gentlemen," said John McGhee,[18] with hat off, "stand back, an don't shout, if you please, or wave any hats, as they come." "All right, Colonel," an' all was still.

They both turn'd into the tracks, even; Ainsworth watchin' the mar, over Ariel's naik, clost as a hawk. Little Maddy, with both han's in the bridle, was watchin' Ainsworth's anxious face, an' smilin'. They both come in a tremblin' squat—"Are you ready?" sed Ainsworth, from between his set teeth. "No!" shouted Hunter, as Kate plunged towards the hoss, lash'd out behine, like a very devil an' shook Hunter like he wer only a rag hung to her bits. Ainsworth, with his hand pattin' Ariel's nose, an' him play-

16. In the Creek War, with the aid of the Tennessee militia, Andrew Jackson surrounded and destroyed Talladega in Alabama, on November 9, 1813, killing more than 500 Indian warriors. On March 27, 1814, Jackson and John Coffee led 3,000 men against the fortified position of the Creeks and Cherokees at the Horseshoe Bend of the Tallapoosa river, slaying between 850 and 900 warriors and capturing some 500 squaws and children. Morris, p. 148.

17. At the battle of New Orleans, on January 8, 1815, under Andrew Jackson's command, 4,500 men, many of them expert Tennessee and Kentucky marksmen, defeated 5,300 British in the last major engagement of the War of 1812. Morris, pp. 151–152.

18. John McGhee was the father of Charles McClung McGhee (1828–1907), noted Knoxville landowner and railroad financier. Mary U. Rothrock, ed., *The French Broad–Holston Country*, pp. 447–448.

fully nippin' at the han', as they both swung roun' agin. Kate this time, cum powerful *low*. Hunter look'd up at the nigger, an' he nodded back the look. "Are you ready." "Go," thundered Hunter, an' he struck at Kate with his whip—a clear miss behine. When Ariel heard the word he jerk'd Ainsworth to his han's an' knees, in lettin' loose. "Ive got you, Bill," sed Hunter, smilin', and wipin' his face. "I have a fifty left," answered Bill. "I take it," sed Hunter, an' they cum walkin' up the track together.

At our aind, every body was still, an' spoke low, as they wer turnin'. "Now they're off"—no,—yes,—by — — —, "here they come." I seed Maddy raise his little arms once, an' bring hit down quick. The nigger was whippin' over the withers, by a turn ove his wrist, strait along. I noticed one thing, I dident like; the niggers head was levil with Maddy's, an' Kate, two han's the highes'. *She was runnin' as low as a greyhoun'.* I tho't too, that I seed her plainer, than I did the hoss, tharfoar she mus' be nearer —my heart wer fairly poundin'. —"The mars got 'im." "No she aint"—"Dont you see, Maddy aint whippin'?" "My soul! they're flyin." —I run two steps, to get opposite the poles, an' I cud see twenty poles an' all ove 'em a dancin'. A noise, like a low fast roll on a kittle drum—a flash—It was the lainth ove Ariel's grey hide, from his bitts to his heels, before Kate's nose. The matchless beauty was *beaten,* an' North Alabama *broke*.

For about two or three common heart beats, that is, if they beat at all,—the very leaves wer still. Nothin' but a muffled sort ove dry swallerin, like children does jist before cryin'. Then a note like a dove cooin', swell'd an' swell'd into a roar, that run on the mountains again, again an' again.

As the riders walk'd them back, the little nigger's tears wer fallin' in Kate's mane, while Maddy, look'd jaded, an' sober, his whip danglin' loose from his wrist. The hoss, as usual slungin along lazily, with scasely a hair turn'd. Kate had a few streaks ove sweat, that look'd like ink on her glitterin' gown ove brown. But with head up yet, an' a purple fire blazin in her eye. —Beat, but beautiful still* * * * "What was thar time?" "Who hilt a watch?" "John McGhee did." "Oh! yes," "an' so did Tom Upton, an' Tom Callaway." I seed the three git together, with open watches in thar han's, an' talk a moment. Then Col. McGhee turn'd to the crowd, an' sed, in his quiet way, "Nineteen seccons, gentlemen," an' he wiped the sweat off his brow, like he'd been at hard work. The fastes' quarter race, ever run, was over. An' the dark hoss, "hadent won." . . . "Now Sut, tell us about that 'tick' business; you have dodged it hansomly."

Oh! no, Ise sleepy.

"You never intended to tell that story; you are *ashamed* of it."

No, I aint sham'd—you be durn'd, I'l swear I'l tell hit—some time.

"WELL! DAD'S DEAD"

THAR never wer a man yet, so mean, but what some time, or other, done at least one good thing. Now, my Dad, put off doin his good thing, for an awful long time, but at last he did hit, like a white man. He died, by golly! prefeckly squar—strait out, an' for keeps. Aint you glad? Don't be fear'd to say so on my account, boys, for hits so reasonable. Mam declar's that Gineril Washington never did a better thing in his whole life. She only grumbles that he dident ketch the idear twenty years sooner, for then, she mout "a done sumthin." But no, he hilt on, jist to spite her, ontil she broke off her last tooth, crackin' a corn bread crust, an' then he immegintly went. Why! the very las' reques' he ever made ove her, wer to "let him look in her mouth." Good people, an' passuns, make a heap ove fuss over what they call the onnatralness ove folks towards the sick. Now, hits all a dad-rabbited lie, for the neighbors acted jist as natral to dad, as could be. Nara durn'd one ove 'em ever come a nigh the old cuss, to fool 'im into believin' that he stood a chance to live, or even that they wanted him to stay a minit longer than he wer obleeged to, by givin him sups of warter, fannin' off the flies—axin him if he wer hongry, or any other meddlesome interfarances with na-ter—not them. I tell you, boys, if ever a man did git a fair launch, every way, into the river sticks, that man wer my dad; he went on time to a seccon', an' no body a holdin on to his coattail. They acted natral clean thru, too, for when he wer a kickin' his last kicks, old Muddleg's wife come to the fence an' call'd mam out, to know if she cudent spar the frock she had on, in pay for sixty cents, that dad owed her husbun', for three drinks ove "hoss botts." [1] "That she thought mam mout afford to run in her petti-

This story appeared in Knoxville *Daily Press and Herald*, II (November 15, 1868), 3.

Knoxville *Press and Messenger*, III (November 19, 1868), 1. Reprinted without editorial revision.

1. Presumably, another name for rotgut whiskey. Actually the "botts" is an animal disease caused by maggots, particularly common to the horse;

coattail a while, as the weather wer good, an' hit bein' black, would pass for fust rate mournin." Hits a wonder that las' idear hadent cotch mam, for she's great on style an' bein' in fashun, but hit dident; hit did git her back up tho' for she jist bleated like an old ewe, an' jump'd the fence to her. An' don't you believe! mam kicked her bustle clean off ove her, the passun, an' his wife a ridin' apast at that. Her nose bled, an' mam cried, an' sich a snortin' as they had. The las' words dad ever spoke, wer, "which whip'd?" I meant to tell 'im, that mam had nearly turned the old crane inside out with her foot, but he cud hear nothin' then, for the roar ove the river.

Well! as I wer saying, the neighbors acted natral, an' thats the right way—do as you wants to, by golly! Dad shave the hipocracy ove fixin' a dead man away nice, arter lettin' him starve. Many, many a time, has people spent enough in plantin' a corpse, that if they had ever a loan'd the half ove hit to the mortul a livin', hit would a put off a funeral. But then the cuss wudent a went, when his time had come. Thars the devil ove hit—flustratin' doctrines so bad, you know.

Well! when dad got cool, an' stiff enuff to handle, we cudent raise ara coffin, without diggin' one up, an' totein hit a long mile. We had an old accoutrement box, hit's true, but then mam wanted hit, to ketch rain water in. So, we just sot in, an' made a regular mummy out ove him, by sowin' him up, body an' soul, in an old, black bed spraid. Who knows, boys, but what he'l git dug up, some three thousan' years arter this, an' be sot up in a glass case, for a King Pharaoo, an' a devil ove a fuss raised, about the bed spraid bein' a royal mantle? Aint that a future for a Lovingood, arter him actin' hoss, an' bein' daddy to sich a varminty fixin' as me? But thar's plenty durn'd fools, ready to do hit for him, if they only happen to find him. Arter we got done, I swar that I wondered to see how much like a rich man's iron corpse case he look'd, an' hit sorter made me proud, hit did. I look'd roun', an' thar stood sister Sall, a blubberin'. I ax'd her what wer the matter? for the gal 'stonish'd me. Sed she, "Sowin' on that bed spraid 'minds me so much ove the time he made me sow him up in a raw hide, when he opened his dorg school.[2] Bo! hoo! hoo!"

hence, colloquially, the word is used to refer to a belly-ache or the colic among humans.

2. A reference to the events in "Dad's Dog-School," the concluding story in *Sut Lovingood, Yarns*, pp. 277–299.

I told her to shet right up least he mout hear her, an' want to go at hit agin, an' then we'd loose all our trouble, besides hit's bein' so disap'intin' to mam, for she had comb'd her har an' flour'd her face.

I know'd whar Old Stump Snodgrasses' steers wer a grazin', with the yoke on. So I goes an' gits 'em, an' hitch'd on to a big shingle sled, what somebody had left on the chestnut ridge, an' we loaded dad up. Mam an' the childer wer strung along on each side, a holdin' on by the standards. "Now," sez mam, a fixin' on her sun bonnet, "hit's the rule to go slow." I sot in front an' was driver, an' a feelin' come over me, like I think a durn'd, starvin', one-hoss lawyer mus' a had, when he fust foun' hissef Captain ove Company A, at the beginnin' ove the war. I'd a cuss'd a man in a minit, but fortinatly for any mam, he warnt about just then. So, when I promised mam that I would "go slow," I did hit, with dignerty and 'sponsibility. I'd a liked durn'd well to a hearn *any*body venter to order me to go fast, or to go at all, for that matter. I meant to make the most out ove that persession, an' my persition in hit, you understan'.

Now, durn'd fool like, in my big strut, I never tho't wonst about the smell ove the corpse a skeerin' the steers—hit always does, you know. So, jist as soon as they cotch the first whiff ove hit, they snorted—bawl'd—histed their tails up strait, an', with one mind, run away, hoss fashion. I be dam, if they dident git from thar, like they thot' that dad wud be too late for the boat. When I look'd up in the air at the wavin' tails, with the tassels hangin' the wrong way, I tho't ove the plumes ove a hearse, an' their bellerin' minded me ove the brass horns, blowin' some ove the Dead March in Saul; [3] an' dad shave me, if I dident feel proud agin. Thar was *some* style about us, if we wer nothin' but Lovingoods. Hit's strange, I know, but I swar the tho't come over me ove the time dad acted hoss, an' instid ove hollerin "Wo, Buck!" I bawled "Wo, dad!" jist as I had done fifteen years before, in the saidge field, an' it seem'd to me I cud hear ho'nets a hummin' somehow. [4]

You orter a seed that old sled waltz, an' dad an' the rest ove 'em bounce, him a buttin' the childer off, one side an' then

3. The oratorio "Saul" by George Frederic Handel, first performed in London on January 16, 1739.

4. A reference to events in the first Sut Lovingood story, "Sut Lovingood's Daddy, Acting Horse," *Sut Lovingood, Yarns,* pp. 19–28.

t'other. Mam sez, "Consarnd him, he's at his old tricks agin. Roll 'im overboard." But, dadrabbit me, if I hadent a died fust; I meant to steer them cattil *thru* the graveyard anyhow, jist for the name ove the thing. So, I jist sot a foot against each steer's bar sturn, for a purchase, clampin' the roots ove thar histed tails atwix' my big toes an' the nex' ones, an' I froz fast to the ropes with both han's. One aind ove my back-bone (an' I scasely know which aind) wud bounce from the sled floor, fur enuff to almost skin my snout on the yoke. Then I'd balance back agin on the ropes, until I'd meet the sled somewhar in the air, on hits jumps—yere I'd come, overhanded, for the yoke agin. Dad shame me, if I dident think hit would jar my heart out at the top ove my head. To a look'd at me, you'd a thought I wer a tryin' to butt the oxe's brains out, but I warnt. My toes hilt like vices, an' I kept on a freezin' to the ropes; an' jist sich a game ove over-handed, high see-saw, you never seed—sorter like a walkin' beam [5] steamboat, you know. You see, I hilt on in the hope that mam wud hev sence enuff to roll 'im overboard, hersef, somewhar nigh the hole, but she wer entirely too busy a fendin' off his butts to think ove enything. I generley look'd over my shoulder, as I'd be a balancin' back, towards that cussed, hard sled, to form some idear how hard the next lick wud be onto my lacerated sturn, an' to see how the rest ove 'em wer a makin' hit. When I seed his head take mam a rale goat butt in the ribs, thinks I, "now we'l hear from her." Arter gruntin' a time or two, an' makin' a face like a burnt saddle seat, she sed, "I'd like to know when the devil *will* go out ove *him.*" An' then she cried, dryin' her tears on the tail ove her bonnet. I wer right glad to see her show some feelin' for the old hoss, now he had started to be gone so long.

When we struck the aidge ove the graveyard, I look'd back agin, an' foun' mysef alone with dad. Mam wer left behine, about a hundred yards, tryin' her levil best to git out ove the jaws ove a tall, forked stump, that had her fast by the waist. I never did see jist sich a glimmer ove arms and laigs a reachin' for ground. I tho't about an alligator, an' my chances for bein' a full orphan, an' how flustrated mam must be.

I found that the dad rabbited steers wer aimin' to run plum astradle ove the grave. So, I tho't I'd improve the occasion, to

5. An oscillating beam for the transmission of power in a certain type of steamboat.

save some liftin'. Jist as the sled flew over hit, with a slider on each side, I turned roun'—sot my foot agin dad's head, an' done jist *so*. Hit shot him out, like an arrow, an' he chug'd in, as plum and strait, as an 'oman lays a baby in the cradle. Bomp: I never hearn sich a jolt, he wer yearnist dead, or that fall wud a sot him to kicken'. One thing I sorter hated, he fell with his head to the east, an' I'm feared, that will make him a little late a risein'. But, by golly! I cudent help hit, for we come in from the west, an' the dad burn'd steers, wer jist a flayin'.[6] Thars one little comfort in hit tho'—he'l rise with his back to the danger, an' I'l bet he hooves it frum thar. I made my lope from the vehikil, as soon as I could, but had to light on my head among prickly pars, an' slate. When I got the stickers pull'd out ove my eye leds, the steers wer out ove sight, gone glimmerin'. But I dident care, for I consider'd the procesion over, any how. That night, when we wer all hunker'd round the hearth, sayin' nothin', an' waitin for the taters to roast, mam, she spoke up—"oughtent we to a scratch'd in a little dirt on him, say?" "No need, mam," sed Sall, "hits loose yeath, an' will soon cave in enuff." "But, I want to plant a 'simmon sprout at his head," sed mam, "on account ove the puckery taste he has left in my mouth. Law sakes alive! haint hit so pervokin, that we never ken do enything like eny body else? Did you notice, how yer dad kerried on, as we wer sleddin' him along?" "An' us a tryin' our best to be sorry, an' solemn," added Sall. "An then them steers, too," mam went on to say. "Blast thar flecked souls! did you *ever* see the like?" "Well! well!" sez I, "never mind, mam, charm's broke at last." "Hand me the fat goard. I wants to grease atwix my toes, dad shave thar rough tails."

Now, boys, say what you will about hit, thar's one thing you all must admit. That considerin' the family gittin' hit up, it wer an allfired, expidishus, imitation ove a funerel.

6. Fleeing in fright.

SUT LOVINGOOD
ON YOUNG GALS AND OLD ONES

IF you happens to be the fortinit possessor ove one ove them interestin, an' mos' unfathomabil mackinisms, called a darter, (Matilda Japonica Jane, for instance,) an' she is old enuff tu cultivate a peck poke ove hoss har, on the back ove her head, an' properly 'preshiate the vartue an' purvailin power ove cinament draps, an' dime photographs; an' then eny vile cuss in tight britches, an' a biled shut, a totin a cow catcher, or a cattipillar mustach, commences a consultin ove you, an' then keeps on a consultin ove you, on the feezability ove his 'stablishing a seventy-five thousin spindle cotton factory, with a hoop skirt and paper collar attachmint some whar in your back calf pastur—jist you summins morril courige tu your aid, an' tell him in deep base english to go to h––l. An' then, by golly, du yu see tu hit, that he immejuntly obeys yu.

On secon' tho'ts, I b'leve I'd advise, say, somewhar about thirty grains ove the same perscripshun, tu be 'ministered "sub linen ah"[1] tu that aforesed mackinism ove yourn, distributed atwixt the hoss har honets nes' an' the groun', on the same side ove the questin—neither favorin' the upper or lower regins, but sorter bunchin' hit on the neutral groun', you know, a kind o' splittin' the difference atwixt the naik an' the heel strings, whar thar's room. Then, p'raps hit mout be as well to foller hit up with a sprinkle ove keean[2] pepper, as a 'mollient. Yes, I think I would, jist for the benefit ove posterity, if nuthin else; not that I keers much about posterity, no way, for hit bids powerful fair to be rale ornary, the way the present is runnin' the thing. It's rather

This story appeared in Knoxville *Daily Press and Herald*, II (May 13, 1869), 3.

Knoxville *Press and Messenger*, IV (May 19, 1869), 6. Reprinted without editorial revision.

1. Presumably, imitation Latin; the general idea seems to be: beneath her linen, or petticoat.

2. Keen: dialect for strong-tasting; probably derived from Cayenne.

feard that the comin' crop ove brains aint in perporshun tu the tremenjus efforts now bein' made, in all sorts of sile, to grow skulls. Hit wont do eny harm tu set back Matilda Japonica Jane a year or so, eny how. Thar's more babys now than thar's plows.

["Sut" must have been scalded, scratched or scolded, by some worthy spinster. Just hear how the "durn'd fool" goes on to rail—to "onbuzzum hisse'f," as he calls it. He must already be bald-headed, or he would never venture so recklessly. We tremble for him.] [3]

Haint hit strange that a gall (when hit's so ordered for her) can't jist run on to old maidenhood smilen, an' smooth, as they dus intu the popular rut ove cradle rocken an' callimus [4] tea bilen. But they can't. Scarcely one ove 'em ken ever take up the crosses ove a one legged fireplace, whar the tongs has no shovel, or the privashuns ove a one hoss bedstid, eny ways gently. They soon gits nervous and skeery, 'maginin vain things, an' givin' tharsefs up tu a fightin' virtue, an' a ghostly prudery, that's tarryfyin' tu behold in one so knowin', and with sich a tenduncy to ever sot bristles, an' sich a apetite for bitein or scratchin' sumfin he.

Them they firmly believes in, an o' nights dreams ove "a great big, hairy man, with a mane like a lion, an' tushes like a hog," a constantly lyin' in wait, ahine the ash hopper, ahine the chimley, ahine everything, watchin' for them—them individooly by-golly! to grab 'em, an' tote 'em "viney eat armies," [5] in spite ove bar darnin needle, bodkin, an' rectitude, strait fornint an onrelentin passun, who with holybook, an' sober look, hands 'em over 'cordin tu law, to the wrath tu cum, an' double geers. In the dim distance, too, they dreams that they see shaddowy high posters, with drawn curtains, floating cradles, fleecy, cloud like caticornered napkins, an' smokin pap porringers, while the ghost ove a barfooted, bald headed man sits a rockin, rockin, still a rockin—sumfin, she knows what. She sees too, his empty britches, like a banner of doom, a swingin in the wind, from a nail drove in the distant sky, an' *that,* by golly! wakes her, tu find herself a huggin one aind ove the bolster, while her locked feet purvents t'other aind ove hit from kickin or cuttin up.

3. The comments in brackets are presumably editorial additions.
4. Calamus.
5. Presumably, more imitation Latin, the meaning of which remains obscure.

I tell you now, that wen a gall is alowed to run to seed, thar is jis' no knowin what they can't 'madgine, or won't do, except tu go strait along, like they didn't mind hit. I mus' say tho', in justice to them unfortunits, what haint faced a perposal, or a passun, that the very bes' 'oman that I ever know'd, in my whole life, was a old maid, but then, you mus' bar in mine, she were my own mammy. But then, on tother han', the very worst one I ever seed, wer a old maid too; she warnt anybody's mammy, but she pizened a widder's spring—run a two hundred poun' bachelor intu the fastest kine ove a gallopin consumpshun, an' then play'd hyena at his grave.

Dad shave me, if I ain't sorter skeery ove the las' one ove 'em, prim, trim, an proper, as they looks. Yea hoss, verily I watches 'em; a body don't know—you know.

SUT LOVINGOOD "SETS UP
WITH A GAL—ONE POP BAILY"

B Y the light of the campfire, after a hunter's supper, enjoyed
with a hunter's appetite, I am reading aloud Elizabeth Barrett's description of a kiss.

> —— *"A ring of amethyst*
> *I could not wear, were plainer to my sight*
> *Than that first kiss. The second passed in height*
> *The first, and sought the forehead; and half missed,*
> *Falling upon my hair."* [1]

"Stop, stop, George. Duz you happen to know what was the
matter thar?"

"No, Sut, do you?"

This story appeared in Knoxville *Press and Messenger*, IV (September
29, 1869), 1. Reprinted according to a headnote from the Knoxville *Press
and Herald*, but the existing file of that paper is fragmentary and the issue
in which the story first appeared is not extant.

1. Lines 5 to 9 from number XXXVIII of Elizabeth Barrett Browning's
Sonnets from the Portuguese (1850). Harris has misquoted line 6, which
should read, "I could not wear here plainer to my sight"; and the first part
of line 9, which should read, "Half falling on the hair." The use of this
quotation and this story were probably suggested by an editorial filler put
together by E. G. Eastman, Harris's friend and editor of the Nashville
Union and American, and published in that paper on February 2, 1858.
Under the title "Two Ways to Tell a Story," Eastman first quoted a badly
garbled, incomplete (only 11½ lines) version of the same sonnet, then
noted that Sut "has experienced a similar felicity," and quoted finally a
few sentences from an early version of the story "Blown Up With Soda" in
which Sut describes the effect a kiss from Sicily Burns has on him (these
lines were later expanded into the first three paragraphs found on page 80
of *Sut Lovingood, Yarns*). The filler was reprinted in the *Union and
American* on January 26, 1859, with a complete but still badly garbled
version of the poem and the following additional editorial comment between the poem and the quotation from Harris: "And very stupidly told,
too, according to our notion. For instance, what is a 'perfect purple state'?
Sut Lovingood, with whose quaint sayings the readers of the UNION AND
AMERICAN are familiar, explains a similar operation with a good deal
more of graphic truth and fully as much poetry. . . ."

"By gravy, I duz. *She dodged.* They'l all do it, an' it's a powerful pestersome trick ove theirn, it is. A poor feller is bad enough off, at sich times eny how, without the 'saitful pests, a movin his target, arter he's done pull'd trigger. Dad shave 'em all, I say."

"Let *me* tell you somethin a barin on the pint. You all know—everybody duz—that besides bein a nat'ral bornd fool, clean in to the peth, I is as awkward as a left-handed foot adze, with an injun rubber helve, when I is amung the wimmen folks. Thar's kissin ove 'em, for instance, as you has jist read about. Hit's a juty that must be gone through with, if you likes peace better nor you does a freshly grub'd bald head; yet somehow I allways manages to make a momox ove the juty—the kiss, an' now an' then the gal, every time I goes for hit. I reccon it's becauze I don't set much store by the article nohow. Hit's sorter like hot soup, not very fattenin—jist a forerunnin shadder ove vittils, that's all. But the wimmen folks seems to think its somethin worth fightin for—so we must sorter "let on," you know, or thar'd never be a mouthful ove sweet milk about the house. They'd "thunder-slay" [2] it afore it was strain'd.

"I heard 'Tilda Hood, a store clothse gal, with high heels, an' a fringed fan, say that when Doctor Boggis, kiss'd *her,* hit felt like as tho' a hummin bird, as big as a speckled hen, wer playin a stream ove wild honey down her throat, about the size ove a woosted [3] bell cord, while he fan'd her cheeks with wings scented with bargamot an' sparklin with spangles, ontil she seed a rouzin big hoop skirt in the sky, made ove rainbows, an' hearn a mockin bird a whistlin Fisher's hornpipe [4] in her nose, an' that she woudent a holler'd, if she could. Well, maybe she woudent. These store clothse folks has some mighty curious ways, any how. But thar's Denizade Snodgrass, a home made, nat'ral gal, built out ove live meat an' blood, an' har, an' sich, arter fust fightin me all over the yard, went an' told it—that I kissed 'like flingin a poor, flanky slab ove raw beef again a stone chimley. Hit stuck fas' an' *smelt fraish.*' That ar Snodgrass gal is too durned smart to be rale healthy anyhow, an' her kissin's no better than any other

2. Thunder-slain: struck by lightning.
3. Worsted: a type of woolen yarn.
4. "Fisher's Hornpipe," a traditional fiddle tune. The music appears in Ira W. Ford, *Traditional Music of America,* p. 38.

gal's, what keeps thar mouths wiped. I kin kiss an' fly loose as slick as she ken, dad rabbit 'er!

"Now, jist to show you what a pervokin, great lummox I is, I'l tell you all what happened to a right peart gal named Pop Baily. I wer a settin up with 'er, one night at her house, an' she wer in a rale expectunt frame ove mind, from the way she kept on a sighin, an' a lookin in the fire. Her fat, wholesome old mammy had knit herse'f asleep, leanin back again the chimley jamb; her pipe had fell in her buzzum an' the stem stuck out like the handle ove a stew pan, while the cat play'd with her yarn ball on the hath.

"Thinks I, I'd best indulge right now. So I begin to take an off han' sight at Pop's mouth, as well as I could, by the light ove the embers. Jist as soon as she seed me a bowin my naik, up she got an' sot a pot ove lye hominey, that were a gurglin an' a simmerin in the corner, squar in front ove the pile ove embers, sayin, 'Thar, now, I reccon maybe *you'l* bile.' Then she sot herse'f back in her chair, cross'd her han's, an' set up my target again, pufeckly fair for me to shoot, she purtendin to be in a doze. *'Bile,'* the devil! The 'saitful huzzy. She'd sot the hominy pot so as to cast a big shadder all over her face, an' that's what spiled my shootin.

"Ah! lordy, boys, how they all does love a *show* ove shyness. Well, when I tho't that I had a rale fine sight, jist about a short inch below her snout, I pull'd trigger. I mus' do her the jestice to say that *she* dident dodge a bit, for she wer a dozin, you know, but still, I hit her in a thicket ove curls, atwix the eye an' the year, greazin my snout slick with old hogs fat. I wiped off the scent ove hit, as well as I could, on my sleeve, an' listened to hear if the old 'oman still snored. I wer feard to look round, least Pop mout wake up, you know, an' *move my board.* I foun' when I got my buzzin years sorter quieted that she *wer* a snorein—that is, if you'd call a hoss snortin in a copper still, snorein. So I fixes up for another shot, an' dont you believe? I hit her on the throat this time, an' her sleepin calm an' still as a baby—an' hit sounded like drappin ove an oven led *flat* into a tub ove cow slop. Dad shave me, boys! if I warnt stone bline for a moment, an' when I did come to see, the room wer full of lightenin bugs, a hummin like bees, an' my laigs wer asleep. Pop fairly flounced out ove the chair, an' tuck up the ladder to bed, so *mad* that she smoked. Jist afore her head got into the loft, she turn'd round on the rungs, with her years flat on her naik, an' her eyes as green as a bottle, an' sez she, in a rale cat hiss, 'If I had a blind mule that cudent fine its own stable door at *two* trials, I'd jist cut its dad blasted throat, so I would.' Then her stockins flash'd out ove sight, an' about the time I hearn her empty shoes drap hard on the loft floor, I found out that I was 'settin up' with a hominy pot. I studied a power to find out next who I was, an' what wer the matter with whoever I mout be. The old 'oman's laig, that hung down on my side ove the chair, were seemingly spinnin round so fast that her foot looked like a wheel, an' I'l swar I hearn hit hum.

"Presently, in comes the old man from huntin, with a yearlin deer slung on his back, an' a rifle gun on his shoulder that I thought had about twenty-nine barrels. His stompin the snow off ove his feet waked the old 'oman up. So drawin her pipe out ove her buzzum, like hit war a bowie knife, she ax'd him, 'Dident—you—*shoot*, wonst or twise't awhile ago, old man?' He never answered her, but takin a 'stonished sort ove look at me, sed, 'Why, you blasted, hongry lookin galiniper,[5] what have you been doin? Been a spoonin in Moll's hominy, haint you?'

"Pop hollered down, 'Oh! no pap, if you wer to take the led off, an' hold a torch, *that thing* haint sence enuff to git the spoon into the pot, atwix this and Chrismus, an' if he did, he'd fetch it out empty—I wish if you aint *too* tired, pap, that you'd jist kick 'im out.' I sorter come to myse'f at this, an' midnight as it wer, I walked two miles to git to a still house. I wer powerfully tuck down, I tell you—I gin the matter a whole Sunday's study, an' at last the idear struck me how to make a centre shot, every pop, an' I haint made ara gal mad since—*that* I haint."

"How do you manage, Sut—sneak up on your target, as you call it?"

"N––o, not adzackly. I jist makes a target out ove myse'f, an' then lets 'em do all the shootin. I tell you boys, I likes the plan, for besides thar bein all dead sure aim, I think the flimsy truck tastes better than when you go arter hit yourse'f. You see them jist keep a comein a lettle closter, an' a lettle closter—thar eyes half shut, with a 'you stan' still now, sir,' sort ove a look, an' as they fastens to you, they finishes shettin 'em. Then, when they

5. Gallinipper: a large mosquito.

hears the report, they blares 'em wide open, makin 'em ax you the question as plain as thar tongue cood, 'Why, what upon the face ove the yeath was *that?*' Then, hoss, is the tickilish time *with you,* for if you aint *very* keerful how you kerries yersef, they'l fall into spittin an' scratchin immejuntly, an' they'l cross bar yer snout with their nails, a heap quicker nor a cat could, with a wooden clothse pin sprung on her tail. Powerful provokin critters am wimmen, powerful provokin in*deed.* I can't raley hate 'em tho', for they do leave a good taste in a body's mouth, sometimes. Don't they? Ha! ha! Now watch me cut the 'pigeon wing' in these yere ashes."

Satires

The satirical sketches of Harris, which have been collected for this edition, have already been fully discussed in terms of their content by Donald Day.[1] The central facts they reveal about Harris is that he remained all his life a faithful member of the Democratic party, a conservative defender of the ante-bellum South as a superior civilization, a militant foe of the encroachment of modern "progress" and materialism on Southern society, and an unreconstructed Southern patriot. Whenever political or social events on the national scene appeared to threaten the safety and influence of what Harris believed in, he was moved to pick up his pen and produce some of the most vigorous and imaginative satires of his day.

Although Harris's achievement as a satirical artist is not comparable with that of such masters as Jonathan Swift or Alexander Pope, an examination of his satiric technique reveals that he was aware of and used the three major rhetorical divisions of satire: invective, burlesque, and irony.[2] Historically, there have been two types of satire: formal verse satire and Menippean satire. All of Harris's work belongs in the latter category, which, according to Alvin Kernan, "originally referred to those satires which were written in a mixture of verse and prose, but . . . has gradually come to include any satiric work ob-

1. Donald Day, "The Political Satires of George W. Harris," *Tennessee Historical Quarterly,* IV (December, 1945), 320–338. Day feels that Harris's political impulse in his work is not confined to the obviously satirical stories and comments. In a personal letter to the writer, dated May 4, 1960, Day comments, "If you will dig deeper into Harris's writings you will find all sorts of political implications and tieups. For instance the piece on Sut and his shirt, when he gets skinned [*Sut Lovingood, Yarns,* pp. 29–36], is unquestionably about Andrew Johnson. At one time I had all sorts of political implications worked out. . . ."

2. See David Worcester, *The Art of Satire.*

viously written in the third person or, to put it another way, where the attack is managed under cover of a fable." [3] It is interesting to note that in the second part of "The Early Life of Sut Lovingood, Written by His Dad," Harris does include some burlesque poetry, true to the Menippean mode in its original form.

When Harris discovered the convenience of Sut as an effective, artistically controllable outlet for his humorous impulses, he also realized that Sut could be manipulated as a mouthpiece for satirical attacks. Thus, the second Sut story Harris wrote, "Playing Old Sledge for the Presidency," was prompted by the desire of Harris to make a satirical comment on the 1856 presidential election in which James Buchanan, Millard Fillmore, and John C. Frémont participated. The story is structured as a dream allegory. Sut recounts to George his dream in which he found himself in Washington, the nation's capital, at a big tavern where a card game of old sledge, or seven-up, was in progress between the three presidential candidates, whose names are slightly altered by misspelling. Allegorically, the plays and strategy of the card players equal the political maneuvering which will be necessary on the part of the candidates to cop the prize. Naturally, the Democratic candidate Buchanan, whom Harris was supporting, out-maneuvers the others and wins, and the fact that such proved to be the outcome makes this story seem prophetic, especially since Harris correctly forecasted victory by a very slim margin. But Harris would have written it this way regardless of the outcome, obviously, and his estimate of the voting margin is simply the result of an interested politician with his eye objectively fixed on current opinion. The accuracy of Harris, however, brought the sketch a wide reprinting after the election and must have given him something of a minor reputation as a political prognosticator.

In the lengthy, four-part political satire called "Sut Lovingood's Love Feast ove Varmints," Harris uses the ancient literary form of the animal fable or allegory. The adoption of this form was suggested by the circumstances in Tennessee in 1859 when the powerful Democratic party was being opposed not by one party but a variety of splinter groups—Whigs, Native-Americans or Know-Nothings, and turncoat Democrats. When these groups

3. Alvin Kernan, *The Cankered Muse*, p. 13. See also, Northrop Frye, *Anatomy of Criticism*, pp. 309–312.

tried to get together for a convention in Nashville and unite their forces in an opposition party to break the Democratic stronghold on the state level, Harris viewed the mixed composition of the group with distaste and was inspired to equate them with a gathering of animals banded together for self-preservation. "Ez a general thing," Harris has Sut, who once again serves as the narrator, say, "afore this, humuns hev hed but wun kind ove varmints tu fite et a time. . . . But things am changed now. The whole dam list ove the inimies tu the humans what am in varmint shape am cum tugether in love feas, an ef they kin do half they wunt tu the coon will be squire, the groun-hog constable, an the wolf preacher, an humans mus dig roots fur a livin and the he's howl on the cliff when they wants the company ove the she's." By thus denigrating the political enemies of the Democrats to the position of animals, their motives also become selfish and animal-like. The only thing the various political elements have in common, Harris indicates, is the desire for power of office and the spoils that come with it; thus, says a wild boar, within the allegorical framework, "Thar aint anuther pint on yeath that we ever kin agree on, an so we wont speak on them, but jist set oursefs on VITTILS. . . . *The fac is we hasent et ontil we hes los all ideas ove size, shape, smell ur taste, an thars but wun thing afore us an that is* 'VITTILS OR DEATH.' "

Harris does not have Sut recount the story of the gathering of the varmints as a dream, but as a whimsical and incredible example of the tall tale. Much of the satiric point and humor is now lost because many of the animals were intended to be caricatures of actual people, and the series closely followed the actual events in Nashville they were meant to ridicule. Although some of the topical references are now impossible to identify, Harris's imaginative skill is evident in the way he could seize upon an actual event, as when a storm nearly tore the roof off the building where one of the convention sessions was held, and use it within the allegory to denigrate the victims satirically: the smell of the varmints in the room, says Sut, "by this time wer must overpowerin tu me, an torrectly I seed the ruff ove the house begin tu rise, an the glass bustin outen the winders. Hit wer nuffin on yeath but the cummulated pressure ove the smell." Also, we see Harris use in these pieces a rhetorical device made famous by Rabelais, the "abusive catalogue," [4] as when he de-

4. John M. Bullitt discusses this device in *Jonathan Swift and the Anatomy of Satire*, pp. 40–43.

scribes the convention as composed of "pole cats, coons, groun-
hogs, minks, house-cats, hoss-cats, hell-cats, weazels, mus-rats,
wharf-rats, bull-bats, owls, buzzards, water-dogs, wild boars, bell
weathers, possums, moles, grub-worms and tumble-bugs. . . ."
This is a device, of course, he used frequently within the nonpo-
litical stories told by Sut, as well as in the other satires.

Harris not only aimed his satiric cannon at local politicians,
but when Abraham Lincoln, a Republican (the party which
eventually emerged from the conglomeration of political elements satirized in the pieces discussed above), was elected President in 1861, he castigated the leader with severity and vicious-
ness. Once again Harris seized on an actual event, the myste-
rious night ride of Lincoln through Baltimore to avoid a hypothet-
ical threat to his life, an action which neither Lincoln nor many
of his friends approved of because of the cowardly appearance it
made. Lincoln's enemies naturally exploited it for this reason,
and opposition press cartoonists caricatured the event. Harris
projects Sut into the situation by first placing him in Baltimore
to witness preparation for the supposed assassination, and then
sending him across country to join Lincoln at Harrisburg, Pennsylvania, to see him safely through to Washington. A series of
three satires were written by Harris describing the journey.

It may be assumed that Harris was not portraying Sut as a
Southern turncoat, a deserter to the enemy. Walter Blair has
written that the formula Harris used here was "to set up a
numb-headed and rather vicious character, show how he traitorously sympathized with the wrong side, have him, in an irritat-
ing fashion, give his rascally aid to the enemy, and then have
him tell his story." [5] But Blair's description is inaccurate. Sut is
not motivated by a sympathy for the Republican or Union cause
but rather by a condescending sympathy for a creature who is
even uglier, more cowardly, and a bigger fool than he is himself.
Says Sut, "I felt that I wer a standin fur the fust time afore a
man I warnt feared ove, an hu I knowd wer scaser ove sence
than I wer, an I wer glad I had found him, fur you know George
that I thot I wer the king fool ove the world, an allers felt shamed
an onder cow about hit." Surely, Harris disliked having a Republican president, but his dislike would not have driven him to
approve of an assassination plot as the solution to a political
problem; thus Sut is only doing what any humane man, South-

5. Walter Blair, *Horse Sense in American Humor*, p. 157.

erner or not, might have done in protecting a human life, inferior though it might seem.

Also, the entire attitude of the satires is one of harsh criticism and denigration, all of it coming from Sut's mouth. Sut is anything but traitorously sympathetic with the new President. Lincoln is described as a coward, who exclaims at the news of the plot against his life, "I hain't perpared tu die, Sutty, my Sun," and sighs trembling with fear, "The party can't spare me now; besides I ain't fit tu die, an my wiskers hev just begin tu grow and I want tu try the vittils in Washintun City. . . ." He is dirty and infested with fleas, and when he asks Sut whether people have trouble with fleas down South, Sut replies that only the dogs do occasionally, "an we allers kicks em out when they scratches." Thus Lincoln is brought down to the animal level of a flea-ridden dog. But Sut draws an even more deadly analogy at another point, often quoted for its vivid but distastefully cruel detail:

> I kotch a ole bull frog once an druv a nail thru his lips inter a post, tied two rocks tu his hine toes and stuck a darnin' needil inter his tail tu let out the misture, an lef him there tu dry. I seed him two weeks arter words, an when I seed ole ABE I thot hit wer an orful retribution cum ontu me, an that hit were the same frog, only stretched a little longer, . . . same shape, same color, same feel (cold as ice) an I'm d--d ef hit aint the same smell.

As Pascal Covici, Jr., has suggested,[6] Harris is here and throughout the series using the satirical device of *meiosis*, that is "belittling" or "dimunition"—"the use of any 'ugly or homely images' which are intended to diminish the dignity of an object."[7] The effect is calculated: Lincoln is not worth taking seriously, and "his ugliness is inhuman enough to suggest that he can be disposed of as easily as any other harmless amphibious reptile."[8]

Naturally, the outcome of the Civil War was to alter radically the temperate balance of humane scorn and invective in Harris's work. In his first postwar satire, "Sut Lovingood Come to Life," Harris tried to control his anger by constructing a fictional framework in which irony could operate, but the invective wins out and overwhelms artistic control. A correspondent of the Wisconsin *State Journal* had traveled briefly through the South and reported that a spark of rebellion still existed there and

6. Pascal Covici, Jr., *Mark Twain's Humor*, pp. 11–12.
7. Bullitt, p. 45.
8. Covici, *loc. cit.*

should forcefully be stamped out, as if Reconstruction were not harsh enough. Harris has Sut appointed by President Johnson as "Fool killer Gineril," and in an "ORFISHUL DOKEYMINT," Sut informs the journalist that his attention has been called to his case as an urgent one.

By requesting the victim to write out a statement in reply to a series of questions, Harris ironically implies what every answer is to be. For example, inferring that the Yankee writer himself shirked military duty, Sut writes, "State fus . . . how meney muskits yu wore plum out a shootin? How meney, you made onsarvisabil, a 'clubbin' em over rebil skulls?" The charge of stealing is laid to the writer when Sut notes: "sit down how meney yu may hev 'lifted' ove the follerin artikils, which am deklared to be contribran ove war: Quilts, frocks, shifts, baby's huckabuck britchis, finger rings, dogratypes ove pepil's dead kin, spoons, love letters. . . ." The catalogue continues with other "personal" items of this sort, in the midst of which appears one item calculated by Harris to arouse a mixture of sentimentality and ire: "the dead baby's shoes." As the mock epistle progresses, the extremity of the charges is intensified in requiring the Yankee to state the number of females he has ruined, "an' class em intu three shades ove culler, jet black—ash black, an' saddil shirt yaller." But Harris does not stop with the charge of miscegenation. Sut also requires him to state the number of legs the females had "ef over two." Thus the irony forces the reader to permit the victim only two types of sexual relations: with Negroes or with animals. As if the charge of animal sodomy were not sufficient, Harris returns to the charge of miscegenation with a vengeance, incorporating as well a reference to the myth of racial odors:

> Stait if ever yu happend by acksident tu git intu the rong bed, an' be foun' thar by an insashiate Sambo; ef so, what wer yer stratergy? Did yu call 'im "a man an' a bruther," ur did yu jis' 'mizzil?' Ef the las' were yer stratergy, hu fotch yer close tu yu? An' how did yu smell thararter, fur say ten days?

Obviously, if Harris must resort to such bare and brutal invective, he has lost control of the artistry. After nine paragraphs, towards the last, Harris in fact completely drops the thin veil of irony Sut has affected in his question technique and makes a frontal attack on the correspondent as a "suck-aig sneak, hu hides ahine the pettecoats at home a suckin the hart's blud ove his country, an' *a fattenin hissef on hit,* while she am strugglin for very life. . . ." Irony and control are replaced by direct, intense abuse. The entire piece is not worked out according to any systematic or logical pattern. It is an exercise in pure invective and insult, and it is to be admired as one would admire the sailor who can curse a blue streak, or in the way that Shakespeare's Hotspur admired a woman who could swear "a good mouth-filling oath." [9] Near the end there is one striking image based upon a sordid aspect of life which would not become acceptable in American literature until the advent of naturalism:

Hit would breathe new life intu the dead blush on the stoney cheek ove a street walker, jis' tu ax her ef he [the Yankee writer] warnt her secun cuzzin's dorg, an' she'd straitway hang herself fur shame.

"The Rome Egg Affair" is only a brief declamation of two paragraphs directed against General William Tecumseh Sherman and the newly organized Union political party. It seems that Sut has been accused of sucking six dozen raw eggs at a sitting. Sut says this is impossible since he hasn't "ownd six dozen eggs, since Sherman come yere, an' biled the hens. . . ." Once again, charges of dishonesty are leveled against the radical reconstruction Northerners, and Sut decides that the man who ate the eggs must have been a Southerner willing to betray himself and his country by joining forces with the Union party, "a Georgia delicate to the poor white trash convenshun."

The next satire by Harris continues to reflect his vitriolic contempt for the Northerner. No attempt is even made at any kind of fable or fictional framework in "Sut Lovingood, On the Puritan Yankee." Sut is simply allowed to deliver, with the slightest touches of irony, a dissertation against the archetypal Yankee character, distinguished by inventiveness, reforming zeal, hypocritical erudition, and especially commercial genius: "As the dorg vomits, as the mink sucks blood, as the snail shines, as the possum sham's death, so dus the Yankee cheat, *for every varmint hes hits gif'.*" Not only does Harris direct his invective against the present generation of their "powerful ornary stock," but he goes back to the very first ancestors who arrived in New England on the "Mayflower":

9. *I Henry IV,* Act III, Scene ii.

What cud our Maker be thinkin about, that he forgot to lay his
finger on her rotten old snout, an' turn her down in the middil ove
the soft sea, wif her pestiferous load of cantin cheats an' moril
diseases.

The Indians, Sut says, should have "carcumsized the head ove
the las' durn'd one, burnt thar clos, pack'd thar carkuses heads-
an-tails, herrin fashun, in thar old ship, sot the sails, an' pinted
her snout the way WARD'S ducks went. . . ." The Indians, then,
would leave "a savory smell in my snout, in spite ove thar grubwurm oder."

By 1867, Harris's anger still ran high, but he at last subordi-
nated it by returning once more to the dream as a framework
device for his satire. Sut relates a dream in which he finds
himself in hell, sent there for "votin the Radikil ticket." Not long
after his arrival, all the famous radical politicians of Harris's day
arrive: Thad Stevens, Charles Sumner, Benjamin Wade, Ben
Butler, Wendell Phillips, and John Forney. Rather than disguise
them in any fashion, Harris borrows the technique of Dante in
his *Divine Comedy*, that of placing them in hell in their own
persons, under their actual names. But their presence proves to
be such a disruptive force in the operation of hell that the Devil
has to expel them. When Phillips tries to persuade the Devil to
run hell backwards, the suggestion is too much for him. He fears
that "they'd raise a rebellion sure an' destroy the institution,
an' then what would the world do, *particularly New England!*" So
one by one, they are placed in a big "bomb mortor," and shot out
of hell, but not before Harris has had a chance to indulge in
pointedly personal caricatures, in which he especially takes advantage of such physical deformities as Butler's defective vision
and Stevens' club foot.

Perhaps the most elaborate and artistic of Harris's satires are
those in the four-part series "The Early Life of Sut Lovingood,
Written by His Dad." Ulysses S. Grant was at the moment running for president, and the New York *Ledger* had commissioned
Grant's father, Jesse Root Grant, to assist in the preparation of a
series for that journal called "The Early Life of Gen. Grant, By
His Father." It was Harris's purpose to burlesque the supposed
efforts of Grant's father, although because of Jesse Grant's foolish character they turned out to be unintentionally farcical. By
directly imitating these pieces, and continually drawing parallels
between Sut and Ulysses as prime examples of the genus fool,
Harris diminishes and degrades his victim, U. S. Grant, and the

literary efforts of his father; hence, Harris's series would most properly be designated a travesty.[10]

In the introductory piece, Harris uses the satiric persona of an "Agent," who proudly announces that Hoss Lovingood has agreed to write the series on his distinguished son Sut. With the purest irony of inversion, he proclaims, "The triumphant close of this important negotiation, should be a cause of gratulation among your personal friends, and will be hailed with joy by the admirers of genius throughout the world." Besides the imaginative way in which Harris has comically imitated the original Grant material, he develops an interesting complexity at one point in the third installment by transforming an incident in the elder Grant's narrative (about the time young Grant broke a wild pony no one else could ride at the circus) into an elaborate, capsule allegory of the entire Civil War in which Lincoln is the ring master, the unmanageable pony represents Robert E. Lee, and the rider who finally breaks the pony is Grant (metamorphosed into Sut).[11]

Once the series has made its point and thoroughly lambasted the purported efforts of the pretentious old Jesse Root Grant, Harris does not continue the travesty on all of the original material. He brings back the Agent to report that the elder Lovingood has received too much unfriendly criticism and that he refused to continue: "really he has been very cavalierly treated, simply for thinking his very black crow [Sut] was a very white one; and, no one else volunteering, he blew his own cracked horn to that note, not dreaming that he would become the laughing stock of the continent."

Harris's last satire, "Sut Lovingood's Allegory," is exactly what its title implies. Resorting to an allegorical story about a billy goat, Harris takes a solid swipe at the advent of "progress, an' higher law" in the South. Harris has George clearly designate the object of attack in an overt statement while Sut reminisces with him over "the good old days":

I was just thinking boys, while Sut was speaking, whether we are the gainer by the discoveries—inventions—innovations, and prayers, of the last forty years. Whether the railway—telegraph—

10. See Richmond P. Bond, *English Burlesque Poetry 1700–1750*, p. 4; David Worcester, pp. 45–48.

11. For fuller details, see note 5, "The Early Life of Sut Lovingood, Written by His Dad," II.

chloroform—moral reform, and other advancements, as they
are termed, have really advanced us any, in the right direction or—

Sut interrupts at this point with a brief parable which indicates
Harris's regard for the past and tradition:

Some ove you minds the boy that started to school one sleety
mornin', an' slipp'd two steps backward for one forrid. He only
got thar, you mine, by turnin' roun', an' gwine tother way. Well!
that's the world's fix today. . . .

A retreat to the standards and mores of the past is the only hope
for the world's salvation, says Harris.

Within the allegory Sut relates, all that Harris disliked in
modern society is embodied in a "progressive . . . meterfistickal,
free will, billy goat . . . forty years ahead ove *his* day." His
Dutch master, Old Brakebill, personifies the good, solid virtues of
the past, a man who does not believe in "out-smarting" anybody
and believes in trading only on the principle of value given for
value received. The sassy billy goat, "a regular, walkin insult to
man, an' beast," who closely resembles the contemporary "business man" ("they am all the go now, you know"), begins to
practice some strange experiments in the farmyard, and "like
mos' ove these yere human progress humbugs, he jis' played
h––l with hissef." Brakebill begins to notice that the recent
offspring of the sheep, pigs, dogs, geese, and donkeys all mysteriously show characteristics of the sassy billy goat. This unnatural cross fertilization eventually produces a "curious, little cuss,
lookin' like a cross atwixt the devel an' a cookin' stove," and the
Dutchman decides that it's time to act. Brakebill whets his knife
and performs an operation so that the goat can never *"raise any
more family."* Thus, taking again that extreme step he so often
did in his satires, Harris suggests that the best method of
straightening things out for "this an' the nex generashun" is to
emasculate the present and return to a now-lost traditional pattern of life.

Although Harris was at his best in his nonsatiric writings, he
at least seems to have tried to channel his indignation into
artistic methods of expression. His contempt and spleen too
often gain the upper hand and obliterate all artistry and control.
When control is lost, his invective reaches fantastic limits and
often approaches indecency. Although Harris's artistry is more
clearly in evidence elsewhere, the satires do tell us much about
the temperament and personality of the man.

PLAYING OLD SLEDGE
FOR THE PRESIDENCY.—
DREAM OF SUT LOVINGOOD'S

WELL, Sut, what was your dream? Tell us; if ever you dreamed anything smart, your friends ought to know it for the benefit of your car-ac-ter, for cuss me if you ever even *thought* anything smart awake."

Thus bantered, Sut leaned against the rough board counter of the doggery, with a tumbler of whisky in one hand, while the other sounded for the bottom of a hole in his breeches, by courtesy called a pocket—took a small sip, and began to tell his dream. Hear him, reader, speak for himself:

"Gentle-men! I dreampt an unpossibility last nite. I wur in Washington City,[1] an I know I never will be thar onless they take me thar tu hang ur crucify me fur drinkin more nur my sheer ov 'the people's drink,' old Rot Gut. But in my dream I was thar, an no mistake—sartin sure—at a thunderin big tavern, whar they rung lettle bells tu keep from hollerin arter the niggers an makin a noise; an whar they called yu to yur mush by ratlin on a big still bottom [2] just fur the sake ov the noise; an whar they took thirty dimes a day fur doin nuthin fur yu; and whar they gin you sass enuf tu make you fite (at home) fur nuthin at all. Darn the seat ov govurnment! Darn the legs an body ov government!—an darn every body, I say!"

"Tell your dream before you get drunk, you long-legged cuss you, or let somebody tell it for you."

Thus reproved, Sut sheered into the channel again:

"Well, arter supper awhile I nosed round ontil I got inter a

This story appeared in Nashville *Union and American*, XXVIII (October 18, 1856), 2.

Austin (Texas) *Southern Intelligencer* (November 26, 1856), 1. Reprinted with minor editorial revision and extensive reparagraphing.

1. That is, Washington, D.C.
2. The bottom of the boiler vessel used in distilling alcohol.

room whar I seed a lite, an thar sat three fellers a playin ov 'old sledge.' "

"Old what?"

"*Seven-up,* you drotted weazel-skinned, frog-legged son ov a kangaroo."

[This was addressed to a young specimen of the order *intensus Americanus, anti-Popeatibus mudleusimus,* who shone resplendent from K————,[3] in tights, small cane and watch-ribbon, and had a laudable desire to learn something of the hidden mysteries of "old sledge." He *played* only on an asthmatic trombone and "schess" when in the "scity."]

"They wur a playin seven up with bran new kerds, spank span new, an no marks, every feller fur his self *seemingly.* Now, gentle-men, I believe I kin smell kerds, ef they ar in motion, as fur as frum here tu the spring, ur how the devil did I happin tu hit onto that room whar gambolling wur a gwine on? But thar I did go by in-stink, I reckin, an the three fellers wur nobody on yearth but Buck-cannon, Fillmore, and Fremount, and thay wur a playin a single game ov seven up for the President's cheer ov these free an awful United E Pluribus States, *thirty one* in number, an kiverin the whole yearth.[4] Thar wur another chap inter that room, with one hand under his coatail, an tother a strokin ov his chin, a walkin about sorter kerrless like, but fust a lookin inter Fillmore's hand an then inter Fremount's, an then a winkin and a frownin, fust at one ov them an then tother. Then he'd tiptoe an try to peep inter Buck's hand. But the old feller hilt it

3. A member of the anti-Catholic and anti-immigrant Know-Nothing or Native American political party, which at this particular time was on its last legs and on the point of merging with the newly formed Republican party. His home state, Kansas, from the time of the Kansas-Nebraska Act (May 30, 1854), was the scene of murderous warfare between proslavery and antislavery elements, both attempting to assert their views as dominant by the formula of "popular sovereignty." In the spring of 1856, actual civil war broke out in which the fanatical John Brown figured; he led a massacre in which several proslavery colonists were executed. The question of "Bleeding Kansas" became a hot issue in the 1856 presidential election. Richard B. Morris, ed., *Encyclopedia of American History*, pp. 218–221.

4. Harris is presenting a prophetic allegory of the 1856 presidential race between Democratic candidate James Buchanan (1791–1868), American (Know-Nothing) candidate Millard Fillmore (1800–1874), and Republican candidate John C. Frémont (1813–1890).

under the shadder ov the table, and sorter looked at it sideways his self, an was a watchin the peepin feller, too, all the while rite clost. His name was Sea-ward,[5] or Hell-ward, ur sumthin ov that sort, no matter which. Now, Gentle-men, I kin play old sledge myself rite peart, an when I seed that it wur a game ov two pluck one,[6] an that Buck-cannon was bound tu be skinned ef his hide didn't grow fast onto his bones, I got as mad as a bee in swarmin time, an I jist thought (mind I sed nuthin) that I'd like tu nock enuf off ov that chap's skull tu make a bullit ladle, ef I dard tu. He is a darn'd snake in the grass, sure.

"Well, arter they had played out thar hands, Mister Buck-cannon sez, a bowin mity purlite, 'I believe, gentle-men, I made high, jack, an that has sot me six, ef I aint mistaken.' Then both on em, Fillmore *and* Fremount, spread all o' Buck's tricks out onter the table till they saw *his* ace ov trumps on *the* jack ov trumps which he had cotch from Fillmore with the king, and then they agreed that he *was* six. Sea-ward sed, 'Yes, he reconed that was the state of the game.' Fillmore then, as modest as a fifteen year old gal, sed, 'I made low; you kotch my juice [7] with yer old ace, Mister Buck-cannon, and that sits me three.' All agreed on that count, an Fremount leaning his cheer back whis-pured behind his hand tu me, 'an d——d low it was too, don't yu think so?' an his black must-tuch-us twisted up like onto two corkscrews; but all agreed that Fillmore was *three,* an no mis-take. Fremount then sed, 'I made *game,* an that sot me six with you, Mister Buck-cannon.' Buck bowed agin tu that, but Fillmore said, "Si-r-r, I'll *count* game with you; this is not adzactly accor-din to our understandin, Si-r-r;' an fur the fust time he looked like he mought be made to fite. Sea-ward frowned, shook his head, winked, and sweated mightly. Fremount did so too, *an all at old Fillmore,* but it warn't no use, count game he would; and Fremount beat him *one.* So that sot the game—Buck six, Fre-

5. William Henry Seward (1801–1872), then Senator from New York, unsuccessful presidential nominee for Republican candidacy, and leader of a large New York state Whig following, is portrayed by Harris as uncertain to which candidate he will lend his support. Actually, Seward consistently refused to have anything to do with the anti-Catholic element of the American party, and gave his full support to the Republicans. Eugene H. Roseboom, *A History of Presidential Elections,* pp. 157–163.

6. Cf. *two poll one:* to be swindled by two confederates.

7. Deuce.

mount six, and Fillmore three—an Buck's deal, an Fremount's beg or stand.[8]

"Buck licked his thumb an delt em mity slow an keerful. I looked at Fillmore's kerds as he got em from the deal, an it like tu knoked me down.—Thar wus *the* ace, the king, the queen, the jack, the ten an *the juice* ov trumps! Thinks I, O, Lordy! an then I looked at him, an thar the old feller sot, his belly kiverin the cheer all over, an nearly out tu his knees, as solemn, as big, an about as wise as an ole Dutch squire a tryin ov a bastardy case with good proof agin the daddy. I tell ye, boys, he looked jist like he had his fust big horn ov whisky fur the nite, an felt it in his boots. I tho't, O Lordy! agin.

"Buck never turned up his hand, but axed Fremount what he ment tu do. He looked at his kerds, sorted em, then looked at em agin, then up at the lamp, then at Buck, scratched his year, shot up his eyes, an very slowly sed— 'I—b-e-g.' By the jumpin Jehosephat! Buck run em quick, an I thot it no harm tu take another look at old Fill. He fotch a low collicky sort ov grunt, an then he blowed. I swar, the wind come outen his nose, mouth, eyes, an years, an like tu put the lamp out.

"I dodged an tuk a peep inter Fremount's hand, an I now swar, that when a man's six on a big game ov seven up, I never seed jist sich kerds.—He hilt tother three aces, bound to be high let what would cum—an out-an-out President at that. Thinks I, O Lordy, Buck!—O Lordy, Fillmore! an watched to see what suit was to make the President outen that darnd mule eatin Fremount—when thar's nara no nothin in hell ef he didnt turn jack jist as easy as ef thar'd been fifty-two of em in the deck, an then only leaned back an smiled loud *fur a President!*[9] Fillmore rared backards outen his cheer an fainted as comfortable on the floor as an old maid at a quiltin when the kissin begins. Fremount's eyes turned green—the har on the back ov his hed ris up like the teeth ov a comb, his must-touch-us turned up towards his eyes,

8. Seven points will win the game, hence Harris's estimate at this point of the candidates' chances for election are Buchanan six, Frémont six, and Fillmore three.

9. Harris's forecast of Buchanan's victory by a slim margin proved accurate. He beat Frémont by slightly under 500,000 popular votes and 60 electoral votes. The results: Buchanan, 1,838,169 popular and 174 electoral votes; Frémont, 1,341,264 popular and 114 electoral votes; Fillmore, 874,534 popular and 8 electoral votes. Roseboom, pp. 166–167.

he brayed like a mule, an at one jump kivered old Fill as he lay, an then sot in tu bitin an chokin and maulin ov him like the Devil beatin hominy.[10] This sort ov exitement fotch the old feller tu, an as soon as he felt all the hurtin that was a gwine on all over him, *inside* an *out,* he sot rite in tu fitin tu like an old stud hoss, an thar they hed it. I looked at Buck, (who still hilt the kerds in his hand with the jack turned up on top) as much as tu say, 'shall I part em?' He shook his hed, an I put my hand in my pockets an kep outen thar way. They fit *some* by this time, I tell ye:—har-wool-fur-an-feathers flew, sorter like gining cotton. Seaward cut dirt as soon as that awful jack was turned, locked the door on the outside, an went strait tu a prar' meetin in Ninth street, whar I reckon he is yet. Well, thar they fit, an grunted, an every now an then Fremount wud bray like onto a mule, an Fillmore wud grunt out sumthin about somebody's box an 'fusion.' [11] Now ef fusion means *mixin*, they war *fused,* about as well as two pints of bald face in a quart flask on a hard trottin hoss. An, ov all the darnd noises I ever did hear, they shook that big tavern tu the ground. An I waked all ove a lather ov swet, an then jist turnd over in the bed an cried like a baby."

"What for, Sut?"

"Case I waked up afore either hollored, an I never will know which whipped. Old Buck knows, an if ever I set eyes on him, I'll ax im. Give us another horn, old hoss!"

10. A variant of the proverbial phrase, "like the devil beating tan-bark," which Harris used twice in *Sut Lovingood, Yarns,* pp. 82, 263. See also Archer Taylor and Bartlett Jere Whiting, *A Dictionary of American Proverbs and Proverbial Phrases 1820–1880,* pp. 97–98.

11. The expression of Democratic strength in this election did indeed convince the opposition parties of the need for a strengthening "fusion," which many had already attempted to effect. The Whig party disappeared and the Know-Nothings joined forces with the Republicans as sectional lines hardened. The development of the Republican party and the ramifications of this presidential election are traced in Roseboom, pp. 149–167.

SUT LOVINGOOD'S LOVE FEAST
OVE VARMINTS, I

Y OU never hearn, George, how I got into a big meetin ove
varmints to Nashville,[1] an how durnd ni I cum gittin ove

This story appeared in Nashville *Union and American*, XXIX (April 19, 1859), 2.

1. This series of political satires, using the age-old animal fable form, was directed against the convention held in Nashville on March 29 by the self-styled Opposition party to nominate a candidate for governor to run against the Democratic incumbent Isham G. Harris. Actually the Opposition party was an amalgam of various factions—dying remnants of the Native American or Know-Nothing party, the last of the Whigs, and turncoat Democrats—all dedicated to the single purpose of breaking the Democratic hold on the national and local levels. The Democratic *Union and American* paper noted on March 30: "Those who imagine . . . that the present Opposition party is a new thing under the sun are vastly mistaken. . . . It would be tedious to trace it from its first appearance down to the present time, and to note all its gyrations, and to index the innumerable names which it has assumed, disgraced and discarded. . . . Whether as Federalists, Republicans, Whigs, Americans, Know-Nothings, or Oppositionists. . . . One moment you shall hear them screaming about foreign influence, then about Democratic extravagance, then about the Pope, then about Americans ruling America, and always about the Democratic administration. . . ."

The Know-Nothing party had practically expired in 1857, but members of the Opposition party were called Know-Nothings and Whigs indiscriminately. See Sister Mary de Lourdes Gohmann, *Political Nativism in Tennessee to 1860;* W. Darrell Overdyke, *The Know-Nothing Party in the South;* Richard B. Morris, ed., *Encyclopedia of American History*, pp. 187, 218; Robert Loren Hargis, "The Know Nothing Party in Tennessee" (unpublished master's thesis, Vanderbilt University, 1931); Nashville *Union and American*, XXIX (March 30, 1859), 2, 3; Nashville *Daily Gazette*, XIV (March 30, 1859), 3; *Republican Banner and Nashville Whig*, XLIX (March 30, 1859), 2.

The idea of portraying human beings as animals may have been suggested to Harris by Aesop, brought into conjunction with the Opposition convention by way of the following editorial comment of the *Union and American* on a speech made by General James F. Quarles at the meeting: "His speech if written out would be equal to a copy of Aesop's fables, and would amuse the children on account of its highly colored

myself fixt for hapiness an halalujah beyant the grave fur gwine amung 'em. Ketch me ever a mixin ove myself up again with pole cats, coons, groun-hogs, minks, house-cats, hoss-cats, hell-cats, weazels, mus-rats, wharf-rats, bull-bats,[2] owls, buzzards, water-dorgs,[3] wild boars, bell weathers, possums, moles, grub-worms and tumble-bugs; when they's in heat an holdin a love-feast,[4] when all ar ekal an on the squar, and every cussed wun ove 'em actin out hits nater in hits mos onsanctified parts. I kotch a big skeer what I haint over yet. Look at that ar foot how hit trembles, (holding out his long leg at right angles); hit shakes yet like ontu a green gall when a feller thretens tu waller her at a quiltin. Oh durn these quarterly meetins ove permiscus varmints, ove the sneakin an stealin sort, whar good dogs, an steel traps, an guns aint alowed tu cum. Sum infurnel devilment's agwine tu cum ove hit sartin. Ise studied the nater ove beastes monsous well, particular the mean kind ove varmints, caze I spose they's sorter in tu me, an I tell you, sure es youre born, when they meets by waggin loads tu hold a pow-wow, hit dont mean eny good tu eny critter but thar sefs. I had followed a terbacker waggin tu Nashville an sot in tu slungin roun in the openest part ove town, what I'd have room tu run in case eny imedjut vexashun ove spirit overtuck me. Thar wer a big tavrin on wun side ove a open lot an they hadn't tuck the scafflin down yet from the front an hits bin thar ni ontu forty years, an on tuther side the lot wer a monsous long shed an big at the ainds like ontu a silkwum what youse pulled in two an lef a hangin by

---

illustrations." The delegates were also referred to another day as "rats." Nashville *Union and American*, XXIX (March 31, 1859), 2; (March 30, 1859), 2.

    2. Nighthawks.

    3. Dogs trained to enter the water and retrieve game.

    4. Calling the convention a "love feast" may have been suggested by a comment on the reception accorded John Bell, the elder anti-Democrat, in the *Republican Banner and Nashville Whig*, XLIX (April 3, 1859), 2: "In all the exciting scenes in Tennessee politics, we know of nothing that can compare with Mr. Bell's reception on Tuesday night, except the reception of Old CLAY, in 1840, or the triumph of Mr. Bell over Felix Grundy [as a candidate for Congress from Tennessee in 1827]. There was a manifestation of devoted love and unbounded admiration that must have been gratifying in the extreme to Mr. Bell. The feeling exhibited showed how much they loved the old man. It was a spontaneous and uncontrollable outburst of enthusiasm, and proved conclusively that the love of his friends was as strong as the hatred of his enemies."

the gut, an in the middle wer a orful big griste mill ur a terback-er stemmery [5] deserted, an hit lef tu take keer ove hits sef like unto mos things in this yere yeath am.

Well, when I got in site ove the tavrin I never seed jist sich a site in all my bornd days, all that ar scaffolin wer kivered with all the varmints Ive norated tu you, a climbin the postes, a hangin by thar tails from the winder shutters, a sittin on thar starns in the winders, a racin an a playin on the ruff, a rastlin and sham fitin ontu the pavement, a stickin tu the door posts, a rushin tugether arter a piece ove cold chicken flung into the back yard, and then a fitin over hit, evry varmint a usin ove his natral wepuns; a ridin wun anuther down stars, a smellin at people's cotetails, a runnin thar fore paws inter the overcoat pockets what wer a hangin ontu the wall an a lookin tuther way all the time.

Groun hogs a pickin the dirt outen thar tails an a slidin on thar hine aind across the rume. Moles tryin tu bore holes in the walls ove the tavrin; minks a 'zaminin ove the chicken coops; coons a growlin at possums about the respective size, beauty, an proporshuns ove thar tales, rats a smellin' around the corners ove people's har trunks an a eatin' the paste outen the flowered callicker what kivered the walls; cats a smellin ove thar tails an a makin passes at the rats, when a ole coon, monsous grey, so ole that the rings ontu his tail hed almost faded out, would jump atween 'em, wash his face with his paws as much as to say no fitin' among his frien's at a love-feas'.[6] He hed a bell tied roun his neck an hit tinckled when he'd rack [7] roun the room. They sorter wer feard ove him. I never did see jist sich kerrien on in all my bornd days. They had tuck perseshun ove the tavrin bodily, an you could see 'em rackin' in an out ove amost evry house in town, an' ove all the hungry devils you could skeer up in a week's travil among the sand hills, they wer the hungriest; not a durned wun

5. Tobacco stemmery: a building in which tobacco is stemmed.

6. The coon is John Bell (1796–1869), a conservative nationalist, the strongest and most popular opponent of the Democratic party in Tennessee. Formerly a Representative and Senator from Tennessee after many successful elections, and Secretary of War under President Harrison, he was presently preparing to campaign as a candidate for President of the United States on the Constitutional Union Ticket in the 1860 election. See Joseph Howard Parks, *John Bell of Tennessee*.

7. Race.

ove 'em hed tasted a morsel since 1852,[8] an you may jist guess how they looked. Why they wer plumb crazy, an ef they ain't fed purty soon sum orful calamity will cum; an they all says so.

Now all these shines an' kerrins on tuck place in broad day lite, so you may know how they did when night cum on.[9] As that is the varmint's day time they poured outen the tavrin in a solid sluce, an I obsarved that almost every coon toted another varmint ove sum sort ontu his back, (they loves tu ride coons) an aimin fur the terbacker stemmery out in the middle ove the lot. So I sorter sneaked in arter them. Well thar they wer, redy fur work, an I know you wont believe me, but I onderstood the most they sed. I'se been mixed up with wild beastes all my life, an so I jist listened tu lurn ef I could what the devil this inundashun ove the varmints meant eny how. An ole rusty he grounhog sat up on aind on a windersill, and sed that he know'd monstrous well how thar tastes fur vitils differed.[10] "The coon thar (a pintin to the old Bull feller with the bell on) loves ole hens monsous well." Here the bell coon interfered tu say "he did like ole hens but dam thar cacklin and scrachin, he jist wanted tu make his record right," an sot down.

The groun hog then went on tu say that the possum hed a weakness fur simmons, the rat loved cheese and meal, the mink went in fur pullet's blood, and he might add the weasel as agreeing with the possum on *that pint*. The skunk loved strong diet, and the buzzard didn't care a dam what he et so hit hed been dead long enough before hand, an he mout show that every animil in that rume differed as tu what they loved tu eat, but all

8. The Whigs last came into power when President Zachary Taylor was elected in 1848. In 1852, Democrat Franklin Pierce beat the Whig presidential candidate Winfield Scott. On the state level, the last Whig governor of Tennessee had been William Bowen Campbell, who was succeeded by Democrat Andrew Johnson in 1853.

9. Before the beginning of the official convention of the Opposition party on March 29, a preliminary caucus assembled at the court house on the Monday evening previous to draw up a list of officers for the convention. Neill S. Brown (1810–1886), former Whig and governor of Tennessee from 1847–1849, was appointed president. Speeches were delivered by Colonel A. M. Looney of Maury county, Colonel J. R. Mosby of Fayette, and Brown. *Republican Banner and Nashville Whig*, XLIX (March 30, 1859), 2. *Dictionary of American Biography*, vol. III, pp. 147–148.

10. Noted the *Union and American*, XXIX (March 31, 1859), 2: "Orators [at the convention] occupied the same stand who had never held a sentiment in common except a desire for office."

were alike in lovin tu eat sumthin or uther an he wer redy to swar that not wun ove em hed tasted a bite fur seven years. They wus starvin an hed met here tu plan out sum way to get sum vittels, an they ment tu hev hit; an he hoped sum one would offer some plan what could be kerrid out tu the gittin ove thar belly's full—an he quiled up with his tail roun his nose. A varmint then climbed up ontu a box tu make a talk, an durn me ef ever I hev been so bothered in all my life tu make out what hit was.[11] At fust I tuck hit fur a ole billy goat frum hits gray beard an wore-out looks. I happened tu look away fur a minit, an hit hed changed powful; hits har wer es black es a mink, an all slicked up, an hit were shaped like ontu a coon. In fac hit changed shape an color every time I looked away. Hit gin me a sorter skeer, hit wer so many beasts at onct. That hit wer a beastes ove sum sort I knowed by his FOOT. I wish I jist knowd what sort ove bait would catch it. Barnum 'ud gin me forty barrills ove whiskey fur hit an make at that. How would a bar trap do baited with an 'oman or a fat office? I mean tu try the experiment.

Well while hit wer in hits black an shiney shape, hit talked sum, sed hit thought the varmints had orter bild a platform, an be again every thing septin of God amity, big crops and cheap whisky.[12] Thought them three sections would take among the varmints an ketch sum humans, an so on. The bell coon sed he didn't adzactly see where the timber or the workmen wer tu cum from tu bild a platform, an warnt sure they wanted wun; fur his

11. Henry Stuart Foote actually addressed the full convention on the next evening and not at the preliminary assembly with, according to the *Union and American*, "A rambling speech, mostly about himself, of considerable length." Nashville *Union and American*, XXIX (March 30, 1859), 3. Originally a Virginian, Foote (1804–1880) was governor of Mississippi from 1853–1854. His administration was marked by fierce battles with states-rights factions, until his pro-Union sympathies led to his resignation just before his term expired. *Dictionary of American Biography*, VI, 500–501. Harris, in speaking of the changing nature of Foote's appearance, is pointedly referring to the fact that he showed up at the convention sporting a black wig and black dyed whiskers (see Herschel Gower and Jack Allen, eds., *Pen and Sword, The Life and Journals of Randal W. McGavock*, p. 514). The woman Harris suggests be used as bait may be the wealthy widow Mrs. Robert Smiley, whom Foote courted and married in 1859.

12. A ten-point platform or declaration of principles was drawn up during the regular convention session. It is quoted in full in Robert Loren Hargis, pp. 105–106.

part he hed tuck a tree early in the spring, an spected to stay thar, fur dogs coudent climb trees, an *he'd* seed dogs ontu platforms. The biggest and spottedest skunk sed he were fur a platform, caze hit suited his wepuns adzactly; thought ef he wer ontu wun high enuf, he could make all the humans below think hit wer raining fresh damnation. So he went for a platform. As fur dogs, he axed them no odds. A monsous knowin lookin dirty old mus-kat sed he prefared a hole, an there were quite a crowd jined him on the hole question. The Buzzard sed he didn't keer a cuss about a hole ur a platform either. His habits kep humans away frum him any how, an all he axed wer a high pint whur he cud ketch the wind; an all he cum thar fur, wus tu fix sum way tu make the wind fetch him scent ove plenty dead cackuses; and he ment tu hev em, ef he hed tu get the weasel tu make em fur him. But Lordy, George, I'se most starved for sum whisky. This yere trail goes to Fryer's still-house an I'm gwine thar. He made a dubblin [13] yesterday, an hits outen corn at that. Got ary quarter ye wont want till muster? [14] I'll meet you thar an tell you the ballance, an what happened tu the varmints, an how I tuck a skeer. I'll jist be durned ef ever you hearn tell ove sich another time since the lord invented corn, an man invented whisky. You take the right han on top of the devide ef yer are gwine to Turtle town. [15] Take keer ove that little cackus ove yourn. I loves you by jings.

13. Doubling is a distiller's technical word for whisky.
14. Racing jargon: until the horses are assembled at the starting line.
15. A small Polk county village in northeastern Tennessee.

SUT LOVINGOOD'S LOVE-FEAST
OVE VARMINTS, II

WELL, Sut, has Ryan made a doubling?" Yes, hoss, an I got a big drunk outen hit afore I showed the quarter you gin —loaned me. *Hit* filled a crock I'd stole outen ole Clapshaw's [1] spring house. Durn him, I hes a sorter spite et him, eny how, fur marryin SICILY BURNS en I hadnt orter, fur ef I hed got her she'd a run all over me several times afore now. "Stop, Sut, I want to hear how you got out of your varmint scrape at Nashville." Oh, yes, we'll lite an hitch an let us walk down tu the spring. I'se got a remnant here yet, (shaking a cherry pectoral bottle,) [2] set down atween the roots ove that ar Catawby tree [3] an jist lean back, thar's a gourd. Hev sum warter? Mind hits cracked an leaks. Why, durn yer little fool picter, are you gwine tu take yer warter afore you licker? Dont ye no that licker's the lightest an ef ye take hit fust, hit cums up thru the warter an makes a ekel mixtry an spiles all chance ove bein pisened by hit? Allers take yer whisky fust, fur you don't allers know what mout be in hit. I'se monsus keerful about everything fur all natur's agin me an I jist takes keer ove mysef with the help ove God amity, an these yere onapproachabil, onnatral, onekeled laigs. Dye see em? Aint they sum superlativ?

Well, es I wer a tellin ove you, arter the Buzzard quit a talkin, a ole wild Boar cum out intu the middle ove the floor with a bunch ove foam on each side of his mouf es big es a snow-ball flower, an he reached his two fore feet away out forward so, an sot on

This story appeared in Nashville *Union and American*, XXIX (April 21, 1859), 2.

1. Clapshaw is the irreverent, dishonest circuit-riding preacher who figures in some of Sut's other escapades. It is his marriage to Sicily Burns that occasions "Old Burns's Bull Ride," *Sut Lovingood, Yarns*, pp. 86–107.

2. A bottle intended for pectoral, a medicine for lung and chest diseases, but Sut uses it for another kind of medicine—whiskey.

3. The catalpa tree, a shade variety, is known as the catawba tree in the Carolinas and Georgia after a local tribe of Indians.

243

em clost together an commenced a rubbin ove em past each other like he wer tryin to push sumthin further frum him, an a crackin ove his teeth like shettin ove a snuff-box. Arter a while he got thru these yere devoshuns ove hisn, an he commenced a talkin. Sez he, "the groun hog, a sorter kin ove mine, (an here he wall'd a monsous red eye roun at the groun hog,) talked about our tastes all bein ove a differ, but he dident tell yer that our habits had a bigger differ nor our tastes, an in our plannin this mustn't be forgot. Thar's the ole billy goat allers had the name ove a minnit man, while I'se slow ove speech an a dam site slower ove action; but jist gin me time an I aint feard tu show work with any one ove the varmints here. I hev made more votes nor eny ove you septin, p'raps, the minks; they hev hilt thar own. An now I'm fur a narrowin down the talkin tu wun thing, an that's vittils—vittils, that's the watch word, an all the balance is dam stuff."

"Thar aint anuther pint on yeath that we ever kin agree on, an so we wont speak on them, but jist set ourselfs on VITTILS. We mite es well own up; jis look at that thar wolf's belly; hits growd tu his back bone frum the cuplin [4] tu his haslets.[5] Look at that ar owl; dam ef he cant roost in the ar, (mine I'm plain of speech.) Ax that ar fox an he can't tell the taste ove a goose frum a grindstone. Git that dam ole file tail'd possum tu draw the shape ove a 'simmon an he'll make hit like ontu a ace ove dimunts. Ax that ar cussed, sleepy, black snake tu describe the pussonel feelens ove a grown squirrill, an if he minds the stripes at all he'll swar they run cross wise; ur ax that ar rat the shape an size ove a cheese an he'll jist swar that hits made in bars like soap, an each one as big es a rail road ker. *The fac is we hasent et ontil we hes lost all ideas ove size, shape, smell ur taste, an thars but wun thing afore us an that is* 'VITTILS OR DEATH.' "

"Let's take a vote on the vittils ur death question," sed a ole red fox. "All them as am fur vittils hold up thar tails." "That won't do," sed the mole, (he hed no tail tu brag ove in a permiskus crowd) "fur ef ye fix hit that way the goat has voted aready." "I stands on the pint with the mole," sed a ole wolf frum the cliffs

4. Coupling: the part of the body joining the hindquarters of quadruped animals to the front parts of the body.
5. The edible viscera (hearts, lungs, etc.) of an animal.

ove Bedford,[6] what hed but three feet an hed sat on his hunkers in a corner, "fur I coudent vote on that ar questin, caze I've got no tail tu hist, darn humuns an thar invenshuns an traps, especially, I say—an as I'm fur vittils hit woudn't do me jestis; I couldn't spress my sentimints," an he backed inter his corner. A monsous long ole grey possum, what hed swum the Cumberland tu git thar, onwoun his tail frum roun his neck an sed he'd traveled a heap in sarch ove simmons; been tu furrin parts an foun dam few simmons; [7] that simmons, *as* simmons, wer the pint, an that the word vittils didn't kiver the case. In place ove "vittils ur death," he wer fur "simmons ur death," an wanted tu be onderstood as fur simmons fust an death arterwards, in due course ove nater—an he squatted and larfed, without hevin eny thing tu larf at. Possums will do that you know. They's either a hangin by the tail ur larfin ur shammin dead 'sep' when they am up a full simmon tree, an then they must be mistakened for a tax collector, they receives the simmons so easy. An this wun looked like he'd been an orful simmon eater in his time.

Up jumped my critter, Billy goat, mink, coon, pothecary shop, ur whatever it wer, (durnd if he didn't exercise me monsously tu know what he wer, eny how,) an said that this differ about the *kind* ove vittils would break up the lov-feas; that he hed et every thing ever et by a beastes an he thot that he looked younger to-night than he ever did afore; he'd tried buzzard fare in Californy, he'd sup'd with a groun-hog on grub-wums and toads in Massasippi, kotch flies with the bats arter sun down, in Alabama, and hunted with the tom-cats successfully every whar at mid-night; [8] he begg'd the pardon of the rats present, but he

6. The high hills of Bedford county, some with elevations of two hundred or three hundred feet, are capped with sandstones. *History of Tennessee . . . with an Historical and a Biographical Sketch of Maury, Williamson, Rutherford, Wilson, Bedford and Marshall Counties*, pp. 861–862.

7. The opossum seems to be intended as a satiric portrayal of Neill Smith Brown, president of the convention. Although Brown maintained a law office at 66 North Cherry Street in Nashville, his home was actually located in Edgefield, that part of the city lying east across the Cumberland River. He had served once for three years as a minister to Russia beginning in 1850. Nashville *Union and American*, XXIX (March 30, 1859), 3; *Nashville City and Business Directory for 1860–61*, p. 134.

8. Henry Stuart Foote first began to practice law in Tuscumbia, Alabama, where he violated the law against dueling and had to move. He then

cotch only mice; (respected rats tu much to hunt them); and so he could bar with amost eny kind ove vittils if they wer plenty, an so he wer in favor ove but the wun pint, in wun word—a word that toch every varmint intu that ar room ni untu hits haslet, and that word wer "VITTILS"—and then he stroked his whiskers with his fore paws, sot down, histed his hine laig, cat fashun, an adjusted his har. He's a takin monsous good keer ove his sef, an durn me ef hit don't stand him in hand, fur in his wust aspects he looks like a dam old worn out sturn wheel steamboat, what had been totin coal and towin mud scows for a livin.

Well, the smell which I wer indicatin tu you tuther day, by this time wer most overpowerin tu me, an torectly I seed the ruff ove the house begin tu rise, an the glass a bustin outen the winders.[9] Hit wer nuffin on yeath but the cumulated pressure ove the smell. I judged hit tu be ni ontu forty pounds tu the squar inch, an a risin; so when I seed that the ruff wer bound tu be tore off, I thort I'd try an gin them a big skeer afore mine cum on. You know, George, I takes skeers jist es regular es moon risin. Now, mine, they hadn't seed me yet, an I jist ris up so, ni ontu seven feet, an hollered: "Here Rove! here Rove! here Rove! sick 'em! dam 'em, sick 'em! Who-eee!!!" and then I fotch a keen

began a political career in Jackson, Mississippi, eventually becoming governor. He left for California after resigning as governor, returned to Vicksburg in 1858, and then moved to Tennessee. Dunbar Rowland, ed., *Encyclopedia of Mississippi History*, vol. I, pp. 716–720.

9. The roof and windows of the court house were damaged the night of the preliminary Opposition assembly by one of the worst storms to visit Nashville in years. Chimnies and fences were toppled, and besides the court house, the First Presbyterian Church was most severely damaged. "Destructive Storm," Nashville *Union and American*, XXIX (March 30, 1859), 3. The same issue of the paper contained this facetious account on page 2:

"Preliminary to the regular Convention a caucus was held the night previous at the court-house. The clouds lowered and nature wore her gloomiest aspect. But the enthusiasm was up, and on they went. In the midst of their proceedings, and in the height of their enthusiasm, at the very point where one of their most *energetic* orators was lifting his audience above sublunary things, the elemental war without came on and put a period to his flight, by partly unroofing the house and filling their minds with consternation and alarm. In the midst of the fright, some thoughtful or rueful personage, we don't know which, exclaimed in stentorian terms, 'Rats, to your holes!' Such a scattering was never before witnessed, and in a moment more the storm seemed to have swept away the last remains of the caucus. Truly the way of the transgressor is hard."

whistle an smaked my hands like whips a poppin——Now rite here I orter stop talkin an never broach the subjic agin, (and Sut looked puzzled and scratched his hed.) Reach yere that ar specimint ove glass blowin [10]—now the gourd [11]—Well, I feels more confidence in myself, now, an I'll try tu make you onderstand hit, but human tung an the fastes painter ove picters on yeath couldent begin tu impress you with the fac es hit wer. "What fact, Sut?" Why, the konsekenses ove callin a dog, in a love-feas ove varmints, whar dogs ur humans warnt spected.

Here Sut held his head between his knees in deep study for a space, and then looking up enquiringly at me, asked: George, did you ever fling a twenty pound dog inter a room whar a passel ove cats wer a negociatin? "I think I have." Well, now, George, am you prepared to swar that the dog *an* the cats wer in that rume at wun an the same time fur eny wun instant? "Well, Sut, I cannot say; the cats certainly displayed great promptitude of action in leaving." Great promptitude ove ackshun? That's a dam slow, inadekate speech, cumin frum you; hit dont kiver the case. Anser me, dident the cats jist disapear sorter like the flash of a cussion cap in the nite? Did they take eny time et all tu do hit? Didnt they jist scatter tharsefs right whar they wer? "Yes, Sut, they went, and did not stand on the order of their going." [12] No, I recon they dident, nor dam ef they stood on any thing else. Now, all I kin say is that the echo ove my whistle rung through a room full ove emtiness. They went outen the winders in grate bunches es big es a hogshead an struck the pavement a runnin.

They went up the chimleys an just poured down the stars,—an agin I got tu a winder I cud just see thar tails a flutterin thru the gratiss over the cellar winders all roun that big lot. And them as had wings,—the buzzards, owls, chicken-hawks, crows, bats and beetles, arter the ruff cum off jist went up-ards intu the gloom ove the storm. Pieces ove the tin ruff as big es bed quilts an waggon kivers chased sum ove em plumb to

10. A whisky jug.
11. Containing water.
12. Harris is quoting from the *Union and American,* which said of the Oppositionists departing the court house during the storm: " 'The wrathful skies scared the very wanderers of the dark' and drove them to their caves. . . . They 'stood not upon the order of their going, but went at once.' " Nashville *Union and American,* XXIX (March 30, 1859), 2. The newspaper, of course, is quoting Shakespeare's *Macbeth,* Act III, Scene iv.

the tavern porch a smashin tails an a peelin of har an fur es they went. I tell you, George, all that sort ove varmints (per-datory, don't ye call hit,) hes a most wholesum fear ove humans, dogs, an daylite. Hits a instink ove them tu make thur sefs scace et a moment's warnin, an darn ef the show they made ove that instink that nite dident kiver them all with a glory what dont fade by time ur git rusted by years. As tu that onnamable varmint what et every kind ove vittils an looked like eny thing hit pleased,—I wer a watchin ove hit a workin ontu hits har, (es I told you) rite in the middle ove the rume when I hollered fur Rove.

An durn ole Clapshaw ef hit didn't jist disapear rite in hits tracks, an when I sarched the spot whar hit sot, I foun a emty har dye bottle, a bunch ove grey har, like unto a hogs, an a leaf outen a book on slight ove han. Taking ove the whole thing tugether, hit am the durndest, impudentest, skariest affar I ever seed. Well, the sun aint more nor a our high, an thars gwine tu be a quiltin tu Hyram Robinson's, an I've got tu go tu Clapshaw's arter a jug ove truck, so I must go. Whar kin I see you tu tell you ove the ballance ove thar doins next day an next nite? Fur I jist tell you what's tu cum beats the devil. I don't know what this world am comin tu, when all the stealin sort ove varmints holds love-feasts agin the humans. Well I has a perfect reliance in these yere laigs takin keer ove me, but whar'd you be ef yer laigs wer all your pendence? Ef you'd been in my fix at Nashville, durn'd ef they hadn't a picked your bones sartin. Say, George, stop a minit; don't you speak ove what I've tole you in any varminty range.

SUT LOVINGOOD'S LOVE FEAST
OVE VARMINTS, III

I ALLERS tole you, George, that thar war a cross ove beasts intu me an now I knows hit. Just look how all that variety ove varmints tuck on a big skeer when I hollered fur Rove. Hits instink, en hits adzactly my instink. I hes for wun ove my mottoes, "allers stand redy tu travil," an big skeers shows the arfinity jist like the split foot an the teeth dus, an the only thing a botherin me is my appetite fur whisky. The ballance ove the varmint tribe dont hev hit: peraps that's one ove my human streaks, an a infernal wide streak hit iz, aint hit?

Arter I seed the last durn'd varmint scared off in thar holes an roosts, I put fur the country. I staid all night, an nex mornin I wer on han soon, and here they cum.[1] Hunger hed made em bold enuff tu face daylite agin thar instink. Outen the cellars, outen the lofts, outen the stables, outen empty hogsheads, outen ole desarted steamboats, outen the tavrins, outen everywhar, twer varmints and nothin but varmints. How the people ove Nashville stood hit I can't tell, onless hits becase they's sorter varmints thar sefs, "in a state ove nater," es ole Bullin sez. But thar they wer, a kiverin all that ar town, an the scent ove 'em pervaded all creashun. I smelt em ontu everything, even the iron posts what's afire at the top ove nights.[2] I tell you, George, *that hellfired scent ove tharn is tu be thar ruin yet.* The pole-cat may look like a coon an talk like a coon, an the buzzard may sprinkle hisself with meal ontil he looks like *a Eagle;* but durn me, ef the smell dont tell on him in the aind; an when hit does, his time am cum sure.

This story appeared in Nashville *Union and American,* XXIX (April 30, 1859), 1.

1. The official Opposition convention began Tuesday morning, March 29, at 11:30, in the Hall of Representatives in the capitol building. Nashville *Union and American,* XXIX (March 30, 1859), 3.

2. Gas street lamps. The Nashville Gas Light Company was chartered in 1849 and by 1860 had about two hundred public street lights erected for the city. *Nashville City and Business Directory for 1860–61,* pp. 78–79.

Well, all that day they were rackin, trottin, pacin, hoppin, playin, an slidin about through the streets, over the houses, in doors an out, an a follerin ove humans an a smellin at thar cotetails, (I dont onderstand that measure yet.) The flyin part ove the congregashun lit an sot ontu the house whar one ove Jackson's ole Ginerals [3] lived, an ontu the pos offis,[4] an ontu a big pile ove stone coal across the street; an while they pretended to whet thar bills they wer watchin ove a big brick house whar a newspaper am norated from.[5] I thinks they thot that hit wer a storehouse ove vittils, an they were a tryin tu find the weakest door so as tu make a demonstrashun arter humans hed gone tu bed. Oh, durn 'em, you cant trust em ur tell how much smartness tu pervide agin, ef vittils am the question afore em. They kin starve longer an live, an then eat more an live, than eny beasts what has the good will an keer ove humans.

Thar wer one coon that made me notis him more nor eny. He hes his den ni ontu Nashville, an seems tu no all that ar range. He takes fust rate keer ove his hide an har, an I swear his tail am the purtyest thing kivered with fur I ever seed. The rings am as bright as they wer in 1840. He's sum coon, ef he ain't I'm dam. An he dont seem tu like that ole devil with the thimble bell on an the faded tail.[6] I hearn him tell a passle ove possums, minks, an

3. The home of Judge John Catron (c. 1786–1865) was at this time within the capitol area at 11 North Cherry Street. Catron came to Tennessee in 1812 and listed to serve under Andrew Jackson in the War of 1812. He settled in Nashville in 1818 to practice law and was made a judge by the legislature in 1824. Throughout his life, he remained an ardent supporter of Jackson. *Dictionary of American Biography*, III, 576–577; *Nashville City and Business Directory for 1860–61*, p. 142.

4. The Nashville Post Office was then located on the northeast corner of Cedar and Cherry streets, two blocks east of the capitol building on Cedar Street. John Campbell, *Nashville Business Directory*, p. 97.

5. The offices of the *Republican Banner and Nashville Whig*, which supported the Opposition convention, were located at 13 Deaderick Street, about one block south of the Post Office. *Nashville City and Business Directory for 1860–61*, p. 247.

6. The person Harris had in mind here is totally obscure. None of the contemporary newspaper accounts or historical materials relevant to Bell and this period indicates the presence of anti-Bell sympathies within the ranks of the Opposition party. It is true, however, that the Know-Nothing faction never fully trusted Bell's sympathies with them, since he never officially became a member of the party. Actually, his semblance of support was due solely to his hope that they could become the truly

foxes, that ef ever they wanted tu taste vittils agin, the less they follered an noticed that ar ole "anomaly" the better 'twould be for them, an that his dried hide would fetch more money than the livin coon wer worth, an axed them tu think ove what he'd sed, an not tu onderstand him *as wantin murder done,* but only as speakin of relative value, in case Providence wer tu take hit intu his head that the coon with the faded tail's *time hed come.* I noticed that the varmints arter that would sorter shy away from the ole feller, an arter he'd rack past em, they'd turn an smell ove his track, an sorter foller his trail a few steps, sleepy like, an then climb the posts, an shade trees, an the warter spouts ove the houses, an look arter him tu see which way he wer agwine. They am feard ove him, ole as he is, on all pints ove the case. Fust, they'se feard tu foller him least he might lead them over burried steel traps an hidden snars, an they'se feared tu go agin him for fear he mout tell ove robbed hen roosts an perforated meal bags in times a past; an agin he mout be the only wun among 'em what knows the right road tu the futer VITTILS, an tharfore he is ove a monsous site ove value jist now, fur so fur I cant see that the fust durn'd wun ove 'em dus no the road. They'se wuss off than bees in swarmin time in a hail storm, ur ole Burns were atop the Bull,[7] an ef his case wusn't wun ove imejit tribulashun an orful vexashun ove spirit, I dont know what trubbil is, ef I allers did see hit a runnin, an that's what they'll hev tu cum tu at last; I am dam ef good holesum onst gittin away aint the ticket, an the only wun fur eny varmint, ur misef either, an they'll hev tu cum tu it at last, ur gin up their hides; fur the humans will git arter 'em in downright yearnest now, since they've got tu holdin ove love feas an assoshiatin all kinds together in broad day lite in the towns. *Hit attracks an orful attenshun tu em,* and ef I wer in the fur ur hide trade, durn the thing, I'd buy ontil next fall. Hit'll be an orful poor cuss what can't war a fur hat ur tote a leather money puss, arter August, mine that. I would like tu see em hev free excess tu all kind ove vittils, jist fur wun month. The coon would eat isecrem, (they'se ove a cool nater eny how,) ontil the har ontu his tail friz tugether hard enuff tu shell corn ontu hit. The possum wud go hit ontu malaga grapes [8] ontil his tail turned

conservative party he had always advocated to oppose successfully the Democrats. Joseph Howard Parks, *John Bell of Tennessee,* pp. 303–305.

7. See "Old Burns's Bull Ride," *Sut Lovingood, Yarns,* pp. 98–107.

8. A sweet grape grown in Spain and used in making wine.

into a grape-vine an bore white alley marbles [9] and buck shot; the wolf would take mutton roasted until his har turnd tu wool and horns grow from above his years, (sum on em wars horns aready,) an his blood hot enuff tu bile aigs in. The mink, he'd be wus on briled chicken nor surkit riders am, an he'd larn tu crow an pass hisself off fur a chicken cock, early ove a mornin. The wile boar, he'd—but never mind, we'll not speak ove him now. The buzzard, he'd hev young wimmin an fat boys killed and packed away aforehand tu spile an then regale hissef until he'd wear hoop petticoats and play with dolls. The musrat would hev eyesters instead of mussils, an make humans shell em fur him ontil he'd larn tu play billards and drink cock-tails. The skunk would eat cod-fish with otter ove rose sass ontil he perjuced a new smell on the yeath, and try to pass hissef off as a genus what hed dun sum service in the way ove novil scents; the cats, hell cats an all, would demand humming birds fur thar feed, an eat on em ontil they'd be flyin intu the milliner shop winders arter the artificial yarbs hung ontu the bonnets. Jist think ove a durn ole tom cat a tryin tu suck honey outen a fus class bonnet, an hit a top ove a pretty omman, but they'd do hit sartin. Nun on em his eny judgment, but you jist giv em power an durn me fundamentally ef they doesn't interchange with wun anuther, thar taste, voice, shape, color, habit, an all but thar hungry, stealin, hidin nater, faster nor they dus now in a desprit starvin condition. You couldn't tell tuther from which, an I'm not sartin but sum on em would set up fur humans an hev houses built an ax fur wimmin fur wives, so I'm fur a BIG HUNT this summer, an what we don't ketch we'll skare intu actin thar natral parts, so that when we see a coon we ken swar tu him an be able tu tell a possum by his tail ur a buzzard by his smell. We must break up these love-feas an larn em tu travel on thar own hook, for theyse gettin tu sassy fur varmints amung spectable white folks.

Ez a general thing, afore this, humuns hev hed but wun kind ove varmints tu fite et a time. Sometimes hit wer minks; well, we dug 'em out. Then 'twer coons, an the *nigger* dog an ax soon suppres'd them. 'Praps the nex bout wer with possums; well, they surrenders so soon in the fite that the children foch 'em home with a split hickery ontu thar tails, an they'd sham dead ontil

9. Playing marbles made of alabaster or real marble (alley is an abbreviation for alabaster).

their necks wer broke. The rifle shet the bills an opened the claws ove the hawks and owls, if they cum afore axin. Ez tu the buzzards, they wer jist let alone, fur they never wunted what we'd hev. The wolves, all naters agin 'em an the county too, so we kep them thin monsous easey. The rats we lef tu the little dogs and boys, and what with shakin an box traps the wimmen didn't cumplain. Now the black snakes, sum humans am *fur them* and sum *agin 'em,* an as black snakes by thar selfs, they didn't pester any body much, so I doesn't take em inter account. We fit poll cats ur not, cordin tu the wepuns we hed, when we overtuck em. If we hed a rifle and seed one at fifty steps, *he* quit squrtin. If he wer ni onter us, we just run like hell an that ainded the fite.

But things am changed now. The whole dam list ove the inimies tu the humans what am in varmint shape am cum tugether in love feas, an ef they kin do half they wunt tu the coon will be squire, the groun-hog constable, an the wolf preacher, an humans mus dig roots fur a livin and the he's howl on the cliff when they wants the company ove the she's. I'll be ecklesiastically durn'd ef hit aint. Mine what I seys, durn'd natral born fool es I knows I is, hits a battle fur life, ur vittils as they call hit, atween humans and humanity and the varmints an dam rascality. If hit haint you may hev wun of these yere laigs fur a well poll,[10] and that's ekal tu offerin my life tu you. I prizes these here laigs more nor a preacher prizes a rich wife. I'se in yearnest, I is.

"Now, Sut, I am in a hurry, and wish you to stick to your text. What happened next?"

Oh Lordy, George, I'se fear'd I cant tell you all this time. I haint cum tu thar speeches, what they made, ur thar fitin, ur the onspeakable time they hed in a big stone house on the hill,[11] or how they wer made tu separate thar sefs, and my big skeer hit wer ONE: I'm associately durn'd an separately dam ef hit warnt. But es you's allers in a hurry, jist you mind, I lef off talkin about em in the *mornin* while they wer a rackin roun the streets afore they tuck persession ove the big stone house ontu the hill, what

10. A well sweep: a long pole, pivoted on top of a post, used with a bucket attached to the end for raising water.

11. The Tennessee state capitol building, constructed of a stratified limestone, was completed on March 19, 1859, but had been occupied since 1853. It is located on a commanding hill in the center of Nashville. *Nashville City and Business Directory for 1860–61,* pp. 32–38.

hes a big rock lantren a top ove hit,[12] an I'll tell you all ove hit on Monday. About that 'ar quarter you loaned me tuther day: Clapshaw only tuck hit es a pistareen,[13] an Jake Doyle owes me half a dollar. Now give me change for hit, an he may give hit tu you soon. "How much change, Sut?" Oh, another quarter'l do ef hit has a Eagle ontu hit. Mine what I told you tother day; don't tell what I've been talkin about whar thar am any pet coons ur simmon trees in the yard. Don't you get me intu any scrape. I dus all that sorter work fur my sef. An mine, most ove all, every dam oncircumsized, onmitigated, stinkin, stealin varmint on yearth am in love-feas agin the humans, an ef I *aint* one you *am*. Good bye little hoss.

"Now isn't hit a pity sich a purty gall es I, shall go away to Georgy to ketch cold an die. Stay away, stay away, I tell you galls stay away." [14]

12. A tower that rises above the center of the capitol building is topped by a lantern, the entire structure being modeled after the "Lantern of Demosthenes" (or the "Choraqic Monument of Lysicrates") erected in Athens about 335 B.C. *Ibid*, p. 36.

13. A small Spanish coin, the old *peseta*.

14. Presumably, the refrain from a popular song or ballad sung by Sut as he departs.

SUT LOVINGOOD'S LOVE FEAST
OVE VARMINTS, IV

I JIS' wish, George, I may never see a still house agin this side ove the bone yard, ef I haint a bigger fool nor ever. Ise a losin my varmint sense: I never hed much other kind tu brag ove; an I prided myself on my varmint noledge, caze hit actuated my laigs an ontu 'em I puts all my trust. My human sense never did me any good, as I knows on; while hit often got me inter the durndest wust sort ove scrapes. I allers know'd an acnoledged mysef a natral born durn'd fool, as humans look at hit; but the sense I got through the streak ove varmint what's intu me never failed me ontil now, an I sorter wishes fur a test. A test tu see ef hits loss effects the moshun an instincks ove these yere laigs, an ef hit dus you'll never see Sut agin, es Sut. Ef you sees enything ove me at all hit'll be my cackus, my bones, ur a pile ove dirt atop ove me; fur dam ef I stays wun day above the grown without I'se sure ef these yere laigs es they wer when they toted me beyant ole Burn's fox houns; [1] for es I hes often tole you, theyre my only pendence fur life. Take my laigs, an hits wus nor taking my gall ur my puss.

"What has got this foolish notion in your head, Sut?"

Why, the strange ways at the promiscus love feas the varmints hilt, what I wer a tellin ove you about; the way the wolf changed nater with the musrat—hearin a possum talk like ontu a coon, an the coon act human on all fours; ur a ole grown hog put on the ways ove a fox, an the fox in turn act owl, an then the owl act eagle, an all ove em assemblin ove thar sefs fur wun purpos, VITTILS. I've thought onter hit an thought onter hit until I aint sure I'd know a king fisher from a washwoman's indigo rag. [2] Thar ways an thar talk an thar purpos hev run me ni

This story appeared in Nashville *Union and American*, XXIX (May 3, 1859), 1.

1. The text of this story is not extant. It is also mentioned in "Sut Lovingood at Bull's Gap," paragraph four.

2. A cheap cotton cloth dyed with indigo.

ontu crazy. I never hearn tell ove sich contradictions afore, not even amung a gang ove galls at a frolic. But I'll tell you all ove hit, an es you hes sum humen sense you may splain hit an make my mind easy, ef I dont I jis will look forard tu sum calamity tu cum ontu this range, wus nor colery [3] an a scasity ove whisky, ur a loss ove the use ove laigs. Oh, I'm durnd ef hit haint a orful prospec when the varmints ove opposite naters plot together agin the humans, and the only hope I sees is they's dun so much durn stealin and rascality that they's becum cowardly; that is, ef hit work'd on em es hit dus onter humans. You knows that a mean man can't stand up squar tu a fite, and ef he dus he don't fite much to speak ove. If thar water don't change on this pint, I jis wish I may be methodically, numerically, an harmoniously dam ef thar'll be a per-datory varmint lef alive inter the corporate limits ove Tennessee by the middle ove August nex. *I'm* agwine intu *that* hunt; I takes two chances intu that ar raffle, I dus; I'se arter tails, arter hides, arter skalps, arter feathers, arter wool, arter har, arter meat, an, bad es hit is, I'se arter scent. I mean tu gin what time I ken spar frum nessesary runnin whisky, frolics, galls, an kerds tu my country, an help save vittels fur the human instead ove hevin grounhogs eat pouncake; buzzards, sassidge; an pole cats fried chicken; while humans hev carron, simmons, minners and crawfish raw. *The change wud be agin nater,* an I'll jis die fust. Ef hit cums tu that, you just put me down in the nex census es among the starved, an ef you thinks me wuth hit, jist write fur my gravestone, "he died fur the cause ove the humans agin a dam partnership ove the per-datory kind ove varmints ginerally, *an fell monsous late in the fite.*"

But my feelings hev kerried me away. I'se been runnin on an must git back to whar I left my norashun of thar doins jurin the time ove thar love feas, an a hell ove a love feas hit wer, if you take stink an growlin, an changin naters intu considerashun. Well, es I told you, they wer in the streets, roads and trails ove the town jurin ove the mornin, a stickin ontu everything an a peepin outen the holes. Now, thar wer a man, a sorter squire, or general, ur presidin elder, I dono which, amung the humans.[4]

3. Cholera.

4. This is the incumbent Democratic governor Isham G. Harris (1818–1897), a popular, respected, and capable leader, who later served as Tennessee's war governor until the Federal occupation of Nashville. *Dic-*

He stays most of his time in a corner room in the big rock hous,[5] I wer speakin ove. He's sorter scace ove har on top ove his scull,[6] but I be regularly an riteously durned ef he's scase ove sence onder hit. He's monsous quiet an kind tu see him walkin along with a black stick in his hand, but show him varmints ur let him smell em even, an you'd think he war a full pack ove houns, a shot gun, hoss an horn. He jist sends em tu glory, an don't stop tu save scalps; spose he had dun so, why, the tellegraf wire frum Bristol [7] tu Nashville woudent a hilt em, ef a man wer at every post tu pack em agin wun anuther. He never stops tu learn ef hit's a coon actin possum, ur a pole-cat actin mink. He knows the general inemys ove the humans afore he sees em by the trail, an when he ketches up he jist ainds that critter's stealin an hunts fur more. I loves that feller, an ef I warn't feard ove him I'd ax him fur sum lessons on humanity.

The instink ove beastes am ove sum use tu them, eny how, ef hit ain't tu me, fur I could tell when he wer a comin afore I seed him by thar moshuns. Did you ever see a passel ove wimmin an children gittin outen the way ove a runaway hoss? Did you ever see a monkey a gittin intu his cage when a big dog cum intu the ring, a bustin open the pint ove his tail, a snappin ove hit agin the bars in his hurry, an then a suckin hit arter he got in, an a cussin in monkey tung? Did you ever see a cat take a apple-tree es the boys cum home frum school, an the swellin all settle in the tail? Did you ever see a tribe ove turkles drown'd tharsefs offen a log es a steam boat cum by? Did you ever see little chickens run onder the ole hen when she says k e r r r, turnin her eye up tu the sky? Did you ever see a hoss thief about fifty steps ahead ove

tionary of American Biography, VIII, 310–311; William B. Bates, "Life and Character of Isham G. Harris," in *Tennessee Old and New,* II, 212–222.

5. The governor's office was located on the first floor of the capitol building. *Nashville City and Business Directory for 1860–61,* p. 35.

6. As contemporary portraits indicate, Isham G. Harris was prematurely bald. Also, note Parson W. G. Brownlow's vituperative description of him in 1865: "His complexion is sallow. His eyes are dark and penetrating—a perfect index to the heart of a traitor—with the scowl and frown of a demon resting upon his brow. His study of mischief and the practice of crime have brought upon him premature baldness and a gray beard." Cited in Kenneth McKellar, *Tennessee Senators,* p. 393.

7. A city in Sullivan county, northeast Tennessee, on the Tennessee-Virginia line, contiguous with Bristol, Virginia.

the perlice an a jail in site? Did you ever see a ole fox ni ontu his hole an the houns nigher ontu him? Did you ever see a chalk-eyed nigger jis as he seed the fus false face at a shuckin whar he'd been told not tu go tu? An wus nor all, did you ever see me jist arter I'd shouldered the biggest skeer ove my life? Ef you hain't seed all ove these, you can't begin to onderstand the ack-shuns ove the varmints on site ove this man. All sham were laid aside an the natral instink prevailed. The coons racked up the water spouts and posts, the possums sham'd dead in their tracks, the buzzards soar'd alof, the owls tuck chimley tops, the rats run onder lumber piles an packin boxes, the foxes aimed fur open ground, the ground-hogs loved cellars, muskrats tuck the Cum-berland in thar stride, the bugs drapped in the people's pockets, while the bats hid ahind the window blinds, an the wolves an wile boars tried good honest runnin down Water street.[8] They must hav holes ur dens in that range. I never seed a man hev a clearer path in a crowd than they gin him. Es ole Buck reigns,[9] they hes a holesume an a reddy fear ove him. I tells you, varmint sence am good ef applied in time. Hit's jist so. They knows his gifts an they'll live tu know em better. Arter he went intu the tavrin they begin tu accumulate agin, all thar noses pintin tu the rock hous what he'd lef. They thickened es they got nigher, an by the time they clomb the steps hit looked sorter like a sea ove har, fur an feathers, sprinkled with years an tails. They jist over run the hous, a peepin intu all the rooms what wer open, an a smellin ove every thing like it wer strange. There were wun room locked up tite. Hit sed over the door that the men what kep the money staid thar.[10] This door exersized em monsously. They all zamined hit clos. They'd stick thar smellers clost inter the corner ove the crack at the bottom, and draw in a long sniff ove wind, an then blow hit out agin at the hind end ove thar moufs, while the ballance wer four deep atop ove the smellin wuns, with thar hed ained turned down, a tryin tu get thar turn at a sniff, jist as pigs dig tu get hold of a teat. The idear seemed tu be that they smelt vittils thar stronger nor any place they'd been at fur say ni ontur a durn'd long time. Thar war anuther room whar a bureau ur a

8. Water Street, now First Avenue, ran parallel with and adjacent to the Cumberland River in Nashville.

9. James Buchanan was serving as President of the United States.

10. The state Treasury was located on the first floor of the capitol building. *Nashville City and Business Directory for 1860–61*, p. 35.

side board ur a *secretary* staid,[11] I dono which, an when they were a zaminin ove hit a owl sed "this am the place whar a fox got fat onst an hed tu skatter his self in furrin ports tu keep his hide outside his cakus. He et durn'd ni all the vittils tho afore he run." [12] A big, rusty wolf got mad, and sed in ansur: "That am a dam imprudent remark to make jist at this time cummin es hit dus frum a varmint what am looked on es powerful wise."

The words wer scasely outen his mouf when a big sortment ove varmints, ni ontu thirty, went squar at the owl, moufs open an tails up. But ef he can't see good he know'd the safe road tu travel, so he flew up an struck agin the stem ove a big brass ten barreled candlestick, what wer a hangin frum the loft, an only left ahind in the ar a few mouffuls ove feathers. They forgiv him arter a ole coon told him ef ever he toch that subjec agin jurin that ar love feas, dam if they didn't gin him a free ticket tu kingdom cum by the fust train, an they ment tu see that he got aboard. An the owl sed he woudent, an he shot an opened his eyes monsous nowin, an wiped his bill ontu the brass work like he'd et sumthing dirty.[13]

11. The Secretary of State's office was also on the first floor. *Ibid.*

12. On May 23, 1858, the Nashville *Union and American* reported that an investigative committee appointed by the Tennessee Legislature had discovered a defalcation of more than $30,000 on the part of Whig F. N. W. Burton, then Secretary of State. At the same time $123,000 worth of bonds disappeared. Burton addressed a letter to the newspaper on May 27 in which he defended himself, wrote a letter of resignation to Governor Harris on May 28 purportedly so as to have time to "vindicate" himself, and by June 10 was declared a "fugitive from justice." Nashville *Union and American*, XXIX (May 23, 1858), 2; (May 28, 1858), 3; (May 29, 1858), 2; (June 10, 1858), 2.

13. There may be an indirect reference contained in this incident to something noticed by the *Union and American:*

"Another amusing circumstance [at the convention] was their much talk about the heavy appropriations and expenditures of the government for some years past. This they did in the presence of Mr. BELL and *without a blush;* careless of the feelings of the old gentleman, and seemingly ignorant of the fact that every appropriation denominated extravagant, passed with his vote and his approval. It may have been fun to them but could not have been fun to him. This was evidenced when it came his time to speak. He said it was not the *amount* of public expenditure, so much, that was to be complained of. One hundred millions he thought might be expended 'economically.' . . . It was the *corrupt use* of the public money by the President which Mr. Bell thought ought to be harped upon; not the *amount* expended, which he had himself approved by his votes. It

Well, they went up stars intu a big room,[14] an jist fill'd hit with stink an tails, and then cummenced a regular pow wow. The long ole possum what went so strong ontu the simmon question, he tuck ontu hissef the highest seat he could find an thar he staid. A sorter musrat lookin varmint got ontu his hine laigs an let his fore wuns hang strate down, an arter workin ove his whiskers up an down a few times sot intu talkin (mine, George, I only norates what wer sed by the most forard ove em, an I may be rong es tu who talked fust). He sed "his sperience show'd him that ef they ment tu *win* they must be able tu change thar appertites an shape cordin tu the range they wer in. He acted human, even, once, and when they tuck tu rasin simmons in his beat then he turn'd possum, an so on, an he thot they all could make thar sefs at home cordin tu the range whar thar lots war cast." He'd been beatin about in Montgomery county,[15] an his talk tuck monsous well, fur they made him a front varmint in the nex sarch fur vittils jist at once. I seed frum this that they didn't mean tu stand ontu thar personel apertites at all, but jist aim to get vittils *es vittils;* an tu do this, they norated thar oppersition tu humans. Now who ever hearn tell ove sich dam stuff, like every fool didn't know from his cradle that all per-datory varmints hev been in oppersition tu humans sence Adam was a baby, and allers will be? They mout a lef that out. Jis so long es thar am dogs, shot guns, traps, an snars, hit's natural tu suppose they'll be oppersition.

Well, I'll tell you the ballance at Tom Taylor's. You'll be thar, wont you? I speck tu ketch one or two of em afore then. Would you save skalps ur not? Hits a heap ove trouble, and durn'd little profit. I believe I'll jist aind thar stealin an let em lie.

---

was a shrewd suggestion. It remains to be seen whether his less discreet followers will take the cue. Mr. BELL well knew that the Democracy would explain to the people that Congress alone held the purse strings and not the President. . . ." Nashville *Union and American,* XXIX (March 31, 1859), 2.

14. The Hall of the House of Representatives, located on the second floor of the capitol building. *Nashville City and Business Directory for 1860–61,* p. 35.

15. In the northern part of Tennessee. Previous to the convention, delegates had made speeches at county meetings to revive the cause of Americanism and Know-Nothingism. Sister Mary de Lourdes Gohmann, *Political Nativism in Tennessee to 1860,* p. 153.

SUT LOVINGOOD TRAVELS WITH
OLD ABE AS HIS CONFIDENTIAL
FRIEND AND ADVISOR

W HEN I tole you, GEORGE, that I wer agwine tu travel
with ole ABE LINK-HORN, you thought I wer a lyin', but
now ye see I'm here, aint I? I jist struck across the country and
kotch'd up with him at Harrisburg, (durn sich a place, I say,)
and I hev stuck clost to the ole Windin Blades till I got him safe
intu this heer tavrin, they calls hit "WILLARD'S," an I'm durn

This story appeared in Nashville *Union and American*, XXV (February
28, 1861), 2. The editorial column contained the following comment:
"We publish this morning a short hand report of a recent conversation
between our old Friend SUT LOVINGOOD and his little friend George.
Having more confidence in MR. LINCOLN than we have in MR. HAMLIN,
we were exceedingly anxious that he should arrive safely in Washington.
Hence, no sooner had we heard of the probabilities of danger in Baltimore,
than we, knowing SUT'S facility for taking short cuts, loaned him our
military cloak, and Tartan plaid, put a quart in his pocket and a half pint
under his skin and told him to put MR. LINCOLN straight through to
Washington. Of his success, let our readers judge for themselves."
Earlier in the month, President-elect Lincoln had begun his trip to
Washington to take the oath of office, making speeches and participating
in ceremonies along the way. Before reaching Harrisburg, Pennsylvania,
he received a warning on February 22 that an assassination plot was
suspected in Baltimore, and on the advice of his friends, Lincoln made a
secret night journey through the city, accompanied only by his personal
bodyguard Ward Hill Lamon, and arrived in Washington at 6 a.m. on
February 23. For a full account, see John G. Nicolay and John Hay,
Abraham Lincoln, A History (New York, 1890) III, 302–316. Lamon's
report of the event is included in Paul M. Angle, ed., *The Lincoln Reader*
(New Brunswick, 1947), pp. 311–316. In his *Abraham Lincoln, A Biography* (New York, 1952), p. 244, Benjamin F. Thomas comments, "As soon
as the manner of Lincoln's entrance into the capitol became known,
ridicule was added to the hatred being vented by the hostile press. The
story of an irresponsible reporter, describing Lincoln as entering Washington disguised in a Scotch plaid cap and long military cloak, was circulated
country-wide. Lincoln's enemies guffawed and derided his cowardice. Cartoonists caricatured him. Lincoln himself was not proud of the incident.
Had his friends not persuaded him that his welfare and that of the country
were inseparable, he would probably have come through Baltimore accord-

ef the ole hoss ove the house aint a jedge ove liker.[1] I've tasted hit, I has, an I'll tell ye anuther thing, old Windin Blades am sleepin in the same rum what I dreamed ove in one thousand eight hundred an fifty-six, whar Ole BUCK played that orful game of kerds with FILL an FREEMOUNT fur the President's cheer,[2] an won hit, too, an he prides hisself in sittin in hit more by a durnd site nor them dus what set him thar.[3]

But es I wer agwine tu tell you, es I wer a gittin thru Bald-timore I seed a feller a sittin ontu a barrel a filin at the lock ove a durned ole revoltin pistil.[4] Sez I, "Mister, are ye gwine tu war?" "Yes," sez he, "I'm gwine tu bore ole ABE'S years fur him es he cums along."

I went a piece furder an seed another fat ole tub a cuttin a cheese with a nife a foot long. "That's a monsous nife, Mister," sez I. "Y-a-w," sez he, "I means tu feel ole ABE'S haslet with hit," sez he.

I rocked along, an seed another feller a rubbin brite a orful cannon; hit wer es big es a pump log.[5] "Gwine tu shute," sez I? "Not jist yet," sez he, a measurin my hite an heft with his eye. "When are ye gwine tu shute, ef I moute be so bold?" "Day arter tu-morrow," sez he. "I'm jist gwine tu take ole ABE in the place what fust tetches a hoss, an dam ef he don't lite beyant Washin-tun, hit 'il be that this yere powder aint good," an he dipped up a tin cup full outen a barrell an poured hit back like hit wer whisky. Jist about this time the ideur got onder my har that Bald-timore warn't much tu speak ove, fur ole Windin Blades, and that they ment tu hev a funeral outen him when he got thar. So I put out tu meet him an tell ove the imedjut rath tu cum, an the orful tribulashun barrelled up fur his widder an that

---

ing to plan." These were the circumstances that inspired Harris to send Sut along on "Lincoln's secret night journey."

1. Upon arrival in Washington after his secret journey, Lincoln was conducted to Willard's Hotel. Nicolay and Hay, p. 315.

2. See "Playing Old Sledge for the Presidency—Dream of Sut Lovingood's."

3. In the original text this entire piece was printed as one paragraph; the second installment appeared as two paragraphs, the third three. For the sake of readability, the present editor has adopted the paragraphing of Edd Winfield Parks in his edition of *Sut Lovingood Travels with Old Abe Lincoln*, which contains all three parts.

4. Revolving pistol, earlier name for a revolver.

5. A hollowed log used as a water pipe.

promisin sun, Bob,[6] ove his'n. Now, GEORGE, Bob may make a monsous fine man, I don't say he *won't;* but es a boy—mind, I say *es a boy*—I'm d--d ef I fancy him a bit. Sum feller will turn him inside out sum of these days, see ef he dont; an who knows but hit would improve the little critter. He can't live es he is, that's surtain.

Well, when I told old Windin Blades what I had seed an hearn, his eyes sorter bulged and sorter spread, an his mouf swelled out, an sez he, "I hain't prepared tu die, SUTTY, my Sun"—he calls me SUTTY when he wants help, and Mister LOVINGOOD when he's got his dignity on, an a passel of flat backs [7] roun him an he feels good an safe—"I hes dun the things I hadn't orter, an lef ondun the things I had orter," an here he hung down his hed an studied a long time, while I sot still and tuk a gineral observation ove a President, an if he aint a long wun an a narrow wun, I'm durned. His mouf, his paw, an his footzes am the principil feeters, an his strikin pint is the way them ar laigs ove hizen gets inter his body. They goes in at each aidge sorter like the prongs goes intu a pitch fork. Ove all the durned skeery lookin ole cusses fur a president ever I seed, he am decidedly the durndest. He looks like a yaller ladder with half the rungs knocked out.

I kotch a ole bull frog once an druv a nail thru his lips inter a post, tied two rocks tu his hine toes and stuck a darnin needil inter his tail tu let out the misture, an lef him there tu dry. I seed him two weeks arter wurds, an when I seed ole ABE I thot hit were an orful retribution cum ontu me, an that hit were the same frog, only stretched a little longer, an had tuck tu warin ove close tu keep me from knowin him; an ketchin him an nailin him up again, an natral born durn'd fool es I is, I swar I seed the same watry, skeery look in the eyes, an the same sorter knots on the "back-bone." I'm feard, GEORGE, sumthin's tu cum ove my nailin up that ar frog, I swar I am; ever since I seed ole ABE, same shape, same color, same feel, (cold as ice) an I'm d--d ef hit aint the same smell.[8] Sumthin orful es tu happen tu me in spite

6. Robert Todd Lincoln (1843–1926), then a student at Harvard.
7. Slang for bed bugs.
8. The above description of Lincoln, beginning with "His mouf, his paw, an his footzes," was reprinted in the Montgomery (Alabama) *Weekly Post,* I (March 27, 1861), 1, under the title "Photograph of Lincoln, By Sut Lovingood," with the following introductory comment: "Read and laugh,

ove these yere laigs, much as I 'pends on 'em, see ef hit don't.

Well, arter he hed studied an sighed, an sorter groaned, a long time, he ris his head up an sez he, "SUTTY, what had I best do in this orful emergincy? The party can't spare me now; besides I ain't fit tu die, an my wiskers hev just begin tu grow an I want tu try the vittils in Washintun City; hit won't du tu let me be made a sifter by these seseshun bullits just at this time. Will it SUTTY, my son?"

Sez I, "Mister LINKHORN, Ise called a natral born durn'd fool in Tennessee, but I think I ken averidge in these parts purty well, an ef you will jist put yesef onder my keer; an ef ole SCOTT [9] cums a cluckin about with his wings a trailin, or ole SEA-WARD [10] cums a whinin an a smellin an a scrachin onder the door, jist gin the tavrin keeper the hint to hist thur cotails with his boot, an that you'l pay fur toein one of em ef he busts em. I'l be constitutionally, sirkumstantially, an indiscriminately durned, ef I don't put you safe tu bed with Missis LINKHORN at Willard's Tavrin. I'l *du* hit; d'ye see these yere laigs?"; an I hilt one straite out abuv the lamp what sot ontu the tabil.

He looked at me mournfuly fur a minit, an his eyes run over, and sez he, "SUTTY, my son, I'l du hit, an ole ABE won't lie, so gin yer orders an fix things; now I feel like I will be President yit"; an he pulled out a pint bottel frum onder the piller ove the bed, an he measured hit with his thumbs, one over the other from the bottom tu the top ove the whisky, an thar wer jist seven thumbs; he then mesured back four an hilt the last thumb fast an run the neck ove the bottel in onder his nose about four inches, when he turned hit up agin thar wer a half inch clar day lite onder the thumb, an he sot hit ontu the table. When he cotch

---

and laugh and read—read it again and laugh deeper. It will be sure to shake you up and make you fatter."

9. Lieutenant-General Winfield Scott (1786–1866), the professional soldier and Virginian who remained loyal to the Union during the Civil War, later personally commanded Lincoln's bodyguard during his inauguration and set up defenses for the city of Washington when war erupted. There is a story recorded that Harris as a steamboat captain once encountered Scott and refused to submit to his authority; see Donald Day, "The Life of George W. Harris," *Tennessee Historical Quarterly*, VI (March, 1947), 8–9.

10. William Henry Seward (1801–1872) was appointed Secretary of State by Lincoln on December 28, 1860.

his breff, says he, "I never incourages eny wun tu drink,[11] but thar's the bottel an *hit hes your whisky in hit.*" I tuck abourd the ballance, I did, an we went tu bed. Now how I got him tu Washintun Il tell you the next time we meet. Good bye. Say George, ye never seed old ABE, did ye? Well youve missed a site, nur BOB?—No. Nur the ole oman? No. Well, Ise sorry fur you, fur you aint yet ready tu die.

11. Lincoln abstained from liquor. When asked once if he belonged to the Temperance Society, he is reported to have replied, "No, I am not a member of any temperance society; but I am temperate, *in this,* that I don't drink anything." Cited in Angle, p. 204.

SUT LOVINGOOD
WITH OLD ABE ON HIS JOURNEY

WELL, es I told you, we went tu bed arter that onekally divided horn, an I sot in tu sleepin in yurnest, when I hearn "kerdiff, kerdiff" [1]—an thar stood the old par ove Windin Blades, jis as he cum inter the world, his shut hung on top ove the bed postez, an he had his red flannin drawers in his hand by the laigs, a thrashin ove em agin the wash stan; then he peeped down wun laig and then down tother; then he turned em inside out, an zamined onder the seams from aind to aind.

Sez I, "Whats rong? Ar you huntin fur a seseshunist in as narrer a place as them ar drawer laigs?"

He shook his hed, an still zamined the seams. At last sez he, "SUTTY, my sun, are you troubled *much* with flees down South?"

"Not es I no's ove; our dogs are sumtimes," sez I, "an we allers kicks em out when they scratches."

"Well," sez he, "I've allers had more ur less vexashun ove spirit with em, and the nier I gets tu Washintun city, the wus they ar; ef thar number an enterprize encreases es they hev dun, afore I am thar a week, I'll be a dead man," an then he reached down both hands and scratched both laigs, frum his ankles up to his short ribs, an hit sounded like rakin' ove a dry hide with a curry comb, an then he cum tu bed agin, but kep on a rakin' ove hissef an sorter a cussin onder his breff.

Sez I, "holler up a nigger an git sum more tangle-laig."

"What's tangle-laig, SUTTY?"

"Sum truck like what you hed in that ar lonesome lookin feller a standin on the tabil *by hissef*."

"Do *you* want sum more?" sez he.

"I dus that, onless you'l go tu sleep."

This story appeared in Nashville *Union and American*, XXV (March 2, 1861), 2.

1. An onomatopoeic formation, akin to "kerplunk," or "kersplash," etc., conveying the idea of impact or sound.

He got up an drug a ole har trunk from onder the bed. When he turned back the led, thar the bottils stood jis like sogers ove a muster day ur a Doctur's Medicin chist. We divided wun tolerable far atwixt us an wur a fixin fur sleep an a talkin ove fleas an how I would git him safe tu Washintun, when a thunderin knockin cum ontu the door. Ole Windin Blades jumped outen bed an agin the lock at one pop an keerfully opened the door, a holdin tu the handil with boff hands. Ater he seed an knowd em, he opened, when in popped two fellers in store close an a Sorrel irish-mun with flax mane an tail, an he hed a letter.[2] Old ABE sot up cross laiged in a cheer in his shirt-ail an read hit a long time, fust wun side up an then tuther, an ater talkin an whisperin a spell they left.

Sez he, "SUTTY, my sun, this ar a dis-patch from Gineral SCOTT, an hit proves what you sed about Bald-timore tu be true, an a tarnal site wus. He sez that ALEK STEVENS[3] am thar with a twelve-pounder strapped ontu his back an a lit rich pine torch in his hand awaitin fur me, an that hit is loaded with a quart ove escopet[4] (old SCOTT calls everything escopet that's round) balls, three smoothin irons, four par ove butt hinges, an a gross ove shoe tacks, an the ole Gineral thinks frum his nolidge ove perjectils that ef it wer turned loose ontu me that my hide would be es well opened out es a fish net, an my close made redy tu stop cracks in a rain barril."

I jumped plumb outen bed an lit afore him an looked him stedy in the eye fur a minit, an I felt that I wer a standin fur the fust time afore a man I warnt feared ove, an hu I knowd wer

2. On February 21, 1861, a federal detective sent a report to General Winfield Scott in Washington of the plot to assassinate Lincoln in Baltimore. Scott passed it on to William H. Seward, the new Secretary of State, who immediately dispatched his son, Frederick W. Seward, to Harrisburg to deliver the correspondence to Lincoln personally. It was this information received independently of the earlier report that convinced Lincoln's advisors of the credibility to the plot. John G. Nicolay and John Hay, *Abraham Lincoln, A History*, III, 311–313. Why Sut portrays the young Seward as an Irishman is not clear. The "two fellers in store close" perhaps are meant to represent two members of Pinkerton's Detective Agency, who were also instrumental in uncovering the plot.

3. Alexander Hamilton Stephens (1812–1883), Democratic congressman, had been elected Vice-President of the Confederacy on February 9, 1861, after the Georgia convention had adopted the ordinance of secession. Richard B. Morris, ed., *Encyclopedia of American History*, pp. 782–783.

4. A short rifle or musket.

scaser ove sence then I wer, an I wer glad I had found him, fur you know George that I thot I wer the king fool ove the world, an allers felt shamed an onder cow about hit. A-l-e-c-k S-t-e-p-h-e-n-s t-o-t-i-n a t-w-e-l-v-e p-o-u-n-d-e-r. I stood stonished, fust et him an them et old Scott, two bigger fools in the world than me, an boff on em able tu read an rite an a holdin high places in the naseun. SUT'S got a chance yet, thinks I.

Sez I, "Mister LINK-HORN (an I wer skeered at the boldness ove my own voice) du you onderstand southern law?"

"No," sez he, "only es hit tetches niggers."

"Well," sez I, "I'll tell ye sum; nolidge ove hit hes saved my life for the last twenty years, twiest a year an hit may save yourn once a month ef ever ye cum out thar, not tu speak of hits imedjut use in this imargincy. When we lects our Governers we lects a fool-killer [5] fur every county, an furnishes him with a gun, sum asnic, stricknine an a big steel trap, an hit is his juty to travel, say about wun day ahine the Suckit Rider. You see the Suckit Rider gethers the people together an hit makes hit more convenient, an he kills off the stock ove fools tu a considerabil extent every round he takes. Our fool-killers hev dun thar juty, an consekently the South hev seceded. Ise been a dodgen em sence I wer able tu run, and I now tell you, Mister LINK-HORN—"

"Stop, stop SUTTY, my son," sez he, "I wants tu ax you a questun; why don't you stop the breed in a more humane way by emaxulation [6] an still let em live? The decleration ove independence you no sez—"

"Stop," sez I, fur I found I wer on risin groun, "An I'l tell yu why emaxulashen wont kiver the case, no more nor freein or stealin a nigger il make him a white man. Fools break out like measils. They cums from the best familys. An agin, a neighborhood ove fools will sumtimes breed a smart fellow. Just look at SEA-WARD [7] as a sampil, or yerself. Yu cum from Kaintuck. An hit perjused HART,[8] a feller hu makes people outen stone, till they kin du every thing but drink, talk an propugate thar

5. Harris's use of this mythological figure is discussed in note 3 to "Sut Lovingood Come to Life."

6. Emasculation, with a hint at the word "emancipation."

7. William H. Seward.

8. Joel Tanner Hart (1810–1872), born near Winchester, Kentucky, was an American sculptor noted for his busts of Andrew Jackson and Henry Clay.

speeches; an caze they can't du that he's an inmitigated durned
fool for makin em stead ove rale livin folks. Spose the fool killer
wer tu kill (as in juty bound he orter) every 'bolitionist now
livin, woudent the same sile, an climit, an feedin what perjused
the d——d ole cusses what burnt ole, palsied wimmen as
witches; [9] an perjused JO SMITH,[10] an ole MILLER,[11] en Miss
FOX,[12] an WENDIL PHILLIPS,[13] an Misses BLOOMER,[14] with
her breeches an shut, nex year perjuse just such another crop,
say? Ove course hit would, an yet the rich strekes in that ar
country ove cod fish an mullen stalks, perjuced a HANCOCK [15]
an the *Day Book*,[16] so emaxulashen wont du; yu must kill em jist
es yu ketch em, es yu du your fleas, an rely (es I dus on my laigs)
on hard work in follerin arter em frum generashun tu generashun. They onderstand this ere thing in Texas adzactly; give em
a black jack an a pece ove bed cord, an that ar all they ax.''

He studied a long time an scrached, an sez he, "SUTTY,
atween the flees an your talkin, Ise sorty got tu wool getherin; I
swar I hes; when I stopt you tu ax that ar questin, what wer you
gwine tu say about the fool killer in connecshun with my case?''

"Oh, nuthin,'' sez I. "Do you ever speck tu cum down souf
mister Linkhorn?''

"No SIR,'' sez he.

9. A reference to the Salem witchcraft trials of 1692.

10. Joseph Smith (1805–1849), founder of the Church of Jesus Christ
of Latter-day Saints (Mormon), was born in Sharon, Vermont.

11. William Miller (1782–1849), founder of the Adventist church, was
born in Pittsfield, Massachusetts.

12. Margaret Fox (1833–1893) and her sister Kate were mediums who
purportedly heard spirit rappings and inspired a strong movement in
spiritualism in New York during the height of their career. They later
revealed the sounds were artificially produced. See Harry Houdini's exposé,
A Magician Among the Spirits (1924).

13. Wendell Phillips (1811–1884), fanatical abolitionist and reformer,
was born in Boston, Massachusetts.

14. Mrs. Amelia Jenks Bloomer (1818–1894), born in Homer, New
York, advocated around 1850 a costume for women consisting of a short
skirt and loose trousers buttoned around the ankles; these became known
as "bloomers.''

15. Presumably John Hancock (1737–1793), signer of the Declaration
of Independence and native of Braintree (now Quincy), Massachusetts.

16. The daily and weekly *Day Book*, established in New York in 1849
by N. R. Stimson, was one of the chief Northern journals in sympathy
with the Confederacy. It was excluded from the mails for fifteen months
from October 1861 but was revived for a short while in 1863. Frank Luther
Mott, *A History of American Magazines 1850–1865*, p. 154.

"Well, then, hit dont signify," sez I, an we sot in tu plannin how tu get thru Bald-timore, an save his hide hole, an hit were done, an done well, tu, ef not wisely. Me, an ETHREDGE,[17] an ole John,[18] am the only fellers from the souf, what am in the raffle at all. Nex time I see you, George, Il tell you how we eucherd [19] all Bald-timore.

17. Emerson Etheridge (1819–1902), Whig Congressman from Tennessee.

18. Presumably John Bell (1796–1869) of Tennessee, Constitutional Union candidate against Lincoln for the Presidency in 1860.

19. Outwitted.

SUT LOVINGOOD
LANDS OLD ABE SAFE AT LAST

ARTER the flees an the tanglelaig an my talk about the juty ove the fool-killer an hits effecks, we couldn't sleep any more, so we konkluded tu start on the fust train. I hed told a tayleur man—with a white face, a big foot turned out, a long measurin string, an a piece ove chalk—yearly in the nite, tu measure a terbacker hogshead fur the body, an a par ove telegraph poles fur the laigs, an make a jackit an a par ove britches, outen cross-barred truck, an to let them bars run cati-cornered, that is, one what started on the shoulder should aind among the ribs on tother side; an bring along a pot ove red paint, an a small bale ove hay. Well, he did hit. An I run the ole Windin' Blades inter the breeches, an tied a string roun the ankles; then stuffed in a mixtry ove hay an the contents ove the har trunk; I did likewise with the jackit, an perjuced the biggest cross-barred man you ever seed; tu judge by site, he weighed seven hundred pounds, an his hed didn't look bigger nur a apple. I painted the yaller off his face with the red truck, an hit tuck three coats to kiver hit; an I swar, when I wer dun with him he looked like he'd been on a big drunk fur three weeks. When we got outer the train the tavrin keeper didn't know him, an he got off without payin ove his bill; he winked et me es the kers started, an sez he, "thar am two dullars saved, sartin." He hes muney sence, ef he haint eny uther kind.

We hadnt gone fur, when a littil, mild, husband lookin feller in gole specks an a pencil, cum up to me an sez he, "whars yer agent?" Sez I, "what agent?" "The agent fur yer show." I tuck the hint, and sez I, "Ise the agent." "Ah," sez he, "I thought you were the long half ove the show." "So I is; an Ise the smart half too, an am celebrated fur the use of these yere laigs," an I onfolded one an reached hit thru the winder on tuther side ove the ker; sez I, "aint that some laig fur reachin?"

This story appeared in Nashville *Union and American*, XXV (March 5, 1861), 3.

He run his eye twist along hit frum aind to aind, an sez he, "Mister, you hes run powerfully to laigs, didn't a tellergraff pole fall across yer mom afore you wus bornd?" "No," sez I; "but we kep a pet sand hill crane, an mom an him hed a differculty, an he chased her onder the bed."

He sot that down with his pencil, an then he tuck a measurin sorter look et ole Abe, who tended tu be sleep. Sez he shakin his hed, "that am a monsous man, I mout say an orful man. What dus he weigh?" "Seven hundred an ninety even." He sot that down. "Hes he a family?" "Yes, he had thirty-four children, but a sorter diseas hes tuck off seven ove em, an he's spectin more tu die every day." "The ole man mus be in powful trubbil?" sez he. "Not much," sez I; "he don't onderstand his loss." "Is he smart tu speak ove?" "Nun tu hurt," sez I; he sot that down an started.

Ole ABE opened his eyes an reached over an whispered in my year atwixt his sot teeth, "that ar las observashun ove yourn, Mr. LOVINGOOD, am a durn lie," an he straitened up an hunted amung the straw onder his close, till he foun wun ove the bottils, an he gin his sef sum comfort, an never offered me a durn mossel, but hilt the bottil up tu the lite, an sez he, "on thinkin over hit you wer right tu tell him that I warn't smart, ur I woudent be here in sich imedjut danger, jis fur my party an a pack ove durned niggers," an he sot in tu thinkin an I went tu sleep, an when I waked he wer a kickin my shins.

Sez he, "SUTTY, my son, we am in Bald-timore"; an sure enouff, thar wer lites along boff sides the road as far as you cud see, jis like a string ove litnin bugs; an fellers a standin about with clubs onder thar arms an a revoltin pistil fur a brest pin. I seed ole Abe had obsarved hit, an he wer skared, fur the ash culler showd thru the three coats ove red lead ontu his face, an he scrached his hed an tried tu scrach his stern thru about a foot an a half ove straw an bottils. Then he looked out the winder a minit an fotch in his hed with a jerk an a ketchin me by boff hans, sez he, "great hevings, SUTTY, es thar em an orful hell, thar em ALECK STEPHENS now with his drefull canyun."

I tuck a look an thar stud a pale Ytalian with a dubbil barrelled trumpet strapped acrost his back. Hit did glitter sorter skeery like, that am a fac. They calls hit a tombone an sez that hit makes musick.

"Now don't show yerself tu be a fool," sez I. "That feller am in a durned site more danger ove blowin out his own brains with that thing than you am. Sit still an keep yer shut on, will yer," but a big skeer wer on him all over, an I seed that nuthin but a runnin spell would help the old cowardly cuss. Well, I relyed on these yere laigs; I knowd I cud ketch him ef he did break; sez he, a tremblin all over, "SUTTY, my sun, ef ALEX. STEPHENS kills me I want you tu go tu illinois an tell em that I died in the line ove my juty, like a man orter, an mine, tell em I died game an that my las wurds wer the Declerashun ove Independence sez—," an here he tuck a squint et the Ytalian; he hed outstraped his long twisted brass horn an hed hit in his hand sorter shutin fashion, that's a fac—an durn ef he dident go outer that keer like a cat outen a cellar when a broom am follerin; the straw made a monsous swishin sorter soun es he went thru the door an I hearn the bottils a clunkin es he run—I took arter him a hollerin, "Kech him—dont hurt him; Ise a takin him tu an ass-lum; he's crazy as a bed bug but am not dangerous."

Well, a hevy sot yung feller with his shurt collor open an his briches in his boots, an a black se-gar pinted up towards his eye, jist squated ontu his all fours afore the ole durnd crazy cuss, an he flung him two summersets over him, an Windin Blades lit on his sturn an bounced an the bottils rattild agin; es I cum up the feller what throwd him sez tu me, "Be Gawd, that fat feller hes et a glass works fur supper, hesent he?" "Es like es not," sez I, "he's durnd fool enuff tu du eny thing." "I thot he hed frum the jinglin in his inards when he lit thar," sez he, an then he tuck a look et me fur a long spell; sez he, "Mister, let me gin you sum ad-vice; when you takes fatty tu the ass-lum du you stay out side the gate." Sez I, "Il du hit fur I nos you am a frien ove mine." Sez he, "is thar a tax ontu laigs wher you cum frum?" "Why?" sez I. "Caze," sez he, "ef thar am you am the poorest man in Maryland, thats all. How did the ole hay stack go crazy?" Sez I, "he et hissef outen his sences." "Be Jethero.[1] I thot so," sez he, "I no that he never went mad a thinkin." Sez I, "Mister, you am right."

An then ole Abe sot ontu his hine aind all this time either scared or hurt tu bad tu move. I went up an whispered tu him tu git up an git inter the ker, an sez I, "hit won't hurt tu gin 'em a little crazy speech often the platform; hit won't cost you much trubile tu du that, an hit will convince 'em you am addled; jist talk nateral," sez I, "that's all you hev to do."

1. A mild oath. Jethro was father of Zipporah, Moses' wife, and a priest of Midian (Exodus 18).

Well he groaned, and got ontu his all fours, and I swar jist then he minded me ove an orful elephant, called Hanibald, what I wonst seed at a sarcus,—now jist tu think ove this cross barr'd great beastes bein ole ABE, President ove the United States ove North Ameriky. I swar, natral born durn'd fool es I no's I is, I felt shamed, an sorter humbled, an I sorter felt like cuttin ove his throat an a sellin the hay tu pay fur my shame, an drink all the whisky on his carcuss tu make miself feel good agin, but I shook him up, an got him tu the kers an thar he made a sorter talk.

Bout his wiskers an puttin his foot down on the Declerashun ove Independence and so on [2]—Swish—spat—pop cum about a peck ove aigs, an they smelt powful. I jerked him inter the ker an hearn a feller holler, "we wer a savin ove em fur ole ABE to-morrer, but durn ef you aint entitled tu a few, fur being es big a fool es he is." The kers started fur Washinton an I wer glad.

"Now," sez I, "ef you'll jist keep yer mouf shet, Il git yu throu, an hit wouldnt be bad ef yu kep hit shut fur the nex four years." He sot still a while, an at last sez he, "SUTTY, my son, what becum ove ALECK STEVENS an his onyeathly canyun? Did hit go off?" "No," sez I, "but you did; you moved yerself." Sez he, "SUTTY, we orter not be hilt sponsibil, when we are onder a big skeer." "That's a fac," sez I, "an that orter be norated tu the pepil, and get em tu endorse hit, for hits all that'll save you, Mister LINKHORN, jurin yer stay es President. Jis take the persishion that you haint sponsibil while onder a skeer an hit will kiver your hole admistrashun."

"SUTTY, my son, you am great," sez he, an we trundled on, no body knowin the ole feller, an got inter the rume at WIL-LARD'S; an afore I hed time tu git the hay an bottils an cross-barred truck ofan him, I hearn a noise in the passige like the rollin ove a wheel barrer mixed up with a heavy trampin soun; I thot hit wer a Irishman a fetchin coals, when the door flew wide open, an in cum a peacock's feather, six foot long, with all the

2. In harping on Lincoln's feelings about the Declaration of Independence, Harris is satirizing an extemporaneous speech Lincoln had made on February 22 (the day of his secret night journey) while visiting Independence Hall in Philadelphia. Lincoln said, in part, "I have never had a feeling, politically, that did not spring from the sentiments embodied in the Declaration of Independence. . . . But if this country cannot be saved without giving up that principle . . . I would rather be assassinated on this spot than surrender it." John G. Nicolay and John Hay, *Abraham Lincoln, A History*, III, 299.

fuzz stripped off sept the eye at the pint, then cum a hat, shaped like ontu a funnil an kivered with gold, an then har an whiskers enuff to stuff a bed, and then more gold leaf an shiney buttons an then the forrard ainst ove a swo-rarard, with ole Marcy's [3] hed on top the handil; then a par ove boots what mout a been fire buckets footed, and then the hind aind ove that orful swo-rard, cum supported frum the floor by a wheel es big es a wash pan, to keep the scabbard from warin out a trailin on the groun an when hit all got intu the rume an wer tuck together hit proved to be Lieut. General Winfield Scott,[4] commander in chief ove all the yearth; an the whole afar, when straitened up, reached ontu the ceilin about fourteen feet, an that orful swo-rard nearly crossed the rume. Ise too dry to talk eny more now, but will tell you agin what that orful mixtry ove gold feathers, iron, noise, gass, an leather did, an how I wer skeered. Ain't a gineral an orful thing tu meet an contimplate George, perticularly when they am a struttin an a gobblin.

3. Randolph Barnes Marcy (1812–1887), distinguished professional army officer, explorer, and writer.

4. When Lincoln arrived in Washington on the morning of February 23 at 6 o'clock, he was met by Elihu B. Washburne and conducted to Willard's Hotel on Fourteenth Street. It was William Henry Seward, not Winfield Scott, who immediately rushed into Lincoln's room minutes after his arrival. Washburne's account is reprinted in Paul M. Angle, ed., *The Lincoln Reader,* pp. 316–317.

SUT LOVINGOOD COME TO LIFE

BUREAU OVE FOOL KILLING,
DESTRICK OVE SALIM, MARSATCHUTITS,
APRILE—NI ONTU THE LAS' OVE HIT.

ORFISHUL DOKEYMINT.

TU SOLOMIN SUNSTRUCK:
Onder the bed corrispondint ove the WISCOONSKIP STAIT JUNNIL.[1]

This story appeared in Nashville *Daily Union and American,* XXXIII
(May 3, 1866), 1.

1. An editorial note preceded Sut's mock epistle explaining the occasion for the piece:

"Though sorely tried by the ordeal of war, our ole-time and well-known
friend 'SUT' survived. He will be hailed by thousands who have a vivid
recollection of the grotesque humor with which he has so often greeted
them through these columns. 'SUT' has encountered a correspondent of
the Wisconsin *State Journal,* who is writing letters from the south over the
nom de plume of 'Sunstroke,' for the benefit of Senator Sumner in making
up his 'scrap speeches.' He is understood to have been a devoted friend of
the Union, but did no fighting to save it, and became valiant only at its
close. It is to this *Sunstroke* that 'SUT' gives the following mangling *pen
stroke."*

"Sunstroke," after spending a month in Mississippi, wrote a caustic
account of his experiences entitled "Re-Constructed Mississippi—Notes of
a Recent Trip through that State" for the Wisconsin *State Journal,* February 12, 1866, page 2. He noted:

"I had been led to believe that the rebel, after having submitted the
question of difference that existed between the North and the South to the
arbitrament of arms, and the matter in dispute having been decided
against him, had taken the oath in all honesty, kissed the bible with
earnest vigor, planted the old flag over the obliterated 'stars and bars,' and
with devoted love for the Constitution, laws and Government of the United
States, was acting in good faith for the good of the people and Government. I did believe likewise, that they had been persuaded into the opinion
that we were not entirely a set of cowardly Yankees, and that we had
earned, and in a measure enjoyed their respect. But in all this I was
wrong."

The writer encountered, he continued, a spirit of rebellion, a
desire for revenge, a continuing lack of respect for the freedmen, and an

S IR—Es yure gif' seems tu run yu sorter in the Noospaper line,
I takes hit es sartin, that you hes read in the "NU YORK
DAY BOOK," [2] ove my bein 'pinted, by the President, ove all these
yere Yunited States, tu the orfully sponsibil orfiss, ove Fool Killer
Gineril,[3] fur that luvely naik ove the woods, named ontu the top
ove this 'pistil.

I is mons'us sorry tu say that my tenshun hes been 'fishuly
call'd tu yure case. The printid 'pistils, atop ove your surjestif

---

abiding hatred for the "Yankees" (that word usually preceded by a "pro-
fane . . . oath"). Among his examples to back up his charges, he related
the following incident: "At a plantation visited, the lady owner, who was a
widow, spoke so frequently and so bitterly of the 'Yankees,' that it was
getting hard to endure. With a view of checking the unkind expressions
used in speaking of my people, I gently informed her that I was from the
North myself. It had its effect, for thereafter she made handy use of a
pronoun instead of the adjective. 'Madam, have you any milk?' 'No! *you*
Yankees stole all my cows!' 'Boy,' said I, turning abruptly to her son, a lad
of twelve years or more, 'how old are you?' *'Don't know. You d – – – – d
Yanks stole our Bible!'* "

As a proper course of action, "Sunstroke" suggested that the
privileges of the rebels be not enlarged and "that the Federal bayonets
be not decreased, and watch them well, for they will bear it." Subsequently a reader from Trenton, Georgia, challenged the soundness of
his judgment of southern character in the pages of the *State Journal* and
prodded "Sunstroke" to contribute two further indictments: "The South
Revisited, Further Observations among the Reconstructed," April 13, 1866;
and "A Reply from 'Sunstroke'—The Spirit of the South," May 24, 1866. In
the latter piece, he made the bizarre charge that after the Battle of Bull
Run, the "heartless" rebels constructed soup tureens out of Yankee skulls
and parlor ornaments out of knee-pans, spinal columns, and finger joints.
A reading of these prejudiced pieces makes Harris's brutally vituperative
attitude and loss of artistic perspective understandable.

2. See note 16, "Sut Lovingood with Old Abe on His Journey."

3. The Fool Killer is presumably a mythological product of the American folk mind, but it has frequently found its way into literature. See, for
example, Ambrose Bierce's poem "To the Fool-Killer" in *Black Beetles in
Amber* (1892); George Ade's "The Fable of How the Fool-Killer Backed Out
of a Contract" in *Fables in Slang* (1900); O. Henry's story "Fool Killer" in
Voice of the City (1908); Stephen Vincent Benét's story "Johnny Pye and
the Fool-Killer" (1937); and Helen Eustis's novel *The Fool Killer* (1954).
For a discussion of the use of the figure as a *persona* in a series of
newspaper satires by C. N. B. Evans before the Civil War, see Jay B.
Hubbell, "Jesse Holmes the Fool-Killer," *South and Southwest: Literary
Essays and Reminiscences* (Durham, 1965), pp. 250–266. The Fool Killer
is alluded to in two other stories by Harris: "Sut Lovingood's Chest Story"
and "Sut Lovingood With Old Abe on His Journey."

name, norated in the jurnil, menshund by me back yander, a few lines ago, brings yu ready tied, cunvicted an' sentunced, intu my han's, leavin nuffin fur me tu du, but tu put yu, *outen yer misery* es quick es I kin git tu yu. (Ise gwine fur yu, in the mornin.) An' nuffin fur yu tu du, but tu furgiv them, what yu hev injur'd, an' prepar yerself for a big swim in brimstone.

It's dre'full! dre'full! tu think ove, dubbil dre'full to undergo, but the laws ontu fool killin mus' be toted out, ef hit don't leave poperlashun enuff, to raise seed inguns⁴ fur nex' year: the safety ove the government, an' the suckces ove Mister Johnson's⁵ plan ove bildin up a shelter, fur *all* tu stan' under, 'pend 'tirely, on the speedy disolushun, ove the las' damfool, an' in the Providence ove things, my job's *tu disolute 'em*.

Yure case am sich a mark'd one, that I felt like makin up sorter, fur yer maker's (humever that mout be) stinginis, in jis' givin yu no sence at all, by a few hour's warning. Now don't yu waste one minit ove em, in prayin; *hits no use:* you dun passed that pint, when yu rit the fus' line fur the noospaper. But sit down, an' rite out a statemint, ove what *yu hes been a duin*, jurin the las' war; that orful four yeres ove blood, an' bluster an' mixin up ove things, an' totein off things, an' skeerin things. This yu mus' du, tu 'nable the projuce ove yer loins, tu stan' far in avrige 'sciety, arter I hes fed yu tu the wirms, an' yer name, an' yer 'pistels, am only tu be foun', ontu the books ove the fool killer-Gineril.

State fus', on the oath ove sum manbody, ove standin, how meney muskits yu wore plum out a shooting? How meney, you made onsarvisabil, a "clubbin" em over rebil skulls? How meney, you lef' loadid, an' how meney loads yu lef' intu each individoal shootin irun. How meney, cords ove baynits laid sockit an pint, yu split, a stobbin folks, an' how meney, you dran'd the temper outen, a toastin uther ole wimen's hens, over camp fires, an' sich like.

Then, go keerfully in tu the blood seckshun, ove the naratif. Say, how meney barrils ove that easily spiled fluid ove the rebel shade, yu hes pussonely spilt, an' ef thar am a remainder, arter the barrils gins out, sit hit down, in galluns, quarts, pints, an' spoon fulls; yu needent mind the draps, in so large a lot. But you

4. Onions.

5. Andrew Johnson (1808–1875), seventeenth President of the United States, 1865–1869.

mus' cum es low, es the spoonfuls, the law requires hit. You hed bes' siperate the crimsun tied, intu kinds, men's, wimen's, children's, cattil's, hog's, hen's, pole cat's, turnip's, dragon's, an' onconstructid pepil's. Nex, tetch the *'propriatin part,* (sumetimes called, by the onedikated, durnd fool, low down, white trash, "stealin.") Mention the 'zact number ove Peanners, yu "moved," an' the karacter ove the feemails, now playin ontu them, whither A No. I, middlin, I thank yu, or common; also the laingth ove thar respectif feet—in feet; ef codfish, an' 'taters, am eny part ove thar livin, how many, ef eny, ove em, b'leves in the "ontil deth" seckshun ove the marriage seremonie,—the doctrine ove misegenashun—Brigam Young [6]—minks—runnin all night —votin—mustard plarsters, an' a great herearter.

Then, sit down how meney yu may hev "lifted" ove the follerin artikils, which am deklared to be contribran ove war: quilts, frocks, shifts, baby's huckabuck britchis, finger rings, dogratypes ove pepil's dead kin, spoons, love letters, work boxis, sowin mersheans, delf war fron onder the bed, hoops, sent bottils, locks ove har, locks ove chists, an locks ove knittin truck, thimbils, famerly registers, the dead baby's shoes, sittin hens, needil cushuns, camfire flasks, yarb bunches, an' the seed bags. Then state what yu got fur em, in dullers an' sents, how much ove the proseeds yu hev spent toards ristorin the yunion, an' things, how much fur spirrets, how much fur reciprokatin refreshmints, an' how much fur the spread ove the gospil, an' the measills; nex, state arter jew refleckshun, ef yu remembers *ara case,* whar yu *personely,* reconstructid a rebil, an' if so, how yu managed the cuss, an' also, how many laigs, an' arms had he, an' what wer his heft. Yu mus' also say, ef yu hes misfortinatly been the ruin fur this worild, and the worild tu cum, ove eny feemails, (stait the number ove laigs, ef over two,) an' how many ove em, yu kin sartinly say, an' swar tu; gin hit tu me, in roun' hundrids, flingin in the frackshun, an' class em intu three shades ove culler, jet black—ash black, an' saddil shirt yaller. Nex, stait how meney battils yu hes fit, fout, an' spillt fluids in. Nex, stait the number in roun' thousins' ove pursonal skrimages, yu am been in, an' whither yu oppernints wer allers she's, ur never he's es the facks may be.

I larns that yu hes been down South, since the war, a smellin

6. Brigham Young (1801–1877), Mormon leader.

roun' the blackened stumps, and houseless chimbleys, ove a blighted an' conkerd pepil, huntin fur treasun, ur disloyalty; ef yu foun' eny, hav yu been abil tu sell hit fur eny thing, an' is hit worth as much tu you es a trunk ove wimen's close wud be? Also, stait how many doggerys yu pursonely 'xamind, an' the moril status ove the inside ove each one, also, the averige ove the onpaid ballances lef with each afoarsed institushun. Stait how meny meals, vittils, an' night's lodgin, that helpless heart-brokin pepil wudent hev pay fur, an' how many tavrins yu either dodg'd ur "euchered," an' then what yu sed about these pepil arter yu hed put eight ur nine hundred miles atwix yu an' them, and thar just rath.

Stait if ever yu happend by acksident tu git intu the rong bed, an' be foun' thar by an insashate Sambo; ef so, what wer yer stratergy? Did yu call 'im "a man an' a bruther," ur did yu jis' "mizzil?" Ef the las' were yer stratergy, hu fotch yer close tu yu? An' how did yu smell thararter, fur say ten days?

Now, es you hes been a solgerin so long, I wants yu tu keep a stiff upper lip, an' die game—so don't go tu gittin a big skeer intu yu, at these yere legul questins, an' turn tail, an' *swar yu warnt ever in the war at all,* tu keep frum anserin 'em. Hit will jis' be jumpin outen fryin fat intu bilin soap greas. Hits rit on every hart in the woirld, what has a soul behine hit, tu set hit tu beatin, that ove all the cussed, low down varmints, what dishoner the name ove man, the suck-aig sneak, hu hides ahine the pettecoats at home a suckin the hart's blud ove his country, an' *a fattenen hissef on hit,* while she am strugglin for very life, a bleedin at every auger hole, gimlet hole, wurm hole an' crack, an' arter she has barly won the fight, weakly tryin tu stagger tu her feet agin, creeps frum his safe place, an' jackal like, goes scentin roun' amung the dead, the dyin and the starvin, a surchin fur sumthin like a dead fire coal, to tote home and lite wif a lucifer match, and then say, "See yere, they haint whipped yit! Yeres the fire ove war I foun' amung em! They is savin sum tu lite the bonfire ove battil agin!" An' then keeps a bellerin fur sumbody else tu go down thar, an' grind em sum more, to feed his hell's hatred, ought to be SPIT ON—by nuthin livin but polekats, tail tu tail—stink tu stink. Hit would breathe new life intu the dead blush on the stoney cheek ove a street walker, jis' tu ax her ef he warnt her secund cuzzin's dorg, an' she'd straitway hang hersef fur shame.

I'll be roun' soon arter brekfus. Now, I wants no muss made—no more dodgin—no cryin ur leav takin—*meet the lick squar*. What's yer favorit way of shufflin off this mortal quile? [7] Yu is 'sperienced in killin. I is 'commodatin on that pint. Take yer choice—rope, club, meatax, ur slaidge-hammer—Ise got em all. P'raps yu'd like fur me tu string yu ontu a scizzlin, red-hot litenin rod, a startin hit in at yer mouf, ur a lettin it cum out thar. Hu knows but hit mout sorter harden yu tu yer heararter.

Yourn ontil in the mornin after brekfus,
SUT LOVINGOOD, F. K. G.

NOTEY BEANEY.—Thar's a man down in Georgy [8] huntin ove yu wif a snaik pole sharpind. Don't let him cum up wif you, ontil I sees yu, when I'll put yu beyant all yer mortal inemys, 'sceptin the buzzards an' the wu'ms ove the dus'.

SUT LOVINGOOD, agin,
F. K. G., agin.

7. William Shakespeare, *Hamlet*, Act III, Scene i.

8. The correspondent from Trenton, Georgia, mentioned in note 1, above, who criticized "Sunstroke's" articles.

THE ROME EGG AFFAIR

A MAN in Rome, Georgia, sucked six dozen raw eggs at a sitting. "SUT LOVINGOOD" is living in that neighborhood.[1]

When the above was read to "SUT" he thus "onbuzzum'd hisef":

"Say, GEORGE, I dusent much like the soun' ove that ar ho'n; I smell a slur in hit—Ise pow'f'ly feard some ornry cuss am a tryin to pin that ar freak ove genus to my cotail on the sly. I never *et em,* by golly! I haint ownd six dozen aigs, since SHERMAN come yere,[2] an' biled the hens, an' smash'd the delf war. (Wonder if he dont consider hisef a hoss—a hell hoss by geminy! His wife mus' be pow'f'l feard ove him, spechuly when he's in one ove his ways; our wimmen all am; they prays some for im too, they dus.) I 'spects some houn' year'd radicul, for wantin to raise anuther mob by cripplin me wif that breckfus of aigs—wants to construct me, may be. Now, I perposes to advise wif him a little. If he has pressd anybody's spoons, he'd better go back arter the ladle—if any body has busted thar boot, a stumpin thar toe agin his later aind, he'd better hev hit half soled for em, an' sorter squar up his bisness ginerly, for if I don't mean to administer on his estate, three secon's arter sight, damee. Mus' think I is fon' ove aigs, the durn'd raskil.

"But, GEORGE, the kaig ove aigs *were et* at one meal, an' I knows hu did hit; hit were a Georgia delicate to the poor white

---

This story appeared in Nashville *Daily Union and American,* XXXIII (September 2, 1866), 4.

1. Presumably a quotation from an exchange newspaper.

2. In 1863, General Ambrose Burnside moved into Knoxville with 10,000 Union troops to capture the already pro-Federal city and establish a siege. Assuming Burnside could not long survive without supplies, General William Tecumseh Sherman (1820–1891) arrived in Knoxville on December 5 with a large Union force to relieve him, only to discover that to his amazement sympathetic East Tennesseans had amply provided the Federal forces with both the necessities and luxuries of life. Betsey Beeler Creekmore, *Knoxville,* pp. 98–108; Lloyd Lewis, *Sherman, Fighting Prophet,* pp. 327–328.

trash convenshun, whats a threatnin to spread a epademic ove lice in Quakerdelphia; [3] his wife made im do hit, an' twenty-one days arterwards to a dot, he vomited up forty-one chirpin chickens, a little soft-shell turkle, a hens nes' made outen cotten stalks, an' thirty addil'd [4] aigs what smelt like sour'd gunpowder. The las' I hearn from the reptile, he had a six foot buck nigger swaller'd to the kidneys; the nigger bein wide coupl'd, he wer a waitin for sum more grease. That job, when finish'd, is intended to give a extra weight in the convocation of pole cats. I'l swar eny time to his eatin the aigs, for his wife *show'd me the shells.* She calls 'em a dead loss—flung away on him entirely, an' seems ruther down-hearted.

3. A meeting of the members of the conservative Union party gathered in Philadelphia on August 14, 1866, in an abortive attempt to unite all moderates in a new party behind President Johnson to oppose effectively the increasing Radical strength. Eugene H. Roseboom, *A History of Presidential Elections*, pp. 206–207.

4. Addled: spoiled.

SUT LOVINGOOD,
ON THE PURITAN YANKEE

"POWERFUL ornary stock, GEORGE, powerful ornary."

The rale, pure puritan, yankee baby, has a naik like a gourd, a foot like a glut,[1] an a belly like a mildew'd drum head. He gits his eyes open at five days, while uther purps hev to wait nine, an' long afore that time he learns to listen ove a night, for his mam's snorin, when he sneaks in to suck on the sly, not that he's hongry for he's got the usual yankee mess ove biled starch, but becaze stolen meat is sweet even this yearly, to the blue, bline, scrawny young trap maker. He hes cheated his mam, wifout eyes —so I guess he'l make a average yankee, able to keep up the famerly name, an' perhaps invent a cod hook, or a clothes pin.[2] From that night on the varmint's whole life is a string ove cheats —straight along, never restin, never missin until the clock's wore out an the cord's broke. As the dorg vomits, as the mink sucks blood, as the snail shines, as the possum sham's death, so dus the yankee cheat, *for every varmint hes hits gif'.*

He believes in schools an' colleges, as a barber dus in strops, an hones, as bein good tools to sharpen razors on. He'l sing hymes, an' pray prayers for you, an' maybe gin you a dime, but if you dont soon fine out yersef sot back five miles on yer road to heaven, an' ninety cents loser by his zeal, an' charity, you may shoot my eyes out, wif a buck load of cow——slop, an' I wont even say "Phew!" His long, cold, flat back, is the color ove a merlatter-gall's head, jis arter hit has been close shaved, an' hits stuck all over from the scrag to the tail, wif his sins like revenoo stamps on a law suit, an' if you'l zamine em clost, you'l fine a cheat of sum sort in the las' durn'd one. If he sins amung the

This story appeared in Nashville *Union and American*, XXXIII (October 16, 1866), 4.

1. A wedge made of wood used in splitting logs.

2. Harris is denigrating Yankee inventiveness, which along with commercial genius, dry humor, and zeal for reform have characterized the Yankee stereotype in American literature and folklore.

she's, thar's a cheat either in money ur expectashuns. If he sins a cussin, thar's a cheat in the words; he'l try to smuggle in G–d d––n, onder the whinin sham ove "gaud darn." If he sins a stealin chickens, he'l steal back at day break, an' crow jis' to cheat the poor devil inter believin that the ole cock is still on the roost. If he sells you an apple for a cent, arter smellin the copper he'l try to slip a peach ontu you, even if hit is ove the same price, jis' for the sake ove stick'n a cheat intu the trade. If he scalds his leather snout a dippin hit intu your soup, he'll offer you a wooden nutmaig[3] for enuff of the skeemins to grease the burn. He'll eat a codfish, and try to cheat hissef intu believin hit's beef, an' he'll listen tu the chirpin ove the cricket in his fire jamb, tellin his childer that it says, "cheat," "cheat," "cheat." His big, limber foot is a cheat, for hits size and shape makes you think hit *mus'* have guts in hit, when hit haint got one. If you cut his throat, you'll find a cheat, for instead of warm red blood, a stream sky blue will run so cold that hit'l freeze the black ants what gits overtuck by the flood, and when the devil gits 'im, *he'll* be cheated, for he won't burn as good as a salted raw hide. What he wer ever made for is what's a pesterin' me, onless hit were to make us hev a better 'pinion ove pole cats, possums, an' cotton-mouths, or as livin sampils to skeer us out ove the road to hell. I reckon it wud be a tolerable safe rule to do nuffin the Yankee does, an' do mos' enny thing what he lets alone.

I kin sorter bar the idear ove my bein a natral born'd, durn'd fool, my dad a playin h––l actin hoss, the sody bisness, sister SALL'S onlawful baby[4]—everything—everything, even the las' war an' THAD STEVENS[5]—but for the life ove me, I cant reconstruck mysef on the idear ove the landin ove the *Mayflower*. What cud our Maker be thinkin about, that he forgot to lay his finger on her rotten old snout, an' turn her down in the middil ove the soft sea, wif her pestiferus load of cantin cheats an' moril diseases. The wust that cud a happen'd wud a been the pisinin

3. The natives of Connecticut, the Nutmeg state, earned that nickname because of the rumor that they made nutmegs (a hard, aromatic nut or kernel valued as a spice) out of wood and sold them as genuine—another example of Yankee ingenuity and trickery.

4. References to "Sut Lovingood's Daddy Acting Horse," and "Blown Up with Soda," in *Sut Lovingood, Yarns*, pp. 19–28, 75–85, and presumably a yarn about Sut's sister which has not survived (cf. note 11, below).

5. Thaddeus Stevens and other Radical Republicans are more directly satirized in "Sut Lovingood's Dream, Tartarus, and What He Saw There."

ove a shoal or two ove sharks, an' killin the coral whar the old tub lay.

I is mad at the injuns too, for they dident begin to do thar juty to 'em arter they did lan'. If they had carcumsized the head ove the las' durn'd one, burnt thar clos, pack'd thar carkuses heads-an-tails, herrin fashun, in thar old ship, sot the sails, an' pinted her snout the way WARD'S ducks went,[6] they'd desarved tobacker an' whisky, while wood grows or water runs. 'Spose they had a strung three hundred an' one scalps on a willerswitch for bait, an' went a mackril fishin. We'd hev no mackril now a days I reckon, but what a gineral blessin hit wud a been to the hole yeath—the isles ove the sea, the witches, an' the niggers. Wudent them injuns had a savory smell in my snout, in spite ove thar grubwurm oder, an' wudent I rise ove a midnight, or any other night to call 'em blessed, in spite ove thar roastin my grandady. No wooden clocks, horn gun flints, nur higher law. No Miller-ism,[7] mormonism, nor free love. No abolishunism, spirit rappins, nor crowin hens. No Bloomer bit—britches I meant to say, no GREELEY,[8] no SUMNER.[9] Oh! my grashus, hits too good to think about. Durn them leather injuns; they let the bes' chance slip ever injuns had to give everlastin comfort to a continent and to set hell back at leas' five hundred year. I is powerful feard I aint reconstruktid on the injun question ither.

GEORGE, pass the jug, the subjick is overpowerin me, an I aint quite dun onbuzzumin mysef yet. That's powerful fur reachin whisky ove yourn.

Well! everything the yankee does am a cheat in sum way. The word cheat kivers his hole character as pufeckly as the ball ove dirt kivers the young tumil bug, an' like the bug, he lives on hit, wallers in hit, rolls hit, an' at las' is buried in hit. Thar may be a iron coffin, an' silver tassils, thar may be a grave stone from Italy, the side ove his face may be cut outen rock, an' stuck up agin the wall inside his chu'ch, an' they may call thar trottin'

---

6. Presumably a common proverbial phrase, with perhaps a reference to Henry Augustus Ward (1834–1906), American naturalist.

7. The religious doctrines of William Miller, who predicted that the second coming of Christ would occur in 1843.

8. Horace Greeley is more directly satirized in "Sut Lovingood's Adventures in New York."

9. Charles Sumner is also a subject of Harris's satire in "Sut Lovingood's Dream, Tartarus, and What He Saw There."

hoss's, cod boats, an' blue [10] babys arter 'im, yet still onder that black velvit kivirlid, inside that iron coffin, atwix the fine linnen an' that shrivil'd hide ove his'n, *is that ball ove dirt.* He cudent live wifout hit, he cudent die wifout hit, he cudent lie still in his grave wifout hit, an' he never will be wifout hit ontill the sheriff angel at the door ove the last supreme court shells him outen hit with a kick, afore he slings 'im naked into the prisoner's box, whar for the *fust* time frum his fust squall, at the cold air in his snout, up to that orful kickin out, on judgmint day, he'l stan' only on his rale merits—A YANKEE nakid—wif a winder in his breast, like one ove his own hemlock clocks, showin all his inside, springs, traps, an' triggers. Then we'l see what he raley is for the fust time, an' perhaps we'l find out then what he were made for, if he wer made at all, or only jis happin'd like SALL SIMPSON'S baby did.[11] *Now* we jist knows that he is a cuss to the yeath, an' a pest to every human on hit, like fleas, an' lice, an' eatch, made as a cuss, kep' alive as a cuss, an' should be doctor'd as a cuss. *Then* we'l know it all, but whether hit'l pay then to know hit is mightly mix'd wif the doubts. I hopes we'l hev sumfin better to do than to pester our brains 'bout fleas, lice, eatch, yankees or spreadin adders either. Powerful ornary stock, GEORGE, powerful ornary.

10. A word frequently used during and after the Civil War in various combinations ("blue-bellied Yankee," for example) to refer contemptuously to a Northerner, especially a New Englander.

11. A Sall Simmons, who keeps no latch on her door, has several "cum by chance" children, and seems to have had an adulterous relationship with Sut's Dad, appears in "Sut Lovingood, A Chapter from His Autobiography."

SUT LOVINGOOD'S DREAM: TARTARUS, AND WHAT HE SAW THERE

S UT Lovingood having imbibed over freely of "green whiskey," got "tangled by the laigs," tumbled down in the "dorg fennel," dreamed he was in hell and had been sent there for "votin the Radikil ticket." [1] He had not been there long before there arrived "the darndest sluice uv mean looking cusses you ever seed." He proceeds:

They were radicals, the last durn'd one. Some had roaps aroun' their nex, wif a runnin' nuse ahin' the year; some had holes in thar heads; some had a big gill cut under their chins, an' every one shode signs of hard times and hurry. Among 'em I see Stevens,[2] Sumner,[3] Wade,[4] Butler [5]—surnamed the Beast—an' Wendell Phillips.[6] "Hey!" sez the devil, "What's wrong above, cholery?" "Wus nor that," says Sumner, "the Constitution people has riz, an' ove korce *we all are here.* Say, your majesty, is

This story appeared in Lynchburg *Daily Virginian* (January 23, 1867),
1.

1. In the 1866 fall Congressional elections, the Radical Republican party captured two thirds of each house and thus gained effective control of Reconstruction, a situation which would lead to the impeachment of President Johnson and harsh reconstruction policies. Richard B. Morris, ed., *Encyclopedia of American History*, pp. 247–249.

2. Thaddeus Stevens (1792–1868), Congressman from Pennsylvania and Radical Republican leader. For a biographical account, see Richard Nelson Current, *Old Thad Stevens, A Story of Ambition.*

3. Charles Sumner (1811–1874), Senator from Massachusetts and one of the organizers of the Republican party. David Donald has written a biography, *Charles Sumner and the Coming of the Civil War.*

4. Benjamin F. Wade (1800–1878), Republican Senator from Ohio. An early biography by A. G. Riddle is *The Life of Benjamin F. Wade.*

5. General Benjamin F. Butler (1818–1893), Union Army officer, an impetuous, insolent man who inspired antagonism among Northerners and Southerners. See Robert S. Holzman's *Stormy Ben Butler.*

6. Wendell Phillips (1811–1884), noted abolitionist reformer and orator. His life is examined in Oscar Sherwin, *Prophet of Liberty, the Life and Times of Wendell Phillips.*

Preston Brooks [7] here?" "Oh, no," says the devil. "Well," sez Sumner, sorter brightenin' up, an' rubin' his hans, "I am durned glad he aint." "Stop a minit," sez the devil, "wait until I sorts you all out." He took up a needil as long as a harpoon, and with a big quile ove trace chains he threaded it. Then he picked out all the common cusses among 'em and strung 'em on the chain, runnin' the needil in all their mouths, and lettin' it come out thar—I forget which—and then hung the whole bunch over the aidge of the boat into the brimstone. Jehosophat! how they sizzled, an' sloshed, an' dove, an' sprinkled hot iron about wif thar tails. A string ove sun pearch would have been jist no whar.

While the devil were stringin the small fry, Butler, surnamed the Beast, aidged back to whar I sot in the boat, a keepin one eye sot on the devil, an' tother on me, an' he whispered in my ear: "Whars Sisyphus?" [8] Sez I: "Don't know; why?" "Oh! nothin; only I wanted to see which knowed the most ove our trades, him or me." Then he whispered, (that mortal off eye [9] ove his'n still sot on the devil): "Say, do you know whar his majesty keeps his spoons?" [10] Sez I: "Does you see that chain hangin over the

7. On May 22, 1856, a few days after he delivered his "Crime Against Kansas" speech, in which he cast aspersions on the character of Senator Andrew P. Butler (South Carolina), Charles Sumner was the victim of a violent caning in the Senate Chamber by Representative Preston R. Brooks (South Carolina), Butler's nephew. This is the reason Sumner here fears encountering Brooks again. Donald, pp. 285–297.

8. A legendary crafty and avaricious king of Corinth, the father of Ulysses according to later legend. "His task in the world of shades is to roll a huge stone up a hill till it reaches the top; as the stone constantly rolls back, his work is incessant; hence 'a labor of Sisyphus' or 'Sisyphean toil' is an endless, heart-breaking job." William Rose Benét, ed., *The Reader's Encyclopedia,* p. 1036.

9. As most people who saw him noted, Butler was throughout his life noticeably crosseyed and had heavy, drooping eyelids which gave him the appearance of squinting. He was, in general, an unattractive man. See Holzman, pp. 31–32, 34, 163, 167, and 175.

10. Gamaliel Bradford, in his essay on Butler in *Damaged Souls,* pp. 230–231, notes that "it was the commercial dealings connected with his name during the war that laid the greatest burden on Butler's reputation for honesty. . . . It is true that the extreme Southern accusations of theft, as to silver for instance, are utterly unfounded, though there appears to have been a lack of delicacy in the purchase of valuables at low prices wrung from the starved necessity of those who had suffered by the war." Because of a story that he stole silverware whenever he dined out, the sobriquet of "Spoons" Butler stuck with him all his life. Holzman, p. 102.

starn? He keeps 'em in a big pot sunk at tother aind ove hit." He jist went over the starn head fust, and coon'd hit down the chain outen sight onder the brimstone. After bein gone a spell he come back, lookin disappinted like; but his general looks wer powerfully improved by his bath in melted brimstone. I swow he looked a heap more like a human. Sez he: "Gone, pot an' all." I opened my eyes. Sez he: "Hain't Forney [11] got 'em?" Sez I: "May be so—he's been fumblin' round the starn a good while." Dam if he dident sarch every pocket Forney had an' the ole cuss never cotch him at hit, an he *got the spoons.* While this were gwine on, Old Thad were a tryin to claim kin wif the devil, a comparin his foot along wif ole Nick's.[12] I think the pint was to git an office, for I hearn the devil keep sayin: "No, no, I be dam if I do; we has order here now." An' all the time ole Wade wer a pesterin his majesty for a free ticket on his doggery. I seed that the devil wer a gittin monstrous oneasy.

Wendell Phillips kept a watchin fust the side that went down onder the climbers, an' then the side what come up out ove the lake. He jist hopped overboard, an' swum over thar, an' tryin' his durndest *to turn hit tother way,* he grab the sloping side of the cleats, an' held on as long as he could, an' then slosh back agin among the melted dogirons an' brimstone. I reckon he must a made fifty trials afore he quit, an' swum back to the boat, an' then he sot in the most yearnest manner, to persuading the devil to take off the cleats, an' nail 'em on again upside down, so as *to run hell backwards, and ove course the outside world with hit,* without giving a single reason why hit help the matter. This made the devil bile over. He sed: "Not a dam one ove 'em should stay thar another hour. That they'd raise a rebellion sure an' destroy the institution, an' then what would the world do, *particularly New England!"*

I tell ye he jist rared; sez he, "I'll clear my dominions of you durn'd quick," an' he ranged a big bom mortar, where were in the

11. John Wien Forney (1817–1881), Philadelphia journalist and publisher, founded in Washington in 1861 the *Sunday* and *Daily Morning Chronicle,* which supported President Johnson at first but under Republican pressure became a strongly Radical journal. *Dictionary of American Biography,* VI, 526–527.

12. Harris is rather brutally here making light of the fact that Thaddeus Stevens was congenitally lame and walked all his life with a hobbling limp. His biographer notes, "in the minds of many his clubfoot assumed the sinister significance of a cloven hoof." Current, pp. 4, 20.

boat, point blank at the hatch hole, an' he loaded in old Wade, feet fust, and made Forney tetch hit off. By golly! he went whizzen throu the hole, and hit rained whisky on the lake ontil hit burnt blue.—Next he grabbed old Thad; sez he, tremblin', "Please yer majesty, load her in with me," apintin to a she nigger strung on the chain; [13] sez the devil, "no sir, I think we can manage her arter you is gone, and besides, she looks like she needed a little rest."—Bolang! and I jist cotch a glimpse ove Thad's hooked foot scrapin a splinter off the hatch combin. Nex he yoked Sumner, an he begged to be loaded head fust, and he sed he'd always traveled sturn fust throu life, an' he wanted to finish his journey the same way, on account ove his record. So sturn fust he come outen the mortar, sturn fust he went outen the hatch hole, an I recon sturn fust he busted agin sumfin away yonder on the outside. Butler's, surnamed the Beast, turn come nex. While the devil were a loadin him in, I observed him buisy a buttonin up his pockits. When the mortar fired I wer watchin the hatch clost; I dident like the idear ove his leavin; but dam if he went thar, he followed the line ove his cock eye, and busted into a million pieces agin the wall. Spoons and breastpins fell a foot deep all over the lake, and I hearn the wimmen all cheer. The devil then licked his lips, and went for Wendill, but he jist loped overboard and dove, an tu save his life the devil couldn't find 'im. He'll raise trouble thar yet, see ef he don't. Nex he grabbed Forney, his steersman, and sez he, "you don't steer tu suit me," and he commenced a loadin him in, an don't you believe, jist as the cuss's head wer a goin out ove sight, he whispered in the devil's ear that I were Jamison, the actor.[14] The devil remarked,

13. Stevens was once publicly accused of fathering a child on the unwed daughter of a friend, and given his fanatic sympathy for the Negro, it is easy to imagine that among Southerners, the charge of miscegenation also was more than once leveled at the clubfooted politician. *Current*, pp. 68–71.

14. George Jamieson (1812–1868) began his stage career in New York in 1837 and afterwards earned a reputation there as a melodramatic actor. He excelled in the role of Iago in *Othello* and was noted for his impersonation of the Negro on the stage. He also turned playwright, producing rather dull, moralistic dramas with such unlikely titles as *Cheating in Play Never Prospers* (1860) and *As You Sow, So Must You Reap* (1863). In an attempt to counteract the influence of Harriet Beecher Stowe, on March 1, 1860, Jamieson produced *The Old Plantation, or, the Real Uncle Tom*, in which a scalawag Yankee abolitionist abducts a quadroon slave only to be punished in the end. His intent, he said, was to portray "the only truthful

"I've got nuffin agin Jamison, you is the one;" mad at me by golly, jist bekaze he seed the beast outsmarted him in the spoon business. I hearn suffin like quack! quack! down in the bowils ove the mortar, and then hit went off, and so did the duck. Thar'l be peace in hell fur a while, if the devil kin only ketch Wendil an' reconstruct the durn'd raskil. Old Smutty reached for me las' one, and put me down his gun. I sot into beggin hard. Sez he "you mus' go, the prosperity of my kingdom demands that nuffin having the smell ove radical unto his close, kin stay yere. I seed you whisperin wif the Beast, and I'd shoot out ole Robespiere [15] hisself, if I wer tu ketch him at sich an ornary trick, an he's bin belpin roll hell roun' in an orderly way ever sence the French Revolution." By golly! I jist limbered all over, the gun roared an' I wakened. Now what do you think was the matter wif me? Why, old Bob Hays were a tryin his durndest to splinter a four foot clapboard over my sturn, and he wanted me to git outen his paster, afore he shut the gate for the night. I were a sweatin orful, George, perfectly orful.

I sorter wished I had dreamed on a little longer. I'd a liked powerful well to a foun' out what had become of ole Thad arter he wer shot out ove hell. Hit'l sorter injur his standin, won't hit, as he roams through nothin forever? I believe if I'd been him, I'd rather staid thar wif my she nigger. Been hard on her though, poor devil, an' a little too good for him. Ain't I hoss on skeery dreams?

---

stage type of the Southern plantation negro." He was accidently killed when run over by an express train near Glenwood, New York, on October 3, 1868. The events of Jamieson's career may be gleaned from volumes IV, V, and VII of George C. Odell, *Annals of the New York Stage;* Howard Paul and George Gebbie, eds., *The Stage and Its Stars Past and Present,* II, 37; and William Winter, *Other Days, Being Chronicles and Memories of the Stage,* p. 40.

15. Robespierre (1758–1794), French revolutionary leader.

CORRESPONDENCE EXTRAORDINARY.
THE FORTHCOMING EARLY LIFE OF
SUT LOVINGOOD, BY HIS DAD.
NEGOTIATIONS COMPLETED.

*M*ESSRS. *Editors:*
 GENTLEMEN—It affords me pleasure to inform you, that
I have accomplished the important mission which you entrusted
to my management. I have closed a contract with the venerable
father of SUT LOVINGOOD, for "the early life" of that distinguished person, to be written *con amore,* and expressly for your
paper. The triumphant close of this important negotiation,
should be a cause of gratulation among your personal friends,
and will be hailed with joy by the admirers of genius throughout
the world. The early and inner life of the greatest living man, *in
his way,* will be sought after, and read, from the shadows of
Cape Coast Castle,[1] to the gleaming ice spires at the pole, and the
day of its publication will be a white stone on the roadway of
time, a pointer, and a warning, to the coming generations, as
they file past, on their way to the end. This thought cheered me,
as I struggled against the many obstacles thrown in my way
during the negotiation, and doubtless assisted in impelling me
forward to a successful result, not the least of which was a vile
emissary of Bonner's,[2] amply supplied with means, and openly

This story appeared in Knoxville *Press and Messenger,* III (April 30,
1868), 1.
 1. Now Cape Coast, a seaport town and Gold Coast Colony in West
Africa and site of a castle built by the Swedes in 1652 (hence its early
name).
 2. Robert Bonner (1824–1899) was publisher of the New York *Ledger*
(1851–1887), a well-known nineteenth century periodical, which had
recently published the series "The Early Life of Gen. Grant, By His
Father," of which "The Early Life of Sut Lovingood, Written by His Dad"
is a direct parody. Bonner was an exploiter and a sensation-monger, and
next to P. T. Barnum was the most outlandish but effective advertiser in
America. As Harris here suggests, either by trickery or high pay (some-

my competitor for the prize. I am not sure but he would have succeeded, had not the fact leaked out, that Bonner was the means of inflicting on the reading public, that matchless production, "The early life of Gen'l Grant, by his father." [3] When old Mr. Lovingood, became convinced of this, he turned a cold shoulder to all propositions from that quarter, declaring, in his own peculiar manner, "That he never roosted on the pole where another damfool did any of the crowing." This, and other utterances of "Hoss" Lovingood, (as he is familiarly termed, by his acquaintances,) leads me to the belief, that his feelings towards the progenitor of Sut's rival, are none of the kindest; it is natural too, that this bitterness should be most cordially reciprocated by Grant, *pere,* when the sons are so palpably and unmistakably pitted against each other for the same prize.[4] Such hostility, backed as it is, by the obstinacy, prejudice and partiality of a second childhood, is sure to culminate in a personal collision, unless Mr. Bonner and yourself, can rise to the level of the occasion, by joining in keeping the peace between these patriarchs of the flock. When such a man as "Hoss" Lovingood openly avows his willingness and ability to "maul the benzine [5] out of Grant, *pere.*" "To sweat out his lard at his ears." "To sun

---

thing unusual among the era's unscrupulous publishers), Bonner added to his contributors the day's most sensational authors and distinguished personages. Imitating the currently popular *London Journal,* he filled the pages of the *Ledger* with innocuous fiction, moralistic essays, and sentimental verse. Among his contributors were Horace Greeley, Henry Ward Beecher, Bryant, Longfellow, Harriet Beecher Stowe, Dickens, and Tennyson, although they were surrounded by third- or fourth-rate hacks. The highly successful *Ledger* in an altered form endured even beyond the turn of the century. See Frank Luther Mott, *A History of American Magazines,* II, 15, 23–24, 356–363; *Dictionary of American Biography,* II, 437–438. Bonner's *Ledger* was equally popular in the North and South. The fact that Southern periodicals could never compete with the more sensational Northern products led Dr. George W. Bagby to comment satirically in the *Southern Messenger* of September, 1861, upon "the inappeasable desire of Southern patriotism to obtain a copy of Bonner's *Ledger.*" See Susan B. Riley, "The Hazards of Periodical Publishing in the South During the Nineteenth Century," *Tennessee Historical Quarterly,* XXI (December, 1962), 365–376.

3. This series appeared in the *Ledger* issues of March 7, 14, and 21, 1868.

4. U. S. Grant was just preparing to run for the Presidential prize, but Harris suggests that the prize he and Sut are to compete for is national recognition as the day's biggest "nat'ral born durn'd fool."

5. An inferior type of whisky.

his moccasins" [6]—and to "snatch all sich, bald headed," it is high time for the interference of thoughtful friends. As Mr. Bonner and yourself have been the means of placing the jealous old Gentlemen in a belligerant attitude, you owe it to society that they be kept apart, for we have every reason to believe that the finale of the fight among the cats of Killkeney [7] would be a wild and bloodless ending, as compared to a meeting between these sturdy old Aries,[8] of the respective flocks of Lovingood and Grant.

I am satisfied that if Grant, *pere*, has shown the whole strength of his hand, (and I incline strongly to that belief, from the twenty five foot jumping anecdote, the photographic prophecy, touching the Presidency, &c,) that Sut Lovingood, will make a respectable race for the crown. Let no one hug the delusion to his heart that "Ulyssus" will walk over the track unmarked by whip or spur, to be proclaimed the durn'd fool of his day. Neither will his earnest biographer, find in "Hoss" Lovingood, a foeman altogether unworthy of *his* steel. Grant a fair field, and no favor, with the honest wish from all parties, that "the best man may win," and I have a hope for "Sut" yet.

In closing, I may remark, that in addition to your offer of $10,000, I was compelled to add a forty-four gallon barrel, full of Pike's unrectified whisky, a bunch of fiddle strings, and a promise of the postmastership at the village of Soaptail.[9] I further stipulated, and agreed that no daguerreotypes of himself, his wife, or their cabin,[10] are to be "mixed in" with his letters, and that his utterances are not to be "tinkered up," or mended, by the

6. To throw him.

7. "In Irish legend, two cats who fought until only their tails and nails were left: a byword for the ancient enmity between Kilkenny and Irishtown. Legend reports constant fighting between the two groups almost to mutual annihilation." Maria Leach, ed., *Standard Dictionary of Folklore, Mythology, and Legend*, II, 578.

8. First sign of the Zodiac: the ram; a nicer way of calling them old goats. There might also be significance in the fact that "In astrology Aries is held to endow with violent temper those born under his sign, and to presage some physical harm that will come to them, sometimes death by hanging." *Ibid.*, I, 72.

9. Grant's father was appointed postmaster at Covington, Kentucky, by President Johnson, and his son maintained the appointment when he became President.

10. Portraits of Jesse Root Grant and his wife, Hannah Simpson Grant, and a picture of the cabin where Ulysses was born appeared in the *Ledger* with the first installment of "The Early Life of Gen. Grant."

compositor, particularly his poetry if he indulges in any, and he rather thinks he *will* "try it a jump or two," if it comes easy. I was forced to these concessions, and hope they will meet your approval, as without them, (to use his own emphatic language,) he wouldn't "budge a single durn'd inch," and the world thereby would have been left in ignorance of "the early life" of another great man "by his father." If the reading public, will make as much allowance for the partiality and zeal of the "dad," in Sut's case, as they have been compelled to grant to "the father of Ulysses," I shall ask no more, only that all stand back, and watch the fur fly—for two more earnest souls, never entered the lists for their respective "boys" than Grant *pere* and "Hoss" Lovingood. Very Respectfully,

Agent.

THE EARLY LIFE OF SUT LOVINGOOD,
WRITTEN BY HIS DAD, I

M ISTER Ramige,[1]
Dear Sir:—You sent me word, that you wanted to print
sumthin about the yearly life ove my most notorious son "Sut,"
and as how I bein' his dad, (so far es eny body knows) you tho't I
wer most knowin' ove his littil tricks, an' tharfoar the very feller
to rite 'em down for you to print frum. Well, jist you count me
I-double-en in. I ruther like hit, havin' a strong honein arter a
pen enyhow; hevin been ofen called on in my yearly days, to tally
bushels at corn measurin's, to keep count at shootin' matches, or
games ove "old Sledge," witnessin' notes ove han', an' articles for
a hoss race, or a rastilin mach. In fac', almos' all short jobs ove
writin' done off han'. In this way I becum eggspert with a pen. I'd
jist as lief as not butted agin the schoolmaster hissef. Ove late
years, I hev writ so much, that hit has affected the sinnews, an'
puckerin strings ove my coteail, to sich a egstent, that I cant sit
on hit, onless I hole hit down clost to my hams as I squat. The
fac' is, my coteails quirls up like a pine shavin, but then even this
is sometimes both handy an' timely.[2]

This story appeared in Knoxville *Press and Messenger,* III (May 7,
1868), 1.
1. William J. Ramage, publisher at this time of both the *Press and
Messenger* and the Knoxville *Press and Times.* Mary U. Rothrock, ed., *The
French Broad–Holston Country,* pp. 417–418.
2. Cf. Jesse Root Grant's opening paragraph:
"ROBERT BONNER, Esq.—*Dear Sir:* You inform me that you wish to
publish some articles about General Grant; and, in order that they may be
perfectly correct and reliable, you request me to furnish them. I have no
objection to doing so, except the difficulty which I labor under, at present,
of committing them to paper. Having acquired when very young, some
facility in the use of the pen, I was, for many years, made secretary of
almost every public meeting which I attended where clerical services were
required; and through life I have been in the habit of doing a great deal of
writing; but, lately, I have written so much that it has affected the nerves
and muscles of my right arm so as to partially disable it temporarily, and

You say, that you want me to go behine SUT'S bornin' a generashun or two, an' partickulerly, to dwell on mysef, an' my doin's right smartly.[3] Well, "My Son" SUT, comes of as good, and as pure durn'd fool stock, as most public caracters now figurin' on top ove the pot. His great gran'dad, arter a long life spent doin' the durndes fool things done in them durn'd fool days, killed hissef a jumpin down a bluff, two hundred feet into a rocky dry branch, jist to save a half a mile gwine to the still-house.[4]

"My son" SUT'S gran' mamey's cousin, on the she side, must a been a hell ove a feller, in his way; he fit the very best men, in all Noth Caliney, an' Firginey, an' never foun' one that he was abil to whop.[5] He also fit a nigger, name Prince or Jupiter, a pitch battil, for a gallun ove appil brandy, an' a barlow knife.[6] That barlow, war foun' in the pockit ove a dead nigger, on the day arter the race from Belmont to the gunboats;[7] I think from this,

---

make the use of it, for much length of time, inconvenient." Jesse Root Grant, "The Early Life of Gen. Grant, By His Father," New York *Ledger*, XXIV (March 7, 1868), 4.

3. "You inform me that you wish me to tell you something about General Grant's ancestors, and of my own history." *Ibid.*

4. "The General comes of good fighting stock. His great-grandfather, Captain Noah Grant, a native of Windsor, now Tolland, Connecticut, was killed in the battle at White Plains, in 1756. . . ." *Ibid.*

5. "his great-grandfather's brother, Lieutenant Solomon Grant, was killed in the same battle [at White Plains]." *Ibid.*

6. A well-known make of pocket-knife or penknife, named after its originator, Russell Barlow. See Gordon Wilson's brief essay "Saint Russell Barlow," in *Passing Institutions*, pp. 59–60.

7. A reference to Ulysses Grant's most significant military failure. Grant had been ordered to clear southeastern Missouri of Confederate troops, and this included Belmont, little more than a steamboat landing on the Missouri side of the Mississippi. On November 7, 1861, Grant and his troops arrived at dawn by boat accompanied by two federal gunboats, the *Tyler* and *Lexington*, to cover them from the Confederate guns on the bluffs at Columbus just across the river. Earlier, General Leonidas Polk got wind of the planned attack and strengthened the Confederate forces there. But before noon, Grant's men had scattered the rebels, and all resistance ceased. The spirits of the cheering Federals were soon dampened, however, when Polk sent two boatloads of men across from Columbus, rallied the disorganized rebels, and cut off Grant's men from their transports moored up the river. Suffering heavy losses, they had to cut their way back through to the transports, while many men panicked and ran for the gunboats. The entire action accomplished nothing for either side. Bruce Catton, *Grant Moves South*, pp. 40–43, 70–84.

that Prince or Jupiter must a flax'd out [8] our ancestor. I hev in my persession, the written agreement ove this pitch battil, signed with Crassis, only the niggers Crass is a fish hook. I menshun this to show, what they tho't ove niggers, one hundred and twelve years ago.[9]

SUGARTAIL LOVINGOOD, was a son ove his daddy, and bein' my daddy is tharfoar gran' daddy to "my son" SUT—That is, if thar was no stockin' ove kerds,[10] or sich. He didn't git killed often, doin' eny thing, nor never got whipp'd, as I knows ove, becaze he never did eny fightin'. He jist sloshed along lazily, an' this sort ove life spiled him for finanshul business, all except multiplyin' childer, ove which I am one.[11] My mamy, was an 'oman hard to beat, or forget; [12] she had the quickest lick with a hickory, or a clapboard, ove eny 'oman I ever seed, except my BETTS, "my son" SUT'S own mam; she also had a sharp eye for insex. A sunshiney, Sunday mornin', was a day ove doom, to all creepin' things, an' we all had sore heads on Monday, an' scratchin' scasely ever begun afore Wensday.

Down to this point, the Lovingood blood had'nt a single bad crass—Durn'd fools, the last cussed one, that toted the name. Now as to me, myself. I wer hatch'd in Ole Noth Caliney, clost to Firginney line, an' tuck my fust drink ove warter, outen Tar Tiver,[13] whar herrins, gourd martin boxes,[14] an' tupemtime did

8. Severely beaten or thrashed.

9. "I have in my possession an original muster-roll made out by Captain Noah Grant, in 1765—the year before his death. His own name leads it as captain; the names, dates of service, and '*quality*' of the men are duly entered in separate columns; and as illustrative of the sentiments of those early days, one hundred and twelve years ago, on the military aspect of color, I may quote the following designations of some of the privates: 'Prince, *negro.*' 'Jupiter, *negro.*' " Grant, *op. cit.*

10. Fraudulent arranging of the cards, "stacking" the deck.

11. "Captain Noah Grant's son, Noah Grant, also a native of Connecticut, was my father; and if he did not get killed in battle, like his worthy sire, it was not because he did not perseveringly take all the chances of such a death, for he fought in the Revolutionary war, from beginning to end—over seven years. . . . This long period of soldiering spoilt him for all financial business." Grant, *op. cit.*

12. "My mother . . . was an excellent manager; and while she lived, the family were [*sic*] always in comfortable circumstances; and after her death—in April, 1805—we had to separate, and that impressed upon the minds of all of us a lesson which we never forgot." *Ibid.*

13. Located in Beaufort county, North Carolina.

14. Gourds in which martin swallows set up household.

mos' abound. When I wer about so years old, Dad packed plunder, an' we got a three year old bull, to haul hit, while we follered
in the cart ruts to Bunkum county.[15] I led two houn dogs, mam
toted twins, an' the chances,[16] with a dinner pot on her back,
while dad, SUGARTAIL LOVINGOOD, rid the bull, a toatin' a
rifle gun; the rest ove the childer follered durn'd permiskusly,
pickin' huckilberys, an' fightin' the hole way. I never will forget
that bull, (we eat him the nex' winter,) for through his sagacity
we foun' Bunkum at last.[17]

When I wer a littil *more*, so year old, dad moved agin to
Bertie,[18] whar I boun' myself out, to the trade ove varmint
huntin', corn shuckin', an sich. Arter I had sarved out my time
faithfully, I sot up for myself, an' staid sot up ever since, except
when I git knocked down, or lie down apupos.[19] Along about now,
I suffered a sevear, an' perlonged attack ove onintermitunt
durn'd fool,[20] jurin' which I got married. Folks talked a good deal,
said Betts wer too good for me, an' they say so yet. I tho't hit a
good thing, an' don't think so yet. I married BETTS LEATHER-
LAIGS, daughter ove old man LEATHERLAIGS, an' we imejuntly sot in to house keepin' in a bark camp,[21] wher, sooner nor
you would expeck, I foun' mysef the daddy (so called,) ove "my

15. Buncombe county in western North Carolina.

16. A "chance child" is an illegitimate one.

17. "I was born in Westmoreland county, Pennsylvania, January 23,
1794. When I was five years of age, I was taken by my father, who
emigrated with his family, to that part of the northwestern territory which
is now Columbiana county, Ohio." Grant, *op. cit.*

18. A county in northeastern North Carolina.

19. "When I was ten years of age, we moved to Portage county, in the
Western Reserve. At sixteen, I was regularly apprenticed to my half-
brother, to learn the tanning trade, at Maysville, Kentucky. I faithfully
served out my apprenticeship; and, soon after I became of age, set up
business for myself, at Ravenna, Portage county, Ohio." Grant, *op. cit.*

20. "Here [Ravenna, Ohio] I suffered a severe and protracted illness
from fever and ague, which finally compelled me to relinquish business."
Ibid.

21. "In 1820, I settled temporarily at a small place called Point Pleasant . . . and, in June, 1820, I was married to Miss Hannah Simpson, and
commenced housekeeping at that time. . . . A few of the neighbors
expressed their surprise that one of Mr. Simpson's daughters should marry
a young man hardly yet established in business. . . . I was not worth a
dollar when I married; but I did not stay that way long: and as soon as I
was known to be prosperous the neighbors seemed to think the match was
exactly the thing—just what I had thought from the beginning." *Ibid.*

son" SUT, the prominent subject ove a heap ove talk now-a-days, an' sartinly a most remarkabil son in his way. I must be allowed, as his daddy, however, to remark, confidensially—dam such a way as his'n. If the camp whar he fotch his fust squall in is standin' yet, I knows nottin ove hit—I speck hit is rotted down.[22] Seventeen other brats wer cotch in my net, an' strung on my string. I hes retired from business, with a compitancy ove brats,[23] an' I keep a retirin' from hit—you bet.

I has allways had a heap ove reputashun, so much in fac, that if I dident now an' then spree away the surplus, I'd be smothered with reputashun.[24] I never owned a nigger, an' never tried, arter I foun' out how much one cost, an' the danger ove mixin'.

I hev voted for Gin'l Jacksin, sum, that is as often as three times ove a morning; I vote for Jacksin, yet—I never wer much ove a politishiner, owside ove the whisky part. I never wer "technically" term'd a abolisionist, (that means durn'd fool,) but hit has been insinuated to the childer, an' charged purty strong on "My son" SUT.[25] I am proud ove mysef; I hev a constitution like a daug. I am a hoss, in fac' hoss rather perdominates amung the Lovingoods. "My son" SUT was fust engineer to one, for a long spell—we dream hoss, we talk hoss, we act hoss, we smell hossey—in fac' Lovingood an' hoss am now, an' forever one an' inseperable. I may add, that I think nex' arter the nigger, that hosses orter vote, an' thar hides be exempt frum the tan vat.

22. "Here [Point Pleasant, Ohio], on the 27th day of April, 1822, our first child, ULYSSES S. GRANT, was born. The house in which this event occurred is still standing." *Ibid.*

23. "Five other children—three daughters, and two sons—were subsequently added to our family. . . . Industry, frugality, and perseverance made me fortunate in business and enabled me to accumulate a competency for myself and my family. In 1854, at the age of sixty, I measurably retired. . . ." *Ibid.*

24. "My sons . . . continued the business for twelve years. . . . We always had the reputation for making the very best leather—we tanned with nothing but oak, and that made it superior." *Ibid.*

25. "I have taken a pretty active interest, generally, in the political questions of the day. . . . I was never what was technically known as an Abolitionist; but I never held a slave. I made up my mind, when I was a young man, that I would never have slaves. This was the reason that I left Kentucky and went to Ohio. I would not own slaves, and I would not live where there were slaves and not own them. I voted for General Jackson for President every time he was a candidate—that is, three times." *Ibid.*

You reques' ove me my dogratype; now Mister Ramige, I aint down bad (jist at this time,) with a spell ove durn'd fool, so you gits no dogratype from me; a man is powerful low with the disease, when he manages to git his picter into the noospapers. I will tho' give you a small mess ove dogril, jist to put a good taste in your mouth. I ken rite poetrie, in fac' I ken do eny thing I want to, except tanning dorg hides, with saw dust, or sellin' hoss hides with cows tails to 'em; try who will they'll find hit a failur. I mus' repeat afore I put in the dogril so as to impress the great fac' on your mine, that *I am a hoss,* an' if I aint a hoss, I'm nothin', an' *if* I'm nothin', I haint foun' hit out yet—you bet.

> "Mister Ramige, my good kind friend,
> I'd see you durn'd afore I'd send
> A picter, profile or pot-o-graff,
> To give durn'd fools a chance to laff.
> Or bust the box, an' break the glass,
> Strainin' to picter out an ass.
> As for BETTS, she'd take a skare,
> A log chain coudent hold her there
> While a feller sighted her. Through
> A fixin', shiney, bright an' new,
> That shows the hide, throu' shift an' dress,
> She'd never stand such wicked-ness.
> My whiskers, too, Ise shear'd 'em off—
> A hen's nest now, in the stable troff.
> So now to you, I'd look all wrong,
> A dam poor tune, to a sleepy song.
> But if you're dry, an' whisky want,
> Jis' come to me, an' hit I'l GRANT,
> I'l rise, an' shine _____ [26]

26. "In replying to your request for my photograph, I will adopt the response which I recently made to a similar application from a lady in Washington, who asked for my own and Mrs. Grant's:

'Miss G.—My kind, good friend:
As you request, I herewith send
A neatly taken photograph
Of mistress Grant, my better-half.
The picture's good, the likeness true,
Which I now present to you.
I also send you one of mine,
Though that, indeed, is not so fine:
This was taken four years ago,

Thar—if I haint crack'd my skull two inches right in the crown, thar's narra devil. I think I'l stick to plain ritein, strait acrost the paper, hits safest—ain't so strainin'. In my next, I will come squar up to "my son" SUT, an' his wonderous doin's, not forgittin' the hoss part, nor how he rid 'em. Don't forgit, always afore the word SUT, to put in the words "my son." An' bar in mine strait along, that I am his daddy; the time has come, the worild mus' be kept in mine ove that great fac', that "my son" SUT has a daddy, an' that daddy is a hoss, an' I am HE.

> Yours Respectively,
> HOSS LOVINGOOD,
> Sire of the renowned Sut.

NOTEY BENEY—Never another durn'd line ove po*etrie* do *you* git—mine that.

> Before I let my whiskers grow,
> And to you may look wrong,
> And right to those who've known me long.
> My best respects I herewith send
> To you and to your room-mate friend.
> And say to both, for what you want,
> Just send your card to J. R. GRANT.' "

Ibid.

THE EARLY LIFE OF SUT LOVINGOOD,
WRITTEN BY HIS DAD, II

M ISTER *Ramige,*
Dear Sir:—It is said, that every man thinks his own wife, the best woman in the world: But if all men think as I dus—a durnder lie never wer told.[1] When I fasten'd onto Betts Leatherlaigs, for a mate, she wer a rale slide easey, smilin', saft footed gall, but she soon spread, an' hardened into the durndest, scaley heel'd, rule-a-roost 'oman, atwix h——l, an' breakfast time. She stomp'd a heap ove her caracter onto her brats; in fac', I don't think eny ove 'em takes arter me to a suspisious egstent. I have studied a power about this.[2] The leadin' passions uv "my son" SUT, from the time he could go alone, wer skeers—whisky—obstinacy, an' hosses. The fust hoss, he ever druv, wer a muel, an' him he druv crazy, in two secon's an' a half, by comin' at him, sturn formos' on his all fours, an' in his shut tail.[3] That ar animule wer never worth a cuss arterwards—*His hart was broke.* Folks sed then, that if "my son" SUT met with no bad luck or accident, to stunt him, or set him back, he'd make a beautiful damfool some day. Hit don't become me, his dad, to speak. He is before the world, but I mus' be allow'd to remark, that I do believe in perdicshuns. If a suckis, or eny show comes along—an' got away without a slit canvass, a lost dorg, or a

This story appeared in Knoxville *Press and Messenger,* III (May 14, 1868), 1.

1. "It is said that every man thinks his wife is the best woman in the world; and if all men think as I do, the saying is correct." Jesse Root Grant, "The Early Life of Gen. Grant, By His Father," New York *Ledger,* XXIV (March 7, 1868), 4.

2. "At the time of our marriage, Mrs. Grant was an unpretending country girl; handsome, but not vain. . . . Her steadiness, firmness and strength of character have been the stay of the family through life." *Ibid.*

3. "The leading passion of Ulysses, almost from the time he could go alone, was for horses. The first time he ever drove a horse alone, he was about seven and a half years old." *Ibid.*

hamstrung hoss, "my son" SUT wer sick—absint—or drunk.[4]
Wonst there come a suckis, with a little cuss ove a muil, an' they
call'd hit Lee.[5] The ring marster, name Abe, call'd aloud for some

4. "When Ulysses was a boy, if a circus or any show came along, in
which there was a call for somebody to come forward and ride a pony, he
was always the one to present himself, and whatever he undertook to ride
he rode." *Ibid.*

5. Up to this point, Harris has primarily been parodying the Grant
material directly, and simply drawing parallels between Sut and Ulysses,
with the effect that Grant greatly suffers in the comparison. Here a new
complexity is introduced in a capsule allegory of the entire Civil War,
based on an incident in Jesse Root Grant's narrative, which functions by
Sut symbolizing U. S. Grant. The circus, of course, is the Civil War, and
the performing, rambunctious mule is Robert E. Lee. The ring master,
President Abraham Lincoln, calls for an able rider to break the vicious
animal, which on a second level also represents the South. Just as Lincoln
changed the Union command time and again, seeking an officer capable of
breaking the repeatedly victorious Confederate commanders, the ring master continues to seek a capable rider. Among the unsuccessful riders is
John Pope, the boastful, untrustworthy general who was no sooner given a
high command than he lost it after defeat by Lee at the Second Battle of
Bull Run (August 29, 30, 1862). The rider who was flung into the river
represents General Ambrose Burnside, who was severely beaten by Lee at
Fredericksburg, Virginia (December 13, 1863), and had to retreat across
the Rappahannock River after suffering thirteen thousand casualties. A
second host led by the radical "Fighting" Joe Hooker was also whipped at
Chancellorsville and driven back across the Rappahannock. But the tide
turned after Lee's defeat at Gettysburg and Grant's success in winning
Vicksburg. Just as Sut is finally given a chance to ride, Grant was finally
given a chance to show his stuff when appointed supreme commander of
all the Union armies in March 1864. Despite a last few feeble bucks and
upsets by Lee (such as the Battle of the Wilderness in May 1864 and the
suicidal assault against Lee at Cold Harbor in June), the stubborn Southern mule was finally bested. The shouting acclaim of the audience in the
little allegory is the general popularity won by Grant which threatened to
carry him, at the time Harris was writing, into the White House, as it
ultimately did.

Once in the political arena, Grant let himself be dominated by more
powerful manipulators in an area of activity where the courageous officer
was not as adept as on the battlefield. Among them was Elihu B. Washburne, a Congressman from Illinois, who made Grant his protégé from the
time he secured for Grant a promotion to brigadier-general in 1861. Like
the monkey which becomes permanently attached to Sut's hair, Washburne shrewdly recognized Grant's potential and defended, sponsored, and
stuck by him through his unfortunate years to his period of success. Harris
lived to see Grant elected to the presidency and Washburne rewarded for
his faithfulness, first with the position of Secretary of State, and then with
the position of Ambassador to France. Washburne little endeared himself

able bodied boy, to ride this vishus cuss. Well boy arter boy tried hit, an' got flung right, an' left. One hit head fust on the candy stand, then Abe mos' incontintly kick'd him out. Another, name John Pope, lit sturn fust amung the "nashun's wards," an' Abe, in bootin' his rear, misfortinately stove out his brains. I hes watch'd the kareer ove that boy, an' he haint been worth a dam since. Another got flung clean into the Rapahanock. Abe dident stun his sturin, (stun means benumb) for he never drowndid, an' aint fish'd out yet. In stepp'd "my son" SUT, an' offered to ride—got mountid, an' the performince begun. Roun', an' roun', an' roun', they went—Lee's tail gwine roun', an' roun', too, like the crank ove a grindstone. Every now, an' then, the muel would send "my son" SUT, spreadeagle fashion, clean acrost the ring, an' then stan' still, an' wait for him to come agin. The people sot up a great shout, some few for the muel, an' a heap for "my son." So many hollered for him, that the ringmaster wer feard to boot him out, although he wer a smashin' things bad, every fall he got; an' besides all that, go as hit would, the performince wer *payin'*. Arter a while, yere cum a great, ugly, chatterin' monkey, name Washburne, an' up he jump'd ahine "my son" SUT'S shoulders, cotch him by the har, an'—*thar he sticks to this day.* Jurin all this tryin' time, an' up till now, "my son" SUT has never moved a muscle ove his face. Queer, aint it? [6] One time, a poor

---

to Southern hearts when he proved to be among the most ardent radicals during reconstruction. For treatments of Washburne and his relationship with Grant, see William B. Hesseltine, *Ulysses S. Grant, Politician;* Bruce Catton, *Grant Moves South; Dictionary of American Biography,* XIX, 504–506.

6. The anecdote upon which Harris based his brief allegory was thus recounted by Jesse Root Grant:

Once, when he was a boy, a show came along in which there was a mischievous pony, trained to go round the ring like lightning, and he was expected to throw any boy that attempted to ride him.

"Will any body come forward to ride this pony?" shouted the ring-master.

Ulysses stepped forward, and mounted the pony. The performance began. Round and round and round the ring went the pony, faster and faster, making the greatest effort to dismount the rider. But Ulysses sat as steady as if he had grown to the pony's back. Presently out came a large monkey and sprang up behind Ulysses. The people set up a great shout of laughter, and on the pony ran; but it all produced no effect on the rider. Then the ring-master made the monkey jump up on Ulysses' shoulders, standing with his feet on his

blind cuss come along, callin' hissef a freenolegist, an' a tellin peple thar caracter by feelin' ove thar heads. The neighbors, hevin a lively idear ove "my son" SUT'S proness to cussedness, an' damfool, immejuntly sent for him. I havent yet remarked, that at this time ove his life, he was as fat as a butterball, it bein' a great season for 'simmons, an' punkins. Jist as soon as the blind man toch "my son" SUT'S face, he shrunk back, an' said— "Gentlemen, it is unmanly, and a shame, to play tricks on one blind." They all dident onderstan' him, an' swore if thar was a trick, they dident know ove it. "Well! well!" sez he, "It *might* a been a mistake, your puttin' the boy at me wrong aind fore-mos'—fetch him up agin." This time he toutch'd "my son" SUT, first on the snout, an' after feelin' ove hit, for a good spell doubtfully, he went for the bumps, an' give in the verdick, that if he escaped bein' a suckis rider, or a stage driver, thar was no knowin' what he mout come too—hit all depended on luck *en-tirely,* for his was the best ballanced head, to make a damfool, he'd ever felt, an' that he wouldent be surprised to hear of his goin' to the penitentiary, hell, or Congriss, any day—that he was equal to the imergency.[7] I think I have remarked before, that I believe in perdickshun.

Somewhere about this time, a well-to-do neighbor, after tryin'

---

shoulders, and with his hands holding on to his hair. At this there was another and still louder shout, but not a muscle of Ulysses' face moved. There was not a tremor of his nerves. A few more rounds and the ring-master gave it up; he had come across a boy that the pony and the monkey both could not dismount.
Grant, *op. cit.*

7. "When Ulysses was about ten years old, the first phrenologist who ever made his appearance in that part of the country came to our neighborhood. He awakened a good deal of interest in the science, and was prevailed upon to remain there some time. One Dr. Buckner, who was rather inclined to be officious on most occasions, in order to test the accuracy of the phrenologist, asked him if he would be blindfolded, and then examine a head. This was at one of his public lectures. The phrenologist replied that he would. So they blindfolded him, and then brought Ulysses forward to have his head examined. He felt it over for a time, saying scarcely anything more than to mutter to himself, 'It is no very common head. It is an extraordinary head.' At length Dr. Buckner broke in with the inquiry whether the boy would be likely to distinguish himself in the mathematics? 'Yes,' said the phrenologist, 'in mathematics or anything else; it would not be strange if we should see him President of the United States.'" Grant, *op. cit.*, XXIV (March 14, 1868), 4.

to school several boys, an' all ove 'em turnin' out miserabil, *miserabil* failures, concluded, as public opinion had fixed "my son" SUT'S fate, that he'd give him a chance to dodge hit; so, by a sartin slight ove han', not at all necessary to mention here, he got smuggled into school.[8] The marster give him the first five letters ove the alfibat, to git by hart. Ove course, to this good day, "my son" SUT haint recited—he's very taciturn.[9] A powerful sharp boy (as *he* thought,) wonst offered to bet "my son" SUT a dozin marvils, that he ("my son" SUT,) couldent jump foar feet, an' let him (the smart boy,) pick the groun', an' the course to jump. Ove course "my son" SUT tuck him up (he woudent a tuck a dare from the devil.) Well! Smarty tuck "my son" within three feat ove a frame house, an' told him to jump toards the house, an' at hit he went—you bet. The licks could be hearn a mile, but, arter a while, the weatherboards give way; so did the laths, an' plarster—"my son" SUT *won them marvils.*[10] When he come home, his head was as big as a bushell, an' his brains wer churned as thin as water, an' when he shook his head, they sloshed. They slosh yet.

In consequence ove the above norated great feat, the boys

8. Jesse Root Grant acquired an appointment for Ulysses to West Point by an accidental turn of circumstances. The young man appointed from Grant's Congressional district failed the entrance examinations, but his family kept it a secret locally. Jesse somehow learned of this and wrote the Congressional Representative who appointed Ulysses on the day before his term of office ended. As Jesse noted, "A day's delay in the mail that carried my letter would have made some difference in the history of one man, if not of the country." *Ibid.*

9. "As is well known, it is the practice at West Point to get some rig, run, or joke on every new-comer. . . . In the course of the first night, one of the cadets, dressed as an officer, entered the room where Ulysses and his chum were sleeping. . . . He, then, producing a book, ordered that, before morning, they should each commit to memory a lesson of twenty pages. 'All right, all right,' responded Ulysses; and as soon as the pretended officer had withdrawn he went quietly back to bed, while his companion sat up and studied all night. Of course, the recitation has not been called for." *Ibid.*

10. "Ulysses came to him [a schoolmate named John Marshall], one day, and offered to bet a half-a-dozen marbles that he could jump twenty-five feet, at a single jump, he to select his own jumping ground. Marshall took him up, and they made the bet. Near by the tannery was a high, perpindicular bluff. Ulysses went to the top of this and jumped off, sinking up to his middle in the soft mud where he struck; but he won the wager." *Ibid.*

roun' thar concluded that "my son" SUT, warn't fit to live, so they "went for him." He come home arter a shot gun to defend hissef, an never went back again.[11] "My son SUT" was slow to wrath but generally fast *from* hit. He was born a beautiful child, but some how, didn't git purtier as he grow'd up, like tother childer.[12] I shall always think that, bustin' head fust throu' that ar weather boarded house, had sumthin to do with hit. That is his beefey egspression ove head, an' face.

Yours Respectively,
HOSS LOVINGOOD,
Sire of the renowned Sut.

11. "Ulysses had a very peacable, equable disposition, and had no inclination to quarrel, but he would not be imposed upon. On one occasion, when he was quite small, he rescued an inoffensive boy, who worked for us, from a trick which a large number of his companions were able to perpetrate upon him. The whole crowd then made for Ulysses, and he came home for a gun to defend himself." *Ibid.*

12. "In respect to looks he was a most beautiful child; but I thought he did not grow up as handsome as our other boys." *Ibid.*

THE EARLY LIFE OF SUT LOVINGOOD,
WRITTEN BY HIS DAD, III

T O OUR READERS.

We are truly sorry to announce that the last letter from our old friend, "Hoss," closed the series of his letters on the early life of his son "SUT." This truly to be deplored fact is owing to the imprudence of a friend. It seems that this friend called on MR. HOSS LOVINGOOD and informed him that the public looked with anxiety and interest for *his* version of that "playing hoss business," and also the reasons why he had always treated SUT as the black sheep of his flock, until he obtained for himself a national distinction.[1] This palpable prying into private affairs insulted the old man—he took what is commonly termed "the sulks," and swore that "he wouldn't budge another durn'd inch," and he won't. We think, too, that some unfriendly criticism has reached his ears touching his poetry and egotism, be this as it may. We fear that this is "his last appearance on any stage," and we in our heart can not much blame the old man, for really he has been very cavalierly treated, simply for thinking his very black crow was a very white one; and, no one else volunteering, he blew his own cracked horn to that note, not dreaming that he would become the laughing stock of the continent.

This story appeared in Knoxville *Press and Messenger*, III (May 21, 1868), 1.

1. Ulysses had been treated by Jesse Grant as the black sheep of the family when he proved to be totally unsuited for the business world in which the other male members of the family thrived. When Jesse divided up his business interests upon retirement, no portion was given to Ulysses, and he turned a deaf ear toward requests for loans when Ulysses was trying to make a go of farming. But he changed his attitude when his son became a prominent military and political figure. Lloyd Lewis, *Captain Sam Grant*, pp. 333–334, 351–354.

SUT LOVINGOOD'S ALLEGORY

THOSE of us who have not yet reached that ferry, so dreaded by many, yet anxiously looked forward to by the footsore and weary ones, who have passed but few cool fountains, or hospitable shelters, along their bleak road, must well remember the good old days of camp meetings, battalion musters, tax gatherings, and shooting matches. Well! there was the house raising too, and the quiltings, and the corn shuckings, where the darkey's happy song was heard for the last time. And then, the moonlight dance in the yard—"Yas by geminey!" interrupted Sut, "an' the riding home ahine the he fellers, on the same hoss, arter the dancin was done, an' the moon gone down. When, if hit hadent been for the well balanced gall, you couldn't a staid on yer critter, but would a bin foun' nex' morning, with yer hed in the branch, holdin a death holt to a willer root with her teeth, whilst some feller rode like h--l arter the coroner, afore any body would venter to haul you out."—

I was just thinking boys, while Sut was speaking, whether we are the gainer by the discoveries—inventions—innovations, and prayers, of the last forty years. Whether the railway—telegraph—chloroform—moral reform, and other advancements, as they are termed, have really advanced us any, in the right direction or—

"Stop right thar, George, an' take my idear ove the thing, fresh from water. I know powerful well that I is a durn'd fool, an' all that—but I can *see*, by golly! Don't the Bible tell about them seekin' out many strange inventions? Well! thars the tex', now. An' if I wer a practized hardshell, with ontax'd whisky in me deep enuff to swim a rat, I could make these woods quake, an' that ar mountain roar. But bein' as hit is, I mus' just talk, bein' content if ara one ove you boys will stay awake an' listen. Some ove you minds the boy that started to school one sleety mornin', an' slipp'd two steps backward for one forrid. He only got thar,

This story appeared in Knoxville *Press and Messenger*, III (September 17, 1868), 1.

you mine, by turnin' roun', an' gwine tother way. Well! that's the world's fix to-day, an' if heaven is the hotel that they is aimin' to sleep in, if they don't turn an' go tother way, I'm dod-drabitted if they don't 'lie out.'

"Nater, George, teaches the cow not to eat laurel or night-shade, an' the dorg to hunt grass, when he has gorged too much 'turkey with ister [1] stuffin', (dorgs do eat sich things right often, you know). So, as we grow old, nater makes some ove their instinck grow an' brighten in us, showin' one, now an' then, that we is on the wrong road, an' might eat nightshade, for hit's plenty. That's what makes you compar the days ove the fiddle, loom an' cradle with the peaner, ball-room an' wetnurse, ove these days. In comparin' 'em, you may take one person, a family, or a county, at a time, an' you'll find that we haint gain'd a step on the right road, an' if the fog would clear up we'd find heaven behind us, an' not strength enuff left to reach hit alone, if we wer to turn back. No, boys, we aint as *good* as we wer forty years ago. We am too dam artifichul, interprizin an' *sharp*—we know too much. We ought to be sarved like Old Brakebill sarved his black billy goat. We desarve hit, mos' all ove us."

"Old Brakebill was a Dutchman, a rale silver dollar Dutch-man. *He* wer fool enuff to think that both parties to a trade ought to hev the best ove hit. That is, somehow in this way: If you had wheat, an' to spare, an' wanted corn, an' I had corn, an' to spare, an' wanted wheat, an' two bushels ove one was worth one bushel of t'other, all the neighborhood over, then we ought to swap. On that sort ove principle he'd trade, an' on no other. As to 'out smartin'' anybody, he know'd no more about hit than the rulin' politicians ove our day know ove statesmanship, or the doctors ove mullygrubs [2] in the brain. He dident attrack much notice then, for he wer jist like most everybody else. But now, if he wer alive, he'd git his broad sturn kick'd out ove church, an' be shot for a damfool, afore he could git out ove the graveyard. 'Behine the age,' an' all that, you know.

"Well! jist wish I wer behine the age mise'f, say some forty or fifty years."

Well! Sut if you will not let me talk, suppose, you tell us how Brakebill, served his black billy goat. And let us draw no compar-

1. Perhaps, oyster.
2. Mulligrubs: a melancholy, despondent mood.

isons between the lost past and the present, which we must endure.

"Oh! I dont know much about hit. Only hearsay, from the old folks, you know. Hit seems, that he had, what would be call'd now a days, a progressive billy goat—a regular, walkin insult to man, an' beast; he strutted, with his hine laigs, and munched, like a fool gall with hir fore ones. An' then his tail—hit said, 'you-be-dam,' all day long, an' him as black as a coal cellar, at midnight at that. He would a suited our day to a dot tho', an' our day would a suited him. He could a hilt his own, even agin the 'busines men,' (they am all the go now, you know), an' durn my buttons, if he dident look an' act adzackley like 'em—beard, eyes, forred, dress, tail, and chewin, ways, an' voice. He did, by gemi-ney!

"But, he wer altogether too dam smart for Brakebill, or Brake-bill's day, an' generashun beyant all sort of doubt. That ar meterfistickal,[3] free will, billy goat wer forty years ahead ove *his* day. As they say in praise ove some cussed raskil, when he gets a million in a week, when at the gineril rate ove fortin [4] makin, hit had orter took him sixty days. He had been showin many marks ove progress, an' higher law, for a good while, without attractin much notice any way. Sich as buttin old misses Brakebill, bucket an' all, belly down, clean thru onder the cow, as she stoop'd to milk her. An' then buttin the cow herself out ove her slop tub, so that he could wet his own beard in her supper. That wer "higher law," warnt hit? Or he'd watch for the old man, to go from the crib to the hog pen, with thirty big ears of corn, piled on his arm. When he'd make a de-monstrashun in the rear, that would send the old feller, spread eagle fashion, plowin gravel with his snout, while he impudently munch'd the hog's corn. That were financee-rin, I s'pose. Or, he'd jump up an' but the under side ove the scaffol, whar the peaches wer spred to sun dry, an' then 'ap-propriate' all that he jar'd over the aidge. That mus' a been what they now call 'strategy,' dont you recon?

"Old Misses Tardiff, a two hundred pound mother in the church, wer once out in the thicket alone, near the camp-groun', during the fall meetin, at secret prayer, an' hit wer away deep into a tolerable dark night. Benny, (that wer the goat's name)

3. Metaphysical.
4. Fortune.

were in the thicket too, an' seeing her on her knees, bobbin her head up an' down, he tuck hit for a buttin challenge, or pur-tended that he did. So immejeretly he went for the 'bull curl'[5] in her forred, turnin her numerous summersets, down hill, into the branch, an' then runnin over her, with a 'B-Bu-Bub-Baa-a,' by golly. Geminey cricket! dont you recon that ole 'oman tho't that the hill had blow'd up? Well, when she got able, an' her cloths sorter wrung dry—she went into camps, an' give in her 'speri-ence: That she had jist had a pussonel, breeches holt, wrastle, with the devil hissef, an' had come off conquerer, an' ment tharfore to wear the crown, but, that his smell ove brimstone an' hartshorn come mitey near chokin' her dead. Thar was ni onto eighty come up at the next call for mourners. But when they tried old man Brakebill, to git him up, he only smiled an' shook his head, sayin', 'Vait dill I shees if my Benny ishent in der dicket shum var.'

"Now, as I said afore, all this dident give the goat much ove a name, or attract much attenshun. He was look'd on as a raskil, that's a fact. But bein' a *beast,* he warn't dealt with like he would a been had he been a human, by them old time people. If he'd a lived now adays, I'l jist be durn'd if they hadent a made him President ove a college or the passun ove Plymouth Church, an' bilt him a harim or a corectory, which is hit? Them old fogy folks had a mitey poor idear ove progress, that's a fac'.

"But at last Mister Benny overdid the thing; he got to be a little too durn'd progressive for old Brakebill and his times. His sin foun' him out, an' he wer made to simmer down to a level surface with the loss ove all, that makes life wholesome to a goat. The fac' is, like mos' ove these yere human progress hum-bugs, he jis' played h−−l with hissef.

"Old Brakebill got to noticin that thar was something wrong with his sheep. The ewes butted at the ram, spiteful like, butted one another an' behaved powerful bad ginerally. Arter a while, on 'zaminin he foun' that some ove the lambs had patches ove coarse har in their wool, an' wer sproutin' beards. Nex' he found' his young pigs behavin' curious to be dutch hog's children. Rarin' up strait on thar hine laigs, clost fornint one another. Walkin' on top ove the fences—climbin' onto the shed roof ove the milk house, an' then buttin' one another off agin. An' every now an'

5. The curl of hair in the crown of the head.

then, one would hist his tail as strait up as a stack pole,[6] an' put on a stiff strut. Venuses pups, too, seem'd to hev the very devil in 'em. While one ove 'em lived on the goose grass in the yard, another one butted the house cat blind, to pussey's astonishment, wrath, an' hissin' disgust. Then another sprouted periwinkle shells above his ears, an' smelt like a bottom ove hartshorn, with a mouse in hit. An old, one-eyed goose laid aigs with hair on, an' then give milk. A jinny's colt walked half hit's time on aind, an' on a par ove split huffs, chawin' a cud made ove an old shoe sole. The hempbrake even rared on *hit's* hine laigs, threatnin the cuttin' box. Misses Brakebill left the plantation, an' the very devil was to pay generally. If you had a wanted to a bought the farm, you would a axed that dam goat the price ove hit, from his airs an' impudent ways, while the owner looked like a scared dorg, or a stepchild on the out aidge ove sufferance. Now, all this troubled the poor old Dutchman a power. He know'd that at the rate things were gwine on his stock, very soon, wouldent be worth a tinker's durn. He had a hankerin' to believe in witches an' things, anyhow; so he tho't purty strong that some ove 'em must be arter his welfar. He toted a hoss shoe in his pocket, an' got rale serious. He often axed, 'how long it wer to camp meetin' time?' Jist like little children, sittin' round the fire ove a night, axin the knittin' mother, for the fiftieth time, 'how long will hit be till Christmas?' You mus' bar in mind that the poor feller dident know the fust durn'd thing about 'progress.' At last, by the livin' jingo! the *true* idear struck him, as hit mus *us* some time. So one mornin' arter drams, he come acrost a bran new, curious, little cuss, lookin' like a cross atwixt the devil an' a cookin' stove, standin' on hit's hine laigs, a suckin' the muley cow. Arter brainin' hit with a wagon standard, he jist sot down, an' whetted his knife, ontil it would shave the har off his arm. Now, boys, that's about all that anybody now livin' knows ove the matter. Only this much was noticed thararter: That Mister Benny, billy goat, instid ove chawin his cud, with a short, quick, sassey nip, nip, nip, arter that mornin', an' plum on, ontil he dried up, an' died in a sink-hole, he chaw'd hit arter the fashion ove an old, lazy cow, when she is standin' onder the shade ove the willers, bellyfull, an' bellydeep in the creek. His tail never agin flaunted the sky, surjestin 'youbedam.' He wer the very last one that you'd a

6. A pole about which hay is stacked.

thought ove axin about the price ove the farm. An *he dident raise any more family.*

"For the sake ove this an' the nex generashun, I would like to know how Old Brakebill managed to straiten things out. If I only could find out, I'd tell Frank Blair,[7] I would, by golly! He wouldent be afeard to surjest the idear, if he tho't hit a wholesome one. Would he?"

7. Francis P. Blair, Jr. (1821–1875), was the nominee for Vice-President on the Democratic ticket at the convention that met in New York City during July, 1868. The Radical movement had stirred Blair to come to the defense of conservatives and ex-Confederates in Missouri, and he believed that the Reconstruction government should be abolished and the South allowed to reorganize itself without carpet-bag government and military domination. *Dictionary of American Biography,* II, 332–334.

Appendixes, Bibliography, Index

APPENDIX A

SINCE Harris's deft control of imagery is one of the most admirable qualities of his prose style, it is unusual that he seldom felt attracted to poetry as a medium of artistic expression. Only one of his efforts in verse has survived, perhaps the only effort to reach print. The poem is entitled "The Coat of Faded Grey," and was written by Harris for the Nashville *Daily Union and American* and published in its July 1, 1866, issue. The subject-matter is sentimental, and the entire piece displays little competence or poetic ability. It has no relationship to the rest of his writings, and is included here in an appendix in order to make this edition of Harris's uncollected works as nearly complete as possible. The poem was reprinted in the *Confederate Veteran*, XI (May, 1903), 205; and the Chattanooga *News*, May 26–31, 1913, p. 18.

In Harris's own day, someone thought well enough of this poem to set it to music. In 1866, the D. P. Faulds music publishing firm of Louisville, Kentucky, issued "The Coat of Faded Gray, Ballad," with words by G. W. Harris, and music by H. M. Hall. The sheet music was dedicated to "Miss Katie Bean, Aberdeen, Miss." The relationships of both the poem and sheet music to the times in which they were written is discussed in full in M. Thomas Inge, "George Washington Harris and Southern Poetry and Music," *Mississippi Quarterly*, XVII (Winter, 1963–1964), 36–44. A portion of the words from the sheet music appears in Willard A. and Porter W. Heaps, *The Singing Sixties* (Norman, 1960), p. 261. The only known copy of the sheet music is on deposit in the Tennessee State Library and Archives, Nashville.

THE COAT OF FADED GREY.
By Geo. W. Harris.

For the Union and American.]

A low hut rests in Lookout's shade
As rots its moss-grown roof away,
While sundown's glories softly fade,
Closing another weary day;
The battle's din is heard no more—
No more the hunted stand at bay—
The breezes through the lowly door
Swing mute a coat of faded grey,
    A tatter'd relic of the fray—
    A thread-bare coat of faded grey.

'Tis hanging on the rough log wall
Near to the foot of a widow's bed,
By a white plume and well-worn shawl—
His gift—the happy morn they wed,
By the wee slip their dead child wore—
The one they gave the name of May,
By her rag doll and pinafore—
By right it's there, that coat of grey,
    A red fleck'd relic of the fray—
    An armless coat of faded grey.

Her all of life now drapes that wall,
Poor and patient still she waits
On God's good time to gently call
Her, too, within the jewel'd gates;
And all she craves is here to die—
To part from these, and pass away
To join her loves eternally
That wore the slip—the coat of grey,
    The shell-torn relic of the fray—
    Her soldier's coat of faded grey.

APPENDIX B

ALTHOUGH the following story is attributed to George W. Harris, it is decidedly spurious, a clear case of literary plagiarism. It is an unskilled attempt at imitating Harris's style and characterization. What gives it away in the first place is the use of several characters who appear nowhere else in Sut Lovingood's yarns: Deacon Jones, Sister Poll, Suze Harkins, and Em Simmons. Harris has Sut proclaim too often against the institution of marriage to lead him suddenly into it, and the author of this spurious sketch has Sut note of Em Simmons that "Her an me expects to trot in dubble harness one of these daze." The dialect spellings here are also unlike those of Harris: "North Karlina," "famili bizness," "Wozent," "daze," "canda," "ize." Sut's cursing in the piece is much too refined for the genuine thing: "Dog my cats," "My stars alive!", and "ile bust his doggoned hed!" Most telling of all, however, is the lack of the characteristic Harris imagery, that rich profusion of similes, metaphors, and epithets found in his typical work. This sketch is an example, then, of the appropriation of Harris's character for the purposes of another writer, and is included in this edition as a literary curiosity. For an example of a similar appropriation of Johnson Jones Hooper's character, Simon Suggs, see M. Thomas Inge, "Simon Suggs Courts a Widow: A New Sketch," *Alabama Review*, XVII (April, 1964), 148–151.

The text reproduced here is from the Atlanta *Constitution*, I (May 23, 1869), 4, the earliest printing. It was reprinted with editorial revision in *Beadle's Dime Spread Eagle Speaker*, Speaker Series, Number 10 (New York: Beadle and Adams, 1859), pp. 68–69.

SUT LOVENGOOD AT A CANDY PULLING

I had a heep of truble las Chrismas, an Ile tell you how it happened. Deken Jones's gals give a candy pullin and I got a stool, as they say in North Karlina, an so over I goes. Sister Poll and me went together, and when we got to mam Joneses the house was chuck full. Dog my cats ef thar was room to turn round. Thar was Suze Harkins, shese as big as a skinned hoss, and six other Harkinses, and all the Scrogginses, and Williamses, and Simmonses, and Pedigrews, and Deken and the Dekeness, and enough little Dekenses to set up half a dozen young folks in the famili bizness.

Well, bimbey the pot begun to bile, and then the fun begun. We all got our plates reddy, and put flour on our hands to keep the candy from stickin, an then we pitched intu pullin. Wozent it fun? I never saw laffin and cuttin up in all by born daze. I made a canda bird for Em Simmons. Her an me expecks to trot in dubble harness one of these daze. She made a candy goos for me. Then we got to throwin candy balls intu one anothers hair, and a runnin from one side of the house to tother, and out intu the kitchen, till everything on the place was all over gommed with candy. I sot on a pine bench, and Em Simmons sot close to me. Suse Harkins, confound her pickter, throwd a candy ball sock intu one of mi ize. I made a bulge to run arter her, and heerd sumtin rip. My stars alive! Wozent I pickled? I looked around, and thar was the gabel end of my bran new britches a stickin to the pine bench. I backed up again to the wall, sorter crawfish like and grinned.

"Sut," ses sister Poll, "what's the matter?"

"Sut," says Em, "come away from that wall, you'll git all over greasy."

"Let her grease!" says I, and I sot down on a washbord, that was a lying across a tub feelin worse than an old maid at a weddin. Purty soon, I felt sumthin hurt and purty soon it hurt agin. Ice—whiz! I jumpt ten feet hi, kicked over the tub, out flu old Joneses Chrismus turky, and you ought to a seed me git. I cut for tall timber now jumpt staked and ridered fences and smashed down bresh like a runaway herikan till I got home, and went to bed and stade there two daze.

If old dekin Joneses barn burns down next winter, and ime arrested for it, and enyboddy peers as a witness agin me, ile bust his doggoned hed! Them's my sentiments.

SUT LOVENGOOD.

BIBLIOGRAPHY

HARRIS AND HIS BACKGROUND

Editions of Works.

Sut Lovingood. Yarns Spun by a "Nat'ral Born Durn'd Fool["]. *Warped and Wove for Public Wear.* By George W. Harris. New York: Dick & Fitzgerald, 1867.

Sut Lovingood Travels with Old Abe Lincoln. By George W. Harris. Introduction by Edd Winfield Parks. Chicago: The Black Cat Press, 1937. Reprints the Lincoln satires in a corrected text; a limited edition of 150 copies.

Sut Lovingood. By George Washington Harris. Edited with an Introduction by Brom Weber. New York: Grove Press, 1954. Reprints eighteen of the twenty-four stories from the *Yarns*, plus the three Lincoln satires, in a text with modernized spelling.

The Lovingood Papers. Published for the Sut Society. Edited by Ben Harris McClary. Athens, Tennessee: The Sut Society, 1962. Knoxville: University of Tennessee Press, 1963, 1964, and 1965. Each of the four published issues reprints several uncollected Sut stories in original texts, reproduced without corrections or emendations, with introductions by scholars.

Sut Lovingood's Yarns. By George Washington Harris. Edited for the Modern Reader by M. Thomas Inge. New Haven: College and University Press, 1966. Reprints in original but corrected texts the entire *Yarns*, plus a selection of the uncollected stories about Sut.

Bibliography.

Blanck, Jacob. *Bibliography of American Literature.* Vol. III. New Haven: Yale University Press, 1959. Pp. 384–386.

McClary, Ben Harris. "George and Sut: A Working Bibliography." *The Lovingood Papers* (1962), pp. 5–9.

Rickels, Milton. "Selected Bibliography." In *George Washington Harris*. New York: Twayne Publishers, 1965. Pp. 145–151.

Biography and Criticism.

Bass, William W. "Sut Lovingood's Reflections on His Contemporaries." *Carson-Newman College Faculty Studies*, I (1964), 33–48.

Blair, Walter. "Sut Lovingood." *Saturday Review of Literature*, XV (November 7, 1936), 3–4, 16.

———. *Native American Humor* (1800–1900). New York: American Book Company, 1937. Reprinted with additional material, San Francisco: Chandler Publishing Company, 1960.

———. *Horse Sense in American Humor*. Chicago: University of Chicago Press, 1942.

Blair, Walter, Theodore Hornberger, and Randall Stewart. *American Literature, A Brief History*. Chicago: Scott, Foresman and Company, 1964.

Boykin, Carol. "Sut's Speech: The Dialect of a 'Nat'ral Borned' Mountaineer." *The Lovingood Papers* (1965), 36–42.

Brown, J. Thompson, Jr. "George W. Harris." In *The Library of Southern Literature*. Edited by E. D. Alderman, J. C. Harris, and C. W. Kent. Vol. V. Atlanta: Martin and Hoyt Company, 1907. Pp. 2099–2110.

Cohen, Hennig. "Mark Twain's Sut Lovingood." *The Lovingood Papers* (1962), pp. 19–24.

Cohen, Hennig, and William B. Dillingham, eds. *Humor of the Old Southwest*. Boston: Houghton Mifflin Company, 1964.

Covici, Pascal, Jr. *Mark Twain's Humor*. Dallas: Southern Methodist University Press, 1962.

Davidson, Donald. *The Tennessee*. Vol. I. New York: Rinehart and Company, 1946.

Day, Donald. "The Humorous Works of George W. Harris." *American Literature*, XIV (January 1943), 391–406.

———. "The Political Satires of George W. Harris." *Tennessee Historical Quarterly*, IV (December 1945), 320–338.

———. "The Life of George Washington Harris." *Tennessee Historical Quarterly*, VI (March 1947), 3–38.

————. "George Washington Harris." In *Encyclopaedia Britannica.* Vol. XI. Chicago: Encyclopaedia Britannica, 1960. P. 217.

DeVoto, Bernard. *Mark Twain's America.* New York: Little, Brown and Co., 1932.

Henneman, John Bell, ed. *The South in the Building of the Nation.* Vol. VIII. Richmond: Southern Historical Publication Society, 1909.

Hubbell, Jay B. *The South in American Literature.* Durham: Duke University Press, 1954.

Inge, M. Thomas. "Sut Lovingood: An Examination of the Nature of a 'Nat'ral Born Durn'd Fool.' " *Tennessee Historical Quarterly,* XIX (September 1960), 231–251.

————. "William Faulkner and George Washington Harris: In the Tradition of Southwestern Humor." *Tennessee Studies in Literature,* VII (1962), 47–59.

————. "A Personal Encounter with George W. Harris." *The Lovingood Papers* (1963), pp. 9–12.

————. "George Washington Harris and Southern Poetry and Music." *Mississippi Quarterly,* XVII (Winter 1963–64), 36–44.

————. "Stark Young's Sut Lovingood." *The Lovingood Papers* (1964), pp. 45–46.

————. "G. W. Harris's 'The Doctor's Bill': A Tale About Dr. J. G. M. Ramsey." *Tennessee Historical Quarterly,* XXIV (Summer 1965), 185–194.

————. "Sut and His Illustrators." *The Lovingood Papers* (1965), 26–35.

Ives, Sumner. "A Theory of Literary Dialect." *Tulane Studies in Literature,* II (1950), 137–182.

Knight, Donald R. "Sut's Dog Imagery." *The Lovingood Papers* (1965), 59–60.

Long, E. Hudson. "Sut Lovingood and Mark Twain's *Joan of Arc.*" *Modern Language Notes,* LXIV (January 1949), 37–39.

Lynn, Kenneth S., ed. *The Comic Tradition in America.* New York: Doubleday Anchor Books, 1958.

————. *Mark Twain and Southwestern Humor.* Boston: Little, Brown and Company, 1959.

Matthiessen, F. O. *American Renaissance.* New York: Oxford University Press, 1941.

McClary, Ben Harris. "Sut Lovingood Views 'Abe Linkhorn.'" *Lincoln Herald,* LVI (Fall 1954), 44–45.

———. "Sut Lovingood's Country." *Southern Observer,* III (January 1955), 5–7.

———. "The Real Sut." *American Literature,* XXVII (March 1955), 105–106.

———. "Sanky and Sut." *Southern Observer,* IX (January 1962), 13.

McKeithan, D. M. "Mark Twain's Story of the Bull and the Bees." *Tennessee Historical Quarterly,* XI (September 1952), 246–253.

———. "Bull Rides Described by 'Scroggins,' G. W. Harris, and Mark Twain." *Southern Folklore Quarterly,* XVII (December 1953), 241–243.

Meine, Franklin J. *Tall Tales of the Southwest.* New York: Alfred A. Knopf, 1930.

Mellen, George F. "Sut Lovingood's Yarns." Knoxville *Sentinel,* February 11, 1909.

———. "George W. Harris." Knoxville *Sentinel,* February 13, 1909.

———. "Lovingood's Settings." Knoxville *Sentinel,* March 7, 1909.

———. "Sut Lovingood." Knoxville *Sentinel,* January 8, 1914.

Parks, Edd Winfield. *Segments of Southern Thought.* Athens: University of Georgia Press, 1937.

Penrod, James. "Folk Humor in *Sut Lovingood's Yarns.*" *Tennessee Folklore Society Bulletin,* XVI (December 1950), 76–84.

Rickels, Milton. "The Imagery of George Washington Harris." *American Literature,* XXXI (May 1959), 173–187.

———. *George Washington Harris.* New York: Twayne Publishers, 1965.

Smith, Charles Foster. "Southern Dialect in Life and Literature." *The Southern Bivouac,* New Series I (November 1885), 343–351.

Stewart, Randall. "Tidewater and Frontier." *Georgia Review,* XIII (Fall 1959), 296–307.

Tandy, Jennette. *Crackerbox Philosophers in American Humor and Satire.* New York: Columbia University Press, 1925.

Thorp, Willard. *American Humorists.* University of Minnesota Pamphlets on American Writers, No. 42. Minneapolis: University of Minnesota Press, 1964.

Watterson, Henry, ed. *Oddities in Southern Life and Character.* Boston: Houghton Mifflin and Co., 1882.

Weber, Brom, ed. *An Anthology of American Humor.* New York: Thomas Y. Crowell Company, 1962.

―――. "A Note on Edmund Wilson and George Washington Harris." *The Lovingood Papers* (1962), pp. 47–53.

Wilson, Edmund. "Poisoned!" *New Yorker,* XXXI (May 7, 1955), 150–159.

―――. *Patriotic Gore.* New York: Oxford University Press, 1962.

Yates, Norris W. *William T. Porter and the Spirit of the Times.* Baton Rouge: Louisiana State University Press, 1957.

Background.

Avery, S. P., ed. *The Harp of a Thousand Strings; or Laughter for a Lifetime.* New York: Dick & Fitzgerald, 1858.

Anderson, John Q. "Scholarship in Southwestern Humor—Past and Present." *Mississippi Quarterly,* XVII (Spring 1964), 67–86.

Babcock, C. Merton. *The American Frontier, A Social and Literary Record.* New York: Holt, Rinehart and Winston, 1965.

Barclay, R. E. *Ducktown Back in Raht's Time.* Chapel Hill: University of North Carolina Press, 1946.

Beadle's Dime Spread Eagle Speaker. Speaker Series, Number 10. New York: Beadle and Adams, 1859.

Beatty, Richmond Croom, Floyd Watkins, and Thomas Daniel Young, eds. *The Literature of the South.* Chicago: Scott, Foresman and Company, 1952.

Bettersworth, John K. "The Humor of the Old Southwest: Yesterday and Today." *Mississippi Quarterly,* XVII (Spring 1964), 87–94.

Blair, Walter, Theodore Hornberger, and Randall Stewart, eds. *The Literature of the United States.* Vol. II. Chicago: Scott, Foresman and Company, 1953.

Boatright, Mody C. *Folk Laughter on the American Frontier.* New York: Macmillan Company, 1949.

Bond, Richmond P. *English Burlesque Poetry 1700–1750.* Cambridge: Harvard University Press, 1932.

Botkin, B. A., ed. *A Treasury of Southern Folklore.* New York: Crown Publishers, 1949.

Bradley, Sculley, Richmond Croom Beatty, and E. Hudson Long, eds. *The American Tradition in Literature.* Vol. I. New York: W. W. Norton and Company, 1962.

Bullitt, John T. *Jonathan Swift and the Anatomy of Satire.* Cambridge: Harvard University Press, 1953.

Chute, Marchette. *Geoffrey Chaucer of England.* New York: E. P. Dutton, 1958.

Frank, Fedora S. *Five Families and Eight Young Men.* Nashville: Tennessee Book Company, 1962.

Frye, Northrop. *Anatomy of Criticism.* Princeton: Princeton University Press, 1957.

Groce, George C., and David H. Wallace. *The New York Historical Society's Dictionary of Artists in America 1564–1860.* New Haven: Yale University Press, 1957.

Hall, Wade. *The Smiling Phoenix, Southern Humor from 1865–1914.* Gainesville: University of Florida Press, 1965.

Heaps, Willard A. and Porter W. *The Singing Sixties.* Norman: University of Oklahoma Press, 1960.

Hoole, W. Stanley. *Alias Simon Suggs, The Life and Times of Johnson Jones Hooper.* University: University of Alabama Press, 1952.

Hopkins, Robert. "Simon Suggs: A Burlesque Campaign Biography." *American Quarterly,* XV (Fall 1963), 459–463.

Hudson, Arthur Palmer, ed. *Humor of the Old Deep South.* New York: Macmillan Company, 1936.

Inge, M. Thomas. "Simon Suggs Courts a Widow: A New Sketch." *Alabama Review,* XVII (April 1964), 148–151.

Kernan, Alvin. *The Cankered Muse.* New Haven: Yale University Press, 1959.

Kunitz, Stanley J., and Howard Haycraft, eds. *American Authors 1600–1900.* New York: H. W. Wilson Company, 1938.

Link, Samuel Albert. *Pioneers of Southern Literature.* Nashville: M. E. Church, 1913.

Longstreet, A. B. *Georgia Scenes*. New York: Harper and Brothers, 1852.

Meltzer, Milton. *Mark Twain Himself*. New York: Thomas Y. Crowell Company, 1960.

Modern Language Association of America. *American Literary Manuscripts*. Austin: University of Texas Press, 1960.

Parks, Edd Winfield. "Craddock's First Pseudonym." *East Tennessee Historical Society Publications*, No. 6 (1934), 67–80.

———. "The Intent of the Ante-Bellum Southern Humorists." *Mississippi Quarterly*, XIII (Fall 1960), 163–168.

Rickels, Milton. *Thomas Bangs Thorpe, Humorist of the Old Southwest*. Baton Rouge: Louisiana State University Press, 1962.

Rourke, Constance. *American Humor, A Study of the National Character*. New York: Harcourt, Brace and Company, 1931.

Smith, Henry Nash. *Mark Twain, The Development of a Writer*. Cambridge: Harvard University Press, 1962.

Spiller, Robert E., *et al.*, eds. *Literary History of the United States*. Third edition, revised. New York: Macmillan Company, 1963.

Stern, Madeleine B. *Imprints on History, Book Publishers and American Frontiers*. Bloomington: Indiana University Press, 1956.

Thorp, Willard. "Suggs and Sut in Modern Dress: the Latest Chapter in Southern Humor." *Mississippi Quarterly*, XIII (Fall 1960), 169–175.

Trent, William Peterfield, *et al.*, eds. *The Cambridge History of American Literature*. Vol. II. New York: Macmillan Company, 1943.

Turner, Arlin. "Realism and Fantasy in Southern Humor." *Georgia Review*, XII (1958), 451–457.

———. "Seeds of Literary Revolt in the Humor of the Old Southwest." *Louisiana Historical Quarterly*, XXXIX (1957), 143–151.

Turner, Frederick Jackson. *The Frontier in American History*. New York: Henry Holt and Company, 1921.

Watterson, Henry. *The Compromises of Life and Other Lectures and Addresses*. New York: Duffield and Company, 1906.

Welsford, Enid. *The Fool, His Social and Literary History*. London: Faber and Faber, 1935.

Wheeler, Otis B. "Some Uses of Folk Humor in William Faulkner." *Mississippi Quarterly*, XVII (Spring 1964), 107–122.

Worcester, David. *The Art of Satire.* Cambridge: Harvard University Press, 1940.

Wright, Lyle H. *American Fiction 1851–1875.* San Marino, California: The Huntington Library, 1957.

Yates, Norris W. *The American Humorist: Conscience of the Twentieth Century.* Ames, Iowa: Iowa State University Press, 1964.

Unpublished Material.

Day, Donald. "The Life and Works of George Washington Harris." Unpublished Doctoral thesis, University of Chicago, 1942.

―――. Letters to M. Thomas Inge, dated April 20, 1960, and May 4, 1960.

Heflin, John J., Jr. "George Washington Harris, A Critical Biography." Unpublished Master's thesis, Vanderbilt University, 1934.

Inge, M. Thomas. "A Study of the Sut Lovingood Yarns and Other Writings of George Washington Harris." Unpublished Master's thesis, Vanderbilt University, 1960.

Plater, Ormonde. "Tall Tales and Tall Talk in the Sut Lovingood Stories: An Oral Tradition Influences a Literary Technique." Unpublished Master's thesis, Tulane University, 1965.

SOURCES OF TEXTS

Newspapers

Atlanta *Constitution.*

Austin (Texas) *Southern Intelligencer.*

Chattanooga *Daily American Union.*

Knoxville *Daily Press and Herald.*

Knoxville *Press and Messenger.*

Knoxville *Standard.*

Lynchburg *Daily Virginian.*

Nashville *Daily Union and American.*

Nashville *Daily Press and Times.*

Nashville *Union and American.*

Nashville *Union and Dispatch.*

New York *Atlas*.

New York *Picayune*.

Sioux City (Iowa) *Register*.

Weekly Nashville Union.

Periodicals

Confederate Veteran.

New York *Spirit of the Times*.

Nick Nax.

Yankee Notions.

REFERENCE WORKS USED IN ANNOTATIONS

Books

Angle, Paul M. *The Lincoln Reader*. New Brunswick: Rutgers University Press, 1947.

Benét, William Rose, ed. *The Reader's Encyclopedia*. New York: Thomas Y. Crowell, 1948.

Berrey, Lester V., and Melvin Van Den Bark. *The American Thesaurus of Slang*. Second Edition. New York: Thomas Y. Crowell Company, 1952.

Biographical Directory of the American Congress 1774–1961. United States Government Printing Office, 1961.

Blom, Eric, ed. *Grove's Dictionary of Music and Musicians*. 9 volumes. London: Macmillan Co., Ltd., 1954.

The Book of Common Prayer . . . According to the Use of the Protestant Episcopal Church in the United States of America. New York: G. E. Egre and W. Spottiswoode, 1850.

Bradford, Gamaliel. *Damaged Souls*. Boston: Houghton Mifflin Company, 1923.

Brinley, Francis. *Life of William T. Porter*. New York: D. Appleton and Company, 1860.

Burt, Jesse C. *Nashville Its Life and Times*. Nashville: Tennessee Book Company, 1959.

Caldwell, Joshua W. *Sketches of the Bench and Bar of Tennessee*. Knoxville: Ogden Brothers & Co., 1898.

Campbell, John. *Nashville Business Directory.* Vol. II—1855–1856. Nashville: Printed for the Author, 1855.

Carr, Joe C. *Tennessee Blue Book* 1961–1962. Nashville: Secretary of State, n.d.

Chitwood, Oliver Perry. *John Tyler, Champion of the Old South.* New York: D. Appleton-Century Company, 1939.

Clark, Thomas D. *A History of Kentucky.* New York: Prentice-Hall, Inc., 1937.

———. ed. *Travels in the Old South, A Bibliography.* Vol. III. Norman: University of Oklahoma Press, 1959.

Cobb, Howell. *Analysis of the Statutes of Georgia, in General Use.* New York: E. O. Jenkins, 1846.

Collins, Lewis. *History of Kentucky.* Revised by Richard H. Collins. Louisville, Ky.: Richard H. Collins, 1877.

The Congressional Globe. First and Second Sessions, Thirty-fourth Congress. Washington: John C. Rives, 1856.

———. First Session, Thirty-fifth Congress. Washington: John C. Rives, 1858.

Copeland, Fayette. *Kendall of the Picayune.* Norman: University of Oklahoma Press, 1943.

Coulter, E. Merton. *William G. Brownlow, Fighting Parson of the Southern Highlands.* Chapel Hill: University of North Carolina Press, 1937.

Craigie, William A., and James R. Hulbert, eds. *A Dictionary of American English on Historical Principles.* 4 volumes. Chicago: University of Chicago Press, 1938–1944.

Creekmore, Betsey Beeler. *Knoxville.* Knoxville: The University of Tennessee Press, 1958.

Crockett, David. *Col. Crockett's Exploits and Adventures in Texas.* Philadelphia: T. K. and P. G. Collins, 1836.

Cross, Nelson. *The Modern Ulysses, LL.D.* New York: J. S. Redfield, 1872.

Current, Richard Nelson. *Old Thad Stevens, A Story of Ambition.* Madison: the University of Wisconsin Press, 1942.

Donald, David. *Charles Sumner and the Coming of the Civil War.* New York: Alfred A. Knopf, 1960.

Douglas, Byrd. *Steamboatin' on the Cumberland.* Nashville: Tennessee Book Company, 1961.

Ford, Ira W. *Traditional Music of America.* New York: E. P. Dutton and Company, 1940.

Fraser, Hugh Russell. *Democracy in the Making, The Jackson-Tyler Era.* New York: The Bobbs-Merrill Company, 1938.

Gohmann, Sister Mary de Lourdes. *Political Nativism in Tennessee to 1860.* Washington: Catholic University of America, 1938.

Gove, Phillip Babcock, ed. *Webster's Third New International Dictionary.* Springfield, Mass.: G. and C. Merriam Company, 1961.

Gower, Herschel, and Jack Allen, eds. *Pen and Sword, The Life and Journals of Randal W. McGavock.* Nashville: Tennessee Historical Commission, 1959.

Gregory, Winfred, ed. *American Newspapers 1821–1936,* A Union List of Files Available in the United States and Canada. New York: The H. W. Wilson Company, 1937.

Hallum, John. *The Diary of An Old Lawyer.* Nashville: Southwestern Publishing House, 1895.

Hamer, Philip M., ed. *Tennessee, A History 1673–1932.* 4 volumes. New York: The American Historical Society, Inc., 1933.

Haywood, John, and Robert L. Cobb. *The Statute Laws of Tennessee, of a Public and General Nature.* 2 volumes. Knoxville: F. S. Heiskell, 1831.

Hesseltine, William B. *Ulysses S. Grant, Politician.* New York: Dodd, Mead & Company, 1935.

History of Tennessee, From the Earliest Time to the Present. 16 volumes. Nashville: The Goodspeed Publishing Company, 1886–1887.

Hofstadter, Richard, William Miller, and Daniel Aaron. *The American Republic.* 2 volumes. Englewood Cliffs, New Jersey: Prentice-Hall, 1959.

Holzman, Robert S. *Stormy Ben Butler.* New York: Macmillan, 1954.

Hubbell, Jay B. *South and Southwest, Literary Essays and Reminiscences.* Durham: Duke University Press, 1965.

James, Marquis. *The Raven, A Biography of Sam Houston.* Indianapolis: The Bobbs-Merrill Company, 1929.

Johnson, Allen, and Dumas Malone, eds. *Dictionary of American Biography.* 21 volumes. New York: Charles Scribner's Sons, 1928–1936.

Julian, John, ed. *A Dictionary of Hymnology.* Revised edition. London: John Murray, 1907.

Leach, Maria, ed. *Standard Dictionary of Folklore, Mythology, and Legend.* 2 volumes. New York: Funk and Wagnall Company, 1950.

Lewis, Lloyd. *Captain Sam Grant.* Boston: Little, Brown and Company, 1950.

―――. *Sherman, Fighting Prophet.* New York: Harcourt, Brace and Company, 1932.

Mathews, Mitford M. *A Dictionary of Americanisms on Historical Principles.* 2 volumes. Chicago: University of Chicago Press, 1951.

McKellar, Kenneth. *Tennessee Senators.* Kingsport, Tennessee: Southern Publishers, Inc., 1942.

Moore, Thomas. *Irish Melodies and Sacred Songs.* New York: Oakley, Mason and Company, 1869.

Morehead, Albert H., Richard L. Frey, and Geoffrey Mott-Smith. *The New Complete Hoyle.* New York: Garden City Books, 1956.

Morgan, Robert J. *A Whig Embattled, The Presidency Under John Tyler.* Lincoln: University of Nebraska Press, 1954.

Morris, Richard B., editor. *Encyclopedia of American History.* New York: Harper & Brothers, 1953. Revised and Enlarged Edition. New York: Harper & Row, Publishers, 1961.

Mott, Frank Luther. *A History of American Magazines.* Vol. I. New York: D. Appleton and Company, 1930. Vol. II–IV. Cambridge: Harvard University Press, 1938–1957.

Nashville City and Business Directory, For 1860–61. Volume V. Nashville: L. P. Williams & Co., 1860.

Nason, Elias, and Thomas Russell. *The Life and Public Services of Henry Wilson.* Boston: B. B. Russell, 1876.

The National Cyclopaedia of American Biography. 46 volumes. New York: James T. White and Company, 1893–1963.

Neville, Bert. *Directory of Tennessee River Steamboats.* Selma, Alabama, 1963.

Nicolay, John G., and John Hay. *Abraham Lincoln, A History.* 10 volumes. New York: The Century Co., 1890.

Odell, George C. D. *Annals of the New York Stage.* 15 volumes. New York: Columbia University Press, 1927–1949.

Overdyke, W. Darrell. *The Know-Nothing Party in the South.* Baton Rouge: Louisiana State University Press, 1950.

Parks, Joseph Howard. *John Bell of Tennessee.* Baton Rouge: Louisiana State University Press, 1950.

Paul, Howard, and George Gebbie, eds. *The Stage and Its Stars, Past and Present.* 2 volumes. Philadelphia: Gebbie and Co., n.d.

Pioneer Citizens, History of Atlanta, 1833–1902. Atlanta: Byrd Printing Company, 1902.

Ramsey, Dr. J. G. M. *Autobiography and Letters.* Edited by William B. Hesseltine. Nashville: Tennessee Historical Commission, 1954.

Randall, J. G. *The Civil War and Reconstruction.* Boston: D. C. Heath and Company, 1953.

Riddle, A. G. *The Life of Benjamin F. Wade.* Cleveland: William W. Williams, 1886.

Roseboom, Eugene H. *A History of Presidential Elections.* New York: The Macmillan Company, 1957.

Rothrock, Mary U. ed. *The French Broad–Holston Country.* Knoxville: East Tennessee Historical Society, 1946.

Rowland, Dunbar, ed. *Encyclopedia of Mississippi History.* Madison, Wisconsin: S. A. Brant, 1907.

Sharp, J. M. *Recollections and Hearsays of Athens, Fifty Years and Beyond.* Athens, Tennessee, 1933.

Sherwin, Oscar. *Prophet of Liberty, the Life and Times of Wendell Phillips.* New York: Bookman Associates, 1958.

Smith, C. Alphonso. *O. Henry, Biography.* New York: Doubleday, Page & Company, 1916.

Spaeth, Sigmund. *A History of Popular Music in America.* New York: Random House, 1948.

Stedman, Thomas Lathrop. *Stedman's Medical Dictionary.* Edited by Norman Burke Taylor and Allen Ellsworth Taylor. Nineteenth

Revised Edition. Baltimore: The Williams & Wilkins Company, 1957.

Stoddard, Henry Luther. *Horace Greeley, Printer, Editor, Crusader.* New York: G. P. Putnam's Sons, 1946.

Taylor, Archer, and Bartlett Jere Whiting. *A Dictionary of American Proverbs and Proverbial Phrases 1820–1880.* Cambridge: Harvard University Press, 1958.

Teller, James David. *Louis Agassiz, Scientist and Teacher.* Columbus: Ohio State University Press, 1947.

Thomas, Benjamin P. *Abraham Lincoln, A Biography.* New York: Alfred A. Knopf, 1952.

Van Deusen, Glyndon G. *Horace Greeley, Nineteenth-Century Crusader.* Philadelphia: University of Pennsylvania Press, 1953.

Webster's Geographical Dictionary. Springfield, Mass.: G. and C. Merriam Co., 1955.

Williams' Knoxville Directory, City Guide, and Business Mirror. Vol. I, 1859–1860. Knoxville: C. S. Williams, 1859.

Williams, Samuel C. *Phases of the History of the Supreme Court of Tennessee.* Johnson City, Tennessee: The Watauga Press, 1944.

Wilson, Gordon. *Passing Institutions.* Cynthiana, Kentucky: The Hobson Book Press, 1944.

Winter, William. *Other Days, Being Chronicles and Memories of the Stage.* New York: Moffat, Yard and Company, 1908.

Wright, Joseph, ed. *The English Dialect Dictionary.* 6 volumes. London: Henry Frowde, 1898–1905.

Zimmerman, O. T., and Irvin Lavine. *Scientific and Technical Abbreviations, Signs and Symbols.* Dover, New Hampshire: Industrial Research Service, 1948.

Articles

Boggs, Ralph S. "Running Down the Fool Killer." *Texas Folk-lore Society Publications,* XIV (1938), 169–173.

"Federal Census of Atlanta, 1850." *The Atlanta Historical Bulletin,* VII (January, April 1942), 16–82.

Houtchens, Lawrence H. "The *Spirit of the Times* and a New Work by Boz.'" *PMLA,* LXVII (March 1952), 94–100.

Leisy, Ernest E. "Jesse Holmes, the Fool-Killer." *Publications of the Texas Folk-lore Society,* VIII (1930), 152–154.

McCallie, Elizabeth Hamleiter. "Atlanta in the 1850s," *The Atlanta Historical Bulletin,* VIII (October 1948), 92–106.

Riley, Susan B. "The Hazards of Periodical Publishing in the South During the Nineteenth Century." *Tennessee Historical Quarterly,* XXI (December 1962), 365–376.

Unpublished Material

Hargis, Robert Loren. "The Know Nothing Party in Tennessee." Unpublished Master's thesis, Vanderbilt University, 1931.

"Minutes of the County Court of Knox County." Book No. 13, 1824–1826. Book No. 14, 1826–1830. Prepared by the Tennessee Historical Records Survey, March, 1941. (Typescripts in Tennessee State Library and Archives.)

INDEX